Human Genetics and Its Foundations

Reinhold Books in the Biological Sciences

CONSULTING EDITOR: PROFESSOR PETER GRAY

Andrey Avinoff Distinguished Professor of Biology
University of Pittsburgh
Pittsburgh, Pennsylvania

The Encyclopedia of the Biological Sciences, edited by Peter Gray
The Biological Control of Insects, Pests, and Weeds, edited by Paul DeBach
Biophysics: Concepts and Mechanisms, by E. J. Casey
Cell Function, by L. L. Langley
Chordate Morphology, by Malcolm Jollie
Concepts of Forest Entomology, by Kenneth Graham
Ecology of Inland Waters and Estuaries, by George K. Reid
Environmental Measurement and Interpretation, by Robert B. Platt and
 John F. Griffiths
Evolution: Process and Product, Revised Edition, by Edward O. Dodson
Experimental Biology: Measurement and Analysis, by R. H. Kay
Experimental Entomology, by Kenneth W. Cummins, Lee D. Miller, Ned A.
 Smith, and Richard M. Fox
General Zoology, by Clarence J. Goodnight, Marie L. Goodnight, and
 Peter Gray
Introduction to Comparative Entomology, by Richard M. Fox and Jean
 Walker Fox
Macromolecular Structure of Ribonucleic Acids, by A. S. Spirin and A. N.
 Bakh
Management of Artificial Lakes and Ponds, by George W. Bennett
Manual of Insect Morphology, by E. Melville DuPorte
Natural History, by Richard A. Pimentel
Paramedical Microbiology, by Stanley E. Wedberg
Physiology of Man, Third Edition, by L. L. Langley and E. Cheraskin
The Plant Community, by Herbert C. Hanson and Ethan D. Churchill
Principles in Mammalogy, by David E. Davis and Frank B. Golley

Consulting Editor's Statement

IT IS EXTREMELY pleasant to come across a book on human genetics written by a geneticist with no ax to grind, with no special cause to plead, with no apparent interest, in fact, in doing anything except write about human genetics. The subject is, in all conscience, complex enough to justify being the sole subject of a book and well worth the effort that Dr. Whittinghill has so skillfully made in reducing it to a logical coherent sequence of scholarly concepts.

The first nine chapters of the book deal with monohybrid genic segregation. This would, in an experimentally controlled population, merely be Mendel's first law but in small size human families, environmentally controlled or not, requires a great deal more explanation to permit the presentation of the population geneticist's point of view and particularly the point of view of the human population geneticist. The next five chapters deal with fractional expectations in regular chromosomal behavior and require of the reader a rudimentary knowledge of statistical procedures as well as some understanding of the previous chapters. There are then six extremely well-written chapters on the biological and biochemical interactions of genes which lead to eight final chapters on mutation and evolution. These cover not so much the evolution of the human, as he at present exists, as those factors which can and have caused such an evolution to occur and which range from spontaneous gene mutations to genetic changes in virulence. This is, in my opinion, exactly what a book about human genetics ought to be both in its content and in the manner in which the content is presented.

PETER GRAY

HUMAN GENETICS

 ## *and Its Foundations*

Maurice Whittinghill

Professor of Zoology

The University of North Carolina

Chapel Hill, North Carolina

New York

REINHOLD PUBLISHING CORPORATION

Chapman and Hall Ltd., London

To my teachers
both older and younger

Preface

In the rapidly expanding subject of human genetics the need for suitable textbooks is becoming greater. This field was relatively small, although well founded, when the writer was a graduate student seeking information in that area, and the increases in knowledge have been especially great in the last few years. During many years of teaching his course in human genetics, the author has felt the need of a textbook concise enough for a one semester course but not limited by the omission of concepts from general genetics which are now beginning to be illustrated by human examples. As models for the writing of a text which is both comprehensive and concise, I am happy to have known and used Sturtevant and Beadle, *Introduction to Genetics*, A. F. Shull, *Heredity*, and L. L. Burlingame, *Heredity and Social Problems*. Finding such books is a delight to teacher and student alike.

Illustrations and diagrams are the special forte of biology and of genetics in particular. Among many effective diagrams to be found in books about other specialties, this writer was tremendously impressed in his youth by the giant step forward made by Roger Tory Peterson in his *Field Guide to the Birds*. From that remote point in time and space the writer offers, with most valuable help from his publisher, a biologist's guide to people and families. Many of the diagrams in this text are original, having been developed for classroom use or for visitors to the laboratory.

Self-taught readers are not to be ignored among a large body of scholars. To assist the independent reader either in studying or reviewing the subject, the levels of complexity in this text have been arranged so that common and inescapable events have been considered well in advance of rarer events such as mutation. Monohybrid inheritance has been presented from many aspects before venturing into sex-linkage, dihybrid inheritance and higher levels of complexity in Part Two. The treatment is far from exhaustive but will introduce terminology and concepts sufficiently to open doors not previously accessible. The biochemical and other biological complications as well as direct environmental influences on the growing fetus and child are related in Part Three to the foregoing genic and chromosomal framework before concluding with the long range population effects of mutation, selection and evolution in Part Four. The beginning student will find the complete progression easy; advanced students may begin with Part Two, Three or Four. Numerous references will entice the student forward to preview interesting topics appearing on later pages; and on the later pages references to earlier pages may bolster the reader who is looking up a particular subject without reading from the beginning. It is hoped that such an arrangement will greatly aid the self-teacher of any age or calling.

Many students will find that a dispersion of the elementary ideas of statistics and the details of biochemistry is welcome. Statistical methods having many applications are introduced in three separated chapters where each can be immediately used rather than being relegated to an appendix or advanced to an early chapter as a formidable hurdle. The same may be said of the chemical bases of life, DNA and RNA, which are emphasized in widely separated parts of this text for logical rather than historical reasons. Yet, no lack of attention to the classic works of genetics is intended. Although recent works have been favored in the lists of Suggested Reading, the scholar will find in them his way to the older research literature. The lists are short in accord with a belief that an introduction is preferable to an array. Let the student, with a few guides, discover for himself the variety of human knowledge.

The plan of the book and its implementation are products of discussions with students and colleagues too numerous to name but nevertheless esteemed as contributors. The participation of certain persons, however, was very definite. For his reading of an early draft of Part One, the author is indebted to Dr. J. Edison Adams, botanist and author. In discussions of the plan and a review of many of the earlier chapters, I am pleased to have had the suggestions of Dr. Carey H. Bostian, geneticist. Dr. Karl Sax read a draft of Chapter 23 and contributed a plan for diagrams of structural chromosomal rearrangements. From the Genetics Training Program of the University of North Carolina at Chapel Hill many stimulating and informative ideas have emerged. Members of the Genetics Curriculum Committee who kindly read and criticized one or more chapters of the manuscript were Drs. John B. Graham, pathologist; Harry Gooder, bacteriologist; William S. Pollitzer, anthropologist and anatomist; and Robert C. Elston, statistician. Dr. Lillian Y. Lehman, embryologist, read the chapter on development of genetic differences, and Dr. Richard F. Potthoff, my part-time colleague shared with the Department of Mathematical Statistics, read drafts and revisions of Chapters 3, 7 and 14. Those ambiguities and mistakes which remain anywhere in this text are the full responsibility of the author, and correspondence in regard to them will be welcomed by him.

Illustrations were obtained from many sources, most of which are acknowledged where they appear. The generosity and good wishes of authors and publishers of borrowed figures and tables were much appreciated. I am indebted to the Literary Executors of the late Sir Ronald A. Fisher, F.R.S., Cambridge, to Dr. Frank Yates, F.R.S., Rothamsted, and to Messrs. Oliver & Boyd Ltd. Edinburgh, for permission to reprint Table No. IV from their book *Statistical Tables for Biological, Agricultural, and Medical Research*. Not mentioned elsewhere is the assistance of Dr. Harrie R. Chamberlain, pediatrician, in arranging for the illustration of Down's syndrome. Mrs. Sandra McLester Bryan's help with correspondence about many of the illustrations was considerable. Mrs. Judy McNease James drew dozens of carefully executed figures but refrained from signing her initials to them. Many gaps in the logical sequence of available illustrations were filled by her fine work.

MAURICE WHITTINGHILL

Chapel Hill, North Carolina
January, 1965

Contents

PART TWO   REGULAR CHROMOSOMAL BEHAVIOR

PART THREE   BIOLOGICAL INTERACTIONS

part one

Monohybrid Genic Segregation

The chapters in Part One of this book are devoted to the exposition and application of Mendel's first law, the 1 : 1 segregation of gametes of a monohybrid. Whenever one encounters phenotypic dominance, the F_2 result of gametic segregation is the Mendelian ratio of 3 Dominant : 1 recessive; but some human phenotypes segregate in 2 : 1 and other phenotypes appear in 1 : 2 : 1 ratios. These ideally segregating sibships are diluted in human population data by families in which no visible segregation occurs because one of the dominant parents was a homozygote.

The gap between experimental and human genetics may be bridged if one assumes the viewpoint of population genetics. The population expectation for all testcross type parent pairs is some definite figure below 50 percent recessives, depending on the degree of commonness or rarity of the recessive phenotype in the whole population. Similarly, for the offspring of all phenotypically normal pairs of parents it is a certain figure below 25 percent recessive children, depending again on the prevalence of the recessive allele. Any first cousin marriages or other consanguineous marriages will add a fixed risk of additional recessive offspring, a fraction which may be insignificantly small for common recessives but strikingly large for the rarer recessive phenotypes.

Monohybrid segregation of a gene pair can produce many describable differences between the two kinds of offspring because of the manifold and widely placed effects of some genes. The various genetic differences may appear at various scheduled times. Some appear long before birth and others are not evident until long after birth or even after maturity is reached. A group of differences which tend to appear in the same individual or to miss his sib, parent or offspring is conveniently named a syndrome. The rare Turner's syndrome and Klinefelter's syndrome indicate the importance of the Y-chromosome in initiating the numerous differences between man and woman.

The small size of human families allows seemingly wide variation from an expected 1 : 1 sex ratio or other genetic expectation. Attempts to accumulate larger totals by adding sibships introduce problems of ascertainment and sampling. These normal scientific difficulties can be surmounted to the extent that the geneticist may assume a uniform environment for the demonstration and study of monohybrid genetic segregation.

chapter 1

Genetic Similarities and Differences

The science of human genetics is seeking and finding answers to many kinds of questions. Why are children so much like their parents? Why are children not entirely like one parent or the other? How can features appear which have not been seen in several generations of ancestors? Can parents be sure that a long-lost child has been correctly identified as theirs? Will certain good traits be handed on to a prospective child? Can certain known or suspected bad traits be avoided? Are predispositions inherited? Questions like these have long been asked, but some of the answers have been slow in emerging. The reasons for the delay include both matters of method and a lack of background information in the intellectual climate.

Asking too large a question makes for a faulty or superficial answer. Thus, questions like "Why is a man a man? Why does this child resemble his mother while his brother closely resembles his father?" can only lead to the answer "heredity," or "heredity reinforced by the social environment." From this kind of answer one can predict merely that "Like will beget like." More definite answers are desired and are available only when suitable analyses have been made. Thus our knowledge of why humans resemble each other in so many ways is founded upon studies of relatively small *differences* within human, mammal or insect families or strains and differences within and between bacterial and viral *clones*.

Human genetics made scant progress before the year 1900. This was so in spite of man's tremendous preoccupation with himself, in spite of an appreciation of an extra risk associated with cousin marriages or closer inbreeding, and in spite of knowledge of certain fragmentary rules for the avoidance of propagating sons with the blood clotting defect, hemophilia. A comprehensive theory of inheritance was not in the cultural heritage of the educated peoples of the world until the rediscovery and confirmation of the Mendelian laws, which had remained in limbo from 1865 to 1900. From that time on progress in the understanding of the likenesses and dissimilarities attributable to the action of genes and chromosomes has been rapid and even astonishing.

The importance of synthesis in science is well illustrated by an analysis of the contribution of Gregor Mendel to human understanding. Mendel's contribution was not just the idea of the *segregation* of unit factors (his first law) nor the idea of *independent assortment* (his second law) nor the idea of dominance. His genius was in the simultaneous and accurate application of all of these pre-existing ideas with mathematical and even statistical accuracy to one specific series of experiments. Mendel used seven varieties of the garden pea, which were grown, crossbred and carefully counted in the garden of the monastery at what was then Brunn, of the old Austro-Hungarian Empire, ruled by a dynasty possessing an inherited form of lower lip as well as the right of succession to a throne. One inquiring visitor to Brunn has reported that Mendel seems to be better known in other parts of the world than among men-on-the-street, who associated his name with leaving some sort of monetary "inheritance" in the city. He left much more, but the legacy was not claimed and assimilated until the century following his two lectures and the publication of his final paper in 1865. That report makes good reading even today, in German or in English, for it not only synthesizes the major features of unit factor inheritance, but it forecasts certain extensions of his principles to distant generations.

The role of libraries, of communication aids, and of the intellectual climate is well illustrated by the fact that the basic laws of human, animal and plant inheritance lay neglected for 35 years although they were known to a few minds and the publication was distributed to several libraries. During that time and longer the leaders in biology were struggling with a different problem, namely, the idea of organic evolution of one or more species from an antecedent species, as propounded independently but simultaneously by Charles Darwin and Alfred Russell Wallace, in 1858. While attention was focused on the question of evolution or separate creation of species, those principles of observable variation and of inheritance which were of great importance to the understanding of organic evolution remained unappreciated. By 1900 there was rediscovery of Mendel's laws and original publication not just once but in triplicate by the Dutch botanist deVries, by Correns in Germany and by von Tschermak in Austria. Since that time discovery and progress in many fields of genetics have multiplied, sometimes at astounding rates.

The applications of genetic principles were made to many other species more rapidly than to humans. In plants, genetic improvement was relatively easy because of the large size of many experiments and because of an advanced knowledge of environmental influences, thanks to the practice of rather uniform horticultural conditions. Genetical studies of mammals with large litters and of insects with short life cycles proceeded rapidly, while studies of human biological inheritance seemed painfully slow. Yet, leaders at work within the field of human genetics—Dahlberg in Denmark, Galton, Penrose, Fisher and Haldane in England, O. Verschuer in Germany, Sewall Wright in the United States, and numerous others in academically peripheral fields—were making basic discoveries. Questions arising with the beginning of the atomic energy age have added to the volume and meaning of recent research in genetics especially as applied to the human species.

GENETIC DEFINITIONS

The appearance of a person is called his *phenotype*, but it does not always reveal his genetic constitution. Similarity of parents and offspring means in general that individuals with similar genetic endowments have grown up in similar environments. When the offspring are raised in a different environment, some differences may appear in spite of similar inheritance. Conversely, a changed inheritance will produce some kind of difference in the offspring which grow up in surroundings not fundamentally unlike those in which his parents grew. For example, rarely it may happen that unusually favorable changes in heredity combined with a particularly well-fitted environment may lead to an outstanding career, like that of Johann Sebastian Bach in music; or a special diet may prevent the brain damage which would otherwise result from the feeding of a normal diet to an infant having an inherited abnormality of the body chemistry known as phenylketonuria. Thus the research worker in genetics must either assume that environmental changes in diet or in exposure to sunlight or to disease organisms have only slight effects upon the phenotypes he is studying, or else he must control the environment to maintain uniformity. Otherwise he must recognize the separate subdivisions of the environment and consider them appropriately in his study. Similar phenotypes in a sufficiently uniform environment imply that there has been genetic continuity without change.

The mechanism of mitotic cell division provides for the propagation of constant *genotypes* by delivering the same kinds and numbers of chromosomes to each of the two daughter cells during each binary cell division (see next chapter). Rare exceptions to this principle of the unchanging genotype in mitotically dividing cells arise from occasional misdivisions of one or more chromosomes. Thus too many or too few chromosomes arrive in one or both daughter cells. Rarely also one or more chromosomes may break, and when that happens the mitotic mechanism will deliver an *aberration* of one or more chromosomes into one or both daughter cells (Chapter 23). Likewise a change too small to be seen with a microscope may alter one part of a chromosome to produce what is called an *allelomorph* (usually shortened to *allele*) of the pre-existing gene, and that chromosome with the mutant allele will have a chance to be perpetuated by mitotic cell division and also by meiosis (Chapter 2). These three kinds of perpetuated changes result in *mutant* materials: chromosomal mutants in respect to number or form of chromosomes and genic mutants produced by invisible substitutions at the chemical level. There is no necessary correlation between the degree of phenotypic effect of the various mutants and the chromosomal versus genic nature of the mutant. The genetic cause of some severe and even lethal phenotypes is often a mutated gene, and the phenotypic effect of an extra whole chromosome may not show up until long after birth (Klinefelter's syndrome, Chapter 22). Although mutations of genes or of chromosomes are very rare events, there are enough mutant products of the mutation process to demonstrate genetic differences within most laboratory and barnyard species and humans.

GENETIC DIFFERENCE WITHIN FAMILIES: MAN AND WOMAN

Sharp differences among related individuals often stem from a single difference between two alleles of a pair of genes or two members of a pair of chromosomes; continuously graded phenotypes will be shown later (Chapter 14) to depend on the simultaneous transmission and action of several pairs of genes and chromosomes. Wide differences often separate the abnormal from the normal, but such phenotypes are rather rare, for example, albinism, certain dwarfs, polydactyls. The more common minor variations within the normal range, such as the shade of eye color, form of hair and the range of skin color, are not fully explained by simple hypotheses. The common blood group differences which were once obscure but are now well correlated to their genic determiners will be described later (Chapter 8). However, the most obvious difference within our species is sex.

The primary distinction of sex depends on the kind of *gametes* produced, whether eggs or sperm. Production of eggs at fairly regular intervals is characteristic of the mature woman. Production of billions of sperm throughout most of adult life is characteristic of mature men. The tremendous size of the egg and the specialized shape of the sperm may be seen in Figure 1-1. Sperm may meet and surround the egg as the latter comes down the fallopian tube after being released from the ovary by the process of ovulation. Fertilization may take place at this time by a fusion of the two gametes. The whole process includes the penetration of the egg

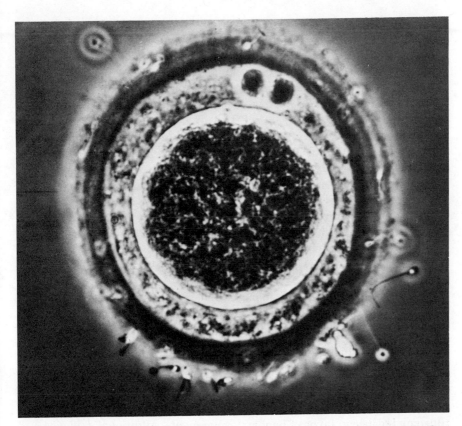

FIGURE 1-1 Living human gametes under phase contrast illumination. One egg surrounded by many sperm, several in sharp focus. The egg usually gives off its first polar body before one or more sperm penetrate into the cytoplasm. This egg shows an uncommon division of the first polar body into two diminutive cells before the regular second polar body will be budded off. From Shettles, *Ovum Humanum*, New York, Hafner, Urban and Schwartzenberg, Munich, 1960.

membrane by a sperm and the combining of the sperm nucleus with that of the mature egg to produce the single nucleus of the zygote. Occasionally, more than one sperm cell have been seen completely within the human egg cell, but the nucleus of only one sperm completes the act of fertilization by combining with the egg nucleus. The genotype of the future child is established at this time of nuclear union, and only rarely does it change in any of the cells descendent from the zygote. The sex of the future individual is decided at fertilization when many other genetic characteristics are also determined.

Sex is an unusually good trait for illustrating a genetic difference because it is highly correlated with chromosomal differences. Men and boys are found to have a short Y-chromosome paired with a much longer X-chromosome in their cells, whereas women and girls lack the Y and have a pair consisting of two equal-appearing X-chromosomes. This seems to be true for other mammals and for some groups of the insects. When the cells of the ovary form mature eggs, only one of the two X-chromosomes remains in the egg, along with only one of each of the other pairs of chromosomes, so that the human egg is capable of developing into either sex, depending on what class of sperm stimulates it and endows it. The sperm come from cells which have matured from earlier cells containing the X and Y, but the members of the X-Y pair are segregated by meiotic reduction into separate sperm. Thus X-sperm and Y-sperm are produced normally in equal numbers. Fertilized eggs containing a maternal X-chromosome and a paternal Y-chromosome develop according to schedule into males. Other fertilized eggs containing just two X-chromosomes, typically one from each parent, develop into females.

Complete correlation in this manner, male with XY and female with XX cells, only indicates a genetically caused difference without specifying the exact manner of inheritance. Thus, equally plausible hypotheses may be made on the above facts: (H_1) presence of a Y-chromosome might of itself alone result in the direction of development toward the phenotype of a male, and lack of the Y-chromosome might result in a female. Equally likely would be the hypothesis (H_2) that one X-chromosome would cause or allow male development but that two such chromosomes would actively tilt some balance in favor of female development. Additional evidence was needed to decide which correlation was the more invariable one, and the analysis of rare exceptions supports the second hypothesis for some organisms, such as *Drosophila melanogaster*, but supports the importance of the Y-chromosome in promoting development of the human male. The observations that those rare persons with only one X chromosome are immature females (Turner's syndrome) coupled with repeated observations that individuals with the rare combination of XXY are more male than female together demonstrate that the main trigger mechanism which starts differentiation resides in the Y-chromosome of man. Additional evidence from the study of sex-linked inheritance further supports the Y-maleness hypothesis for man, and evidence from another mammal, the mouse, is similar.

The strong genetic character of the sex difference is attested by the regular ratio of male to female births. Human efforts to change the sex of the fetus have so far been unsuccessful. It is approximately a 1 : 1 ratio, which is also typical of a Mendelian *testcross* (Chapter 3). Such a 1 : 1 ratio is found among the offspring of a parent who can form only one kind of gamete while the other parent forms just two kinds of gametes. Thus a woman, who is always *homogametic*, and a man, who is always *heterogametic*, may be expected to have daughters and sons in equal numbers, consisting of homogametic females and heterogametic males.

Females homogametic	mother XX eggs X father XY X-sperm and Y-sperm XX daughters and XY sons	Males heterogametic

Thus a phenotypic segregation of the children into girls and boys is consequent upon the genetic segregation of the sex chromosome pair of the father separately into mature sperm. Genotypic and phenotypic segregation correspond without any sign of recessiveness. Consideration will be given later (Chapter 3) to the slight excess of births of male children and to the consequently greater frequency of all-boy sibships as compared with all-girl sibships of corresponding sizes. The fact that examples of wide variations from this equality are observed does not change the overall expectation. The terms "homogametic sex" and "heterogametic sex" are special terms, more cytological than genetical, to designate the sex chromosome pair content in the species. Thus in humans, in other mammals so far as is known and in some flies the male is the heterogametic sex; whereas in birds, butterflies and moths the female is heterogametic and always produces two kinds of eggs even after generations of inbreeding for purity of other genetic differences.

DEVELOPMENT OF A GENETIC DIFFERENCE

An important genetic aspect of the sex difference is that it continues to unfold during most of a lifetime. At fertilization the zygotes of future males and future females are outwardly alike except for the presence in the male of the Y-chromosome in place of the second X. Throughout all the stages of embryogenesis the sexes look alike morphologically.

A cytological distinction between ordinary resting cells of the two sexes may be made in the morula stage. In the nuclei from females a single large spot of *sex chromatin* (also called a *Barr body* after one of its discoverers) lies against the nuclear membrane. Males usually lack this spot. The diagnosis of the sex chromatin body in adults may be made in the resting nucleus of epithelial cells which can easily be rubbed off the inside of the mouth. These or any available cells show a plano-convex dark spot in the nucleus when two X-chromosomes are present but no such sign when only one X-chromosome is present.

In a three month old fetus a histological difference can be detected in the primary sex organs, the gonads. At this time the gonads of female specimens show more rapid growth of their epithelial cells leading to the production of egg strings and egg nests, and finally the Graafian follicles present at birth in baby girls. Meanwhile the same ovary shows degeneration of certain interior gonadal cells which have been present up to the third month of development. In young male fetuses the opposite happens. The epithelial layer regresses, and the rapid growth takes place in the interior sex cords which later elongate, coil, become hollow and are recognizable as the future seminiferous tubules of the adult. The interstitial cells, which are soon to be of importance as secretors of the male hormone testosterone, make their appearance as separate clumps of cells among the seminiferous tubules in fetuses growing from XY human zygotes.

After these differences have begun to appear at the histological level, the first anatomical differences between male and female fetuses can be seen. These include the appearance of a rougher surface on the ovary as Graafian follicles develop, and a greater migration of the testes posteriorly as they leave the main coelomic cavity to descend, usually before birth, into a bipartite scrotal sac. Changes which are secondary to the differentiation of the ovaries or of the testes are the abandonment of one of the sets of potential ducts which have been present and growing simultaneously in early fetuses of both sexes. In males the small oviducts degenerate almost completely, and parts of the intermediate kidney with its mesonephric duct persist and enlarge to become an eventual sperm duct on each side of the body. In females, by contrast, these latter ducts largely degenerate during fetal life, while the parallel Mullerian ducts persist and develop to become oviducts anteriorly and fuse and thicken posteriorly to become the uterus and the vagina. These changes are well advanced by the fourth fetal month.

Other secondary sexual characteristics are developed during the fetal period. The external genitalia cannot be identified as male or female in the three month fetus, when they are said to be in the phenotypically *indifferent stage*, although they are composed of chromosomally different cells in males and females. Signs of male determination are the greater growth of the anterior glans with lateral tissues to form the penis and sidewise fusion in the midline to extend the urinary and genital canals as the penile urethra. Signs of female development in the fetal stage are the less conspicuous growth of the labial tissues and the persistence of a wide vestibular opening receiving separate genital and urinary openings.

These two directions of differentiation do not proceed at equal rates in all male fetuses nor in all female ones, and consequently some aborted fetuses cannot be sexed even by midterm of pregnancy. By four months some 90 percent of fetuses can be readily classified, and it is a rare individual indeed who is not clearly differentiated as boy or girl by the time of birth. These and other differences between male and female are examples of the manifold end results of genetic differences which we here call by the old established name of secondary sexual characteristics. Geneticists speak of the widespread and numerous results of a single gene difference as the *pleiotropic effects* of that gene substitution. Medical men often call such an association of diagnostic signs a *syndrome*.

Some later differences between individuals of XX and XY constitutions are more physiological in nature. These include the greater infant mortality among males and the greater activity of boys. During the teen years girls tend to mature earlier than boys, while the boys have a longer period of growth and thus attain greater height and weight. At all ages men die off with greater frequency than do women, and hence old women are much more numerous than old men. Thus the pleiotropy of the XX-XY difference seems to include the question of longevity, as the insurance actuaries have long ago realized in their calculations. Later we shall point out that earlier death may result from such abnormal phenotypes as Tay-Sachs disease, muscular dystrophy, hemophilia, sickle cell anemia and from such environmental risks as exposure to ionizing irradiation or to other mutagenic agents (Chapter 25).

OTHER PATTERNS OF SEX DETERMINATION

A wide range of mechanisms and devices for differentiating the two sexes is found among animals, and occasionally a prevailing system is replaced or overpowered in some rare line of descent by a mutational *gene substitution* or by a *chromosomal change*. In some species there is no morphologically odd Y-chromosome, and thus one sex may be described as XO while the homogametic sex is XX. In *Drosophila* it was once thought that the absence of the second X-chromosome was the cause of turning the development down the male pathway, but presently it seems clear that maleness results from a certain balance of the number of X-chromosomes, usually one, to the number of sets of autosomes (Chapter 2), usually two sets. A ratio slightly above one-half produces intersexes of great variety, whereas a ratio exactly twice that of the male produces typical females, and an excess of X-chromosomes such as three in a diploid background produces a phenotype even more different from the opposite sex. Such XXX flies are now termed metafemales; they are female-like but sterile. Balance is again operative in the gypsy moth *Lymantria*, but the balance of one or two X-chromosomes is against something cytoplasmic. Furthermore, there are racial differences among moths in the strength of these male-determining and female-determining tendencies, so that families from a certain pair of moths may segregate into equal numbers of males and intersexes; while families from the reciprocal pair segregate into half of the moths intersexes and the other half females instead of the usual equality of males to females throughout most of the species in nature.

Elsewhere other chromosomal, genic and even chance environmental contacts determine sex. In honeybees unfertilized eggs become drones, so the inheritance of the male is entirely via the mother; fertilized eggs become females. Those female larvae which are fed normally become sterile female workers, but those which are fed on royal jelly in a larger cell of the comb become large, fertile queen bees. In the wasp *Habrobracon* unfertilized eggs likewise become males, but so do a percentage of fertilized eggs in very inbred strains, whereas fertilized eggs from crossbreeding are almost invariably female. The rules which seem to apply in *Habrobracon* are (1) that wasps which are heterozygous at a certain locus on a certain pair of chromosomes become females, and (2) that wasps which are homozygous (pure) at this locus or which are haploid (and therefore not heterozygous) become males. A single gene substitution, *tra*, found by Sturtevant in *Drosophila* transforms XX females into sterile males. Perhaps the most surprising situation to one who is aware of the chromosomal and genic switch mechanisms as mentioned above is environmental determination in the marine worm *Bonellia*. This genus has macroscopic females each usually containing a microscopic male which has found its way to live as a parasite in the uterus of its mate. The larvae are free swimming and have the potentiality of becoming either sex; if the larva grows in isolation it becomes a mature female, but if the young larva comes in contact with a mature *Bonellia* soon enough it develops into a tiny but sexually mature male. One would suppose that hormonal influences were decisive in this environmental determination of sex.

If such variety is possible in the animal kingdom, and if more than one influence may be at work within a species, it would be a mistake in human genetics to assume that the common X-Y switch mechanism is the only means of determination of male development. Other forms of genetic differentiation may be at work in a few widely scattered human kindreds. Furthermore, alternate modes of genetic determination (*mimic genes*) are known for dozens of other human phenotypic differences (see Table 4-2).

LIMITED MODIFIABILITY OF THE PHENOTYPE

The environment seems to be able to influence the human genetic sex difference only slightly. Although hormones may be administered for therapeutic purposes later in life, their greatest effect is to modify the functioning of the female or male physiology within the limits of the genetic potentiality. The one sex is not changed into the other. The greatest modifiability of sex among mammals is probably best shown by the case of the *freemartin* in cattle twins. A female calf twinned with a male usually remains immature, and breeders now rarely try to raise such a calf, although the male member of the twin pair grows into a perfectly good bull. Two rather special features of cattle development may explain this widely known phenomenon of the freemartin. The fetal testes grow faster and secrete the male hormone testosterone before the ovaries of heifers have developed, and the placental blood vessels of the bull and heifer in many twin pregnancies connect through anastomoses. Thus it appears that the hormones from this male retard the normal development of the female twin at a crucial time, and this lost opportunity to grow toward female sexual maturity is never regained by the freemartin. An earlier injection of hormone might have even more profound phenotypic results.

The absence of a hormonal effect between twin fetuses during a human pregnancy nevertheless raises a similar question about higher multiple births. The recent Fischer quintuplet birth included four girls, and yet the boy was large and grew vigorously. At least three other such 1 : 4 quintuplet births have been recorded; and conversely, a single girl among four boys has been reported six times without mention of abnormality of the lone individual of one sex. Although none of the babies from the earlier quintuplet births has survived infancy, quadruplets frequently become adults. In a summary of quadruplet births in the United States in the years 1915–1931 Hamlett has summarized the sex distributions, and these included six sets with but a single girl and seven sets with only one boy. Presumably these showed no notable influence of the majority sex. However, other genetic characteristics may not be as well protected against external influences as is this inherited distinction.

It is important to discover and recognize the extent of phenotypic modifiability of normal and abnormal genotypes. Rare individuals exist who are neither clearly male nor clearly female and so may be called by the concise term *intersexes*. From time to time they seek medical and surgical advice, and some are assisted into a normal female mode of life, others into that of a male. The decisions in some of these cases involve not only proper appraisal of the genetic possibilities but also of the personal and social history up to the time of seeking advice. A recommended medical position is to give considerable weight to the apparent sex of the external genitalia and to reinforce that impression surgically and hormonally. This may even run counter to the evidence from the presence or absence of Barr bodies. Thus the *sex chromatin* indicates but does not guarantee femaleness; absence of it usually but not invariably indicates maleness. These qualifications to the previous statement are made necessary by the observation that the chromatin negative XO individuals are phenotypically like immature females, and the chromatin positive XXY Klinefelter's syndrome cases are male but produce no sperm. Even before these cases were explained in chromosomal terms by Barr and by Ford, it would have been prudent to have allowed for other but rarer causes of sex-determination in humans.

SUMMARY

The science of genetics studies the phenotypic (visible) differences between individuals and attempts to relate them to underlying genic or chromosomal differences. Chromosomes and their genes pass from the two parents to a single zygote. The genotype of the fertilized egg is translated into one or more aspects of the phenotype at various times before and after birth. As an example the differences between male and female and the sex ratio are already familiar to the beginning student of genetics. The approximate 1 : 1 ratio is of the testcross ratio type, and it obviously varies between wide extremes in small human families.

Sex is a typical example of a genetic difference in that it is determined at the moment of fertilization but unfolds slowly to produce a constellation of differences both physical and emotional between male and female adults and even old people. The group of differences begins with the Barr body in the typical female nucleus of embryos and ends with the longer length of life of the average woman. The human sex difference is only slightly modifiable by hormonal means. The freemartin heifer twin and the Turner's syndrome girl illustrate environmental and genetic pathways, respectively, to a similar phenotypic result, the immaturity of these females.

SUGGESTED READING

Mayer, C. F., *History of Genetics*, pp. 3–68 in L. Gedda, ed., *De Genetica Medica* Pt. I, Rome. Edizioni Instituto Mendel, 1961. Generously illustrated.

Mendel, G., "Experiments in plant hybridization," translation in J. A. Peters, *Classic Papers in Genetics*, pp. 1–20, Englewood Cliffs, N. J., Prentice-Hall, 1959.

Nordenskiöld, E., *The History of Biology*, New York, Knopf, 1938, 629 pp. On page 490, further background of the evolution controversy among scientists.

Penrose, L. S., *Outline of Human Genetics*, New York, Wiley, 1959, 146 pp. A very brief and excellent summary by an outstanding research leader.

von Tschermak-Seysenegg, Erich, J. Hered. **42**: 163–171 (1951). The last surviving rediscoverer of Mendel's paper reminisces on the rediscovery.

Zirkle, C., J. Hered. **55**: 65–72 (1964). Some oddities in the delayed discovery of Mendelism.

PROBLEMS

1–1 What is the largest family you personally know which consists entirely
  (a) Of girls?
  (b) Of boys?

1–2 Have you personally heard of any theories as to why some families consist entirely
  (a) Of male children?
  (b) Of female children?

1–3 When is the future sex of a human being
  (a) Determined?
  (b) Visibly diagnosable?
  (c) Finally expressed?

1–4 Define briefly but adequately:

  phenotype
  genotype
  mutant
  allelomorph
  testcross

1–5 Define briefly but adequately:

  freemartin
  clone
  heterogametic
  Barr body
  genetic segregation

chapter 2

Chromosomes During Growth and Maturity

A new life cycle in mammals begins when the sperm cell of the male and the egg of the female fuse to form a single cell, the *zygote*. In spite of the very small size of the sperm the paternal contribution to offspring through the zygote is as great as the maternal contribution in respect to most characters, and this fact has pointed to the importance of the nucleus in heredity. A sperm cell consists mostly of a nucleus which, in other animals, has been shown to fuse with the egg nucleus at the first cell division of the zygote. By micromanipulation of the egg nucleus and its removal from the egg cytoplasm before fertilization, embryologists have demonstrated androgenetic hybrids, those offspring showing mainly the characteristics of the father's species. Conversely, fertilization by a sperm whose nucleus has been killed results in gynogenetic offspring, those with all chromosomal inheritance from the mother. We may reasonably assume for man and mammals that most of one's inheritance crosses this tiny bridge of sperm nucleus and egg nucleus from the two parents to form the *diploid* zygotic nucleus. The fact of such nuclear fusion has directed the attention of many biologists to the study of the nucleus and its chromosomal contents as the bearers of heredity. Most of the small volume of the sperm cell is taken up by a mass of chromosomes, and yet the father contributes about as much as does the mother through her much larger egg to the genetic makeup of the offspring.

CYTOLOGY: THE STUDY OF CELLS

The direct study of the gross form and fine structure of chromosomes and of other cellular constituents is called *cytology*, and both optical and electron-microscopical methods are used. Chromosomes of nondividing cells are long and very thin, but they condense during the midstages of cell division, becoming considerably thicker and much shorter. This change is comparable to that produced by winding a long thin wire in tight coils around a

16

pencil. After removing the pencil, one can pull out the thick helical spring to great length and fractional thickness. Most of our information about chromosomes has come from observing, counting and studying them in cells which are dividing to form two daughter cells. Convenient places to find such rapidly dividing cells are in the growing root tips of plants, in the blastula stage of the developing eggs of fish and in cells of the germinal tissue which are forming eggs or sperm.

The number of chromosomes going into a mature sperm cell or remaining in the cytoplasm of the mature egg is only half the number which is characteristic of the dividing blastula cells or the vast majority of cells derived from the zygote. The number of chromosomes in a mature gamete, whether egg or sperm, is called the *haploid* number, and the genes of a haploid chromosome set make up a single *genome*. After the egg is fertilized, the resulting zygote contains the *diploid* chromosome number or set, or two genomes. Characteristically, no two chromosomes of the haploid cell are alike, whereas in diploids there are two chromosomes of each kind forming a pair. The longest chromosome is found twice, the next longest twice and so on. Even if several chromosomes seem to be of approximately the same length so that their partnership cannot be decided with certainty by simple inspection in most kinds of body cells, nevertheless, the superficially similar chromosomes reveal their affinities in a two-by-two pairing, called *synapsis*, in the first of the two maturation divisions of gametogenesis. The synapsing partners are one *paternal* chromosome, that received via the sperm, and one *maternal* chromosome, that received via the egg nucleus. These pairing partners look alike, and it cannot be told by mere observation of the *autosomes* (22 similar pairs of chromosomes in the case of humans) which member of the pair came from the mother and which from the father. An exception is the *heteromorphic pair* concerned with sex-determination and called the sex chromosome pair. In the human male the short Y-chromosome is presumably always of paternal origin, and the longer X-chromosome with which it synapses is maternal. However, in a woman the two members of the X-pair look alike; the one which came from her father cannot be distinguished optically from that partner which came from her mother, even though the chromosomes may contain genes with different potentialities.

It was not easy to determine that the diploid chromosome set in humans contains 46 chromosomes, and before 1956 the number was reported to be two more. Advances in tissue culture techniques are responsible for our present understanding of chromosome number and form. The cells are now grown flatter than most cells within the body, and are subsequently spread farther by the use of hypotonic solutions before fixing and staining for observation. By the use of the alkaloid colchicine from the autumn crocus, it is possible to arrest dividing cells at a stage most favorable for chromosome counting, metaphase, and to accumulate larger numbers of cells for microscopic examination.

The cytological difficulties remaining are concerned with matching partners correctly among four or more chromosomes of almost the same size and shape. When one is studying these preparations, it is well to remember that the use of colchicine makes each chromosome look divided longitudinally but not separated (Figure 2-1). Hence there appear numerous cross-shaped dividing chromosomes which would be V-shaped or J-shaped if the

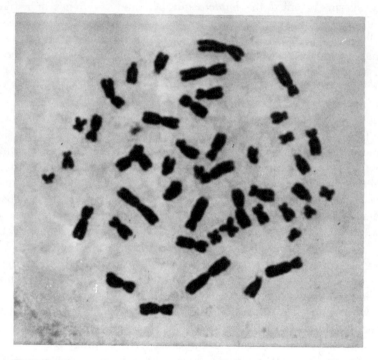

FIGURE 2-1 Chromosomes of a cell in arrested metaphase and having the normal karyotype of a woman. Each chromosome is split into two identical chromatids; each kinetochore is unsplit. Courtesy of Bonny Morgan Lewis.

mitotic division had been allowed to be completed normally. Similarly, V-shaped chromosomes in colchicine-arrested preparations would separate into identical, essentially rod-shaped chromosomes. The union is maintained until the appropriate time in cell division by a special part of each chromosome, the *centromere* or *kinetochore*, which is the point of attachment to the mitotic spindle (see the next section). The kinetochore is at a position characteristic of specific chromosome pairs. It may be in the middle of the chromosome or at any point except the very end, depending on the evolutionary history of the chromosome. For any one chromosome the position of the centromere and the total length are constant. Chromosomes may thus be described diagnostically in respect to total length and to *arm length ratio*, the ratio of the longer arm to the shorter arm (or merely as having a median, submedian or subterminal spindle attachment). Identification is easy among the three largest pairs of human chromosomes, which differ markedly both in total length and in arm length ratio (Figure 2-2).

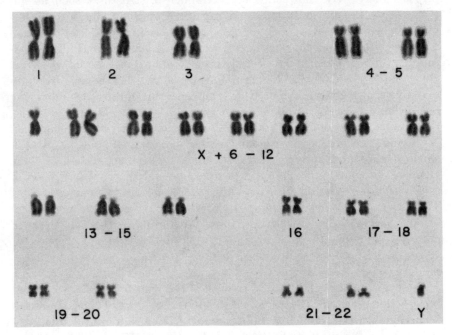

FIGURE 2-2 The normal male karyotype. Mitotic chromosomes rearranged according to probable partners within size groups: groups A and B, top line; C, second line; D and E, third line; F and G groups, bottom line. Men usually have one unpaired member of group C and another unpaired chromosome of group G representing the unequal X-Y pair. Courtesy of Bonny Morgan Lewis.

Chromosomes in the size range of pairs 6 through 12 and including the X-chromosome are presently much more difficult to differentiate. Similarly, the Y-chromosome and the two smallest pairs of chromosomes, numbers 21 and 22, are near enough alike in size and in the location of the kinetochore so that even expert cytologists diagnose the pair number with occasional reservations. Some pairs, such as the 21st, possess an extremely small terminal piece called a *satellite*. However alike some of the chromosomes may look to the scientist, the cell has no apparent difficulty in reproducing its chromosomal complement exactly.

MAINTAINING THE GENOTYPE BY MITOSIS

A precise method of nuclear division is responsible for the constancy of the chromosome number from cell to cell within most of the tissues of a person's body. By contrast, some extranuclear structures such as mitochondria and pigment granules are separated unevenly during the cytoplasmic part of cell division, cytokinesis, as though the uniform distribution of these cytoplasmic materials were not critical. A cell may divide mitotically forming two daughter cells in from 20 minutes (bacteria) to several days; many kinds of cells divide in an interval of a few hours. In representative growing tissue one may see some 5 percent of the cells undergoing recognizable stages of mitotic division.

The chief events of one complete cycle of mitosis are chemical replication of the material of the chromosome, visible longitudinal splitting of each chromosome strand into two parallel *chromatids*, the separation of these identical chromatids into two identical groups and the final formation of each of these groups and of surrounding cytoplasm into two daughter cells. The chromatids in each daughter cell now assume the name of *chromosomes* before they in turn replicate and form chromatids in the next cycle of mitosis. Although the nuclear and cytoplasmic events are continuous, stages in the process are described in the sequence of names, interphase, prophase, metaphase, anaphase and telophase. (See Figure 2-3.)

The typical metabolic state of the cell is the long *interphase*, so named because it is between cycles of actual cell division. Yet the division process begins here with the doubling of the amount of DNA in the chromosomes of the nucleus. No more replication of DNA occurs after interphase, even though the visible doubling of chromosomes may not be detected until later.

During *prophase* of division the chromosomes become visible under microscopic examination. The strands are very thin and usually too long to trace in early prophase, but they gradually thicken and shorten and become discrete. During late prophase the *mitotic spindle* is organized from the divided centrioles which were outside the nucleus during interphase, and the

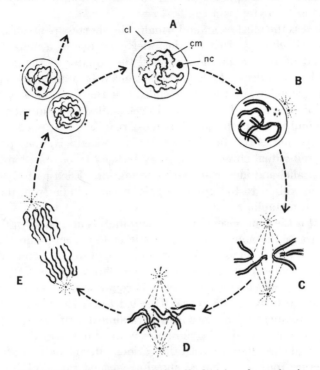

FIGURE 2-3 Diagram of cell division by mitosis illustrated in a cell with two pairs of chromosomes, V-shaped and J-shaped. (A) Interphase, synthetic phase, or "resting" nucleus; cl, centrioles; cm, centromere or kinetochore; nc, nucleolus. (B) Prophase. Each chromosome is visibly double, the duplicates still joined by the centromeres, which have not yet divided. (C) Metaphase. The double chromosomes are aligned at the equator between the poles of the spindle. (D) Anaphase. The centromeres have split, and the chromosomes are beginning to move toward the poles. (E) Telophase. The chromosome halves have moved to the poles, one complete set (two pairs) going to each pole. (F) Daughter nuclei. Each chromosome set is included within a new nucleus, in each of which the conditions at (A) are restored. (From *Principles of Genetics*, 5th edition by Sinnott, Dunn and Dobzhansky. Copyright 1958. McGraw-Hill Book Company. Used by permission.)

nuclear membrane disappears so that the chromosomes and spindle figure seem to lie in the cytoplasm.

Metaphase is the most exact and usually the shortest phase of mitotic cell division. It is characterized by the brief existence of a metaphase plate arrangement of all chromosomes around the equator of the spindle; and considerable movement of chromosomes may be detected in time-lapse photomicrographs before this stage ends, as if they were jockeying toward one pole and then toward the other. In cells killed and stained at this time the total number of chromosomes is most readily determined. Colchicine stops cell division as this favorable stage is reached. By metaphase if not earlier the individual chromosomes may be seen to be split longitudinally into two parallel and identical sister chromatids. Each half of the former chromosome will go to the opposite pole of the spindle from its identical chromatid as metaphase ends.

Anaphase is the time of separation of chromatids into two identical sets of chromosomes of the number characteristic of the species and tissue. The anaphase begins as soon as the kinetochores begin to move toward opposite ends of the spindle, pulling their respective chromatids with them. Each such chromatid, which can be called a chromosome as soon as it is fully separated from its sister, moves as if pulled toward the pole by its kinetochore. Consequently, chromosomes with almost terminal spindle attachments appear rod-shaped; chromosomes with central kinetochores appear V-shaped; and chromosomes with the various intermediate locations of the centromere are roughly J-shaped showing various ratios of long arm to short arm. This time, however, is not suitable for making exact chromosome counts and identifications because of the occasional lagging of some chromosome and its apparent inclusion in the anaphase group in the other half of the spindle. Hence chromosome counts are usually made in mammal cells which are at metaphase even if it takes a poison to hold them there with undivided spindle attachments. As anaphase proceeds the chromosomes soon bunch together in two dense groups.

The *telophase* completes the division process by separating the cytoplasm of the parent cell to comprise that of the two daughter cells. In animal cells a cleavage furrow forms around the location of the former metaphase plate, and this pinches in until the cytoplasm has been partitioned to the two new cells. Meanwhile the separation of the chromosomes has continued; a new nuclear membrane forms around the two separated chromosome complements, and the chromosomes themselves lose their visible identity as the nucleus again takes on its interphase appearance. In this condition the cells carry on their normal metabolic activity, and it is a rather long time before one or both of them may enter a new cycle of cell division.

In this manner the chromosome number and composition are maintained. The normal 46 chromosomes of the parent cell are represented by 46 chromosomes in each of the two daughter cells. If by some rare mutational misdivision a chromosome is lost and a cell receives only 45 chromosomes, further division of that abnormal cell will produce daughter cells with 45 chromosomes present in each. If the loss does not kill or severely handicap the cell, still further mitoses will produce more cells and tissues with the same number of chromosomes. For example, in individuals showing Turner's syndrome, the chromosome pairs 1 through 22 and a single X-chromosome have been faithfully reproduced throughout the body, presumably from the zygote stage. Should a rare event deliver 47 chromosomes to the fertilized egg, mitotic cell division conserves that number for as long as the organism lives. With the chromosome complement of the Klinefelter's syndrome, XXY, the extra member of the sex "pair" is regularly reproduced and transmitted within the body cells on into adulthood. Other abnormal numbers and combinations will be described in Chapter 22.

MEIOSIS: THE TWO MATURATION DIVISIONS

The fusion of egg and sperm nuclei once in each generation of individuals does not increase the number of chromosomes for the species, because two maturation divisions have reduced the number in an exact proportion yet in numerous assortments. The two special divisions, collectively called *meiosis*, produce four haploid nuclei from one diploid nucleus. The everyday fundamentals of genetics are bound up with the manner in which 46 chromosomes are sorted out so that 23 arrive in each gamete usually without extras of one kind of chromosome and without deficiencies of another. Even with these restrictions a great variety of individuals is created within a sexually reproducing species.

The essence of meiosis is that the chromosomes come together in pairs, and only a single lengthwise replication of each into two chromatids occurs although two cell divisions follow. The obvious result is that the chromosome number is reduced to one-half, that is, from the diploid to the haploid number. A corollary result is that the maternal and paternal chromosomes of any one pair tend to *segregate* to opposite haploid nuclei (unless the pair undergoes crossing over, Chapter 11). A second main result is the *independent assortment* of the maternal members of the different chromosome pairs to one or the other pole of the spindle while each is separating in obligatory fashion from its partner, the paternal chromosome of the same size, shape and general content. For no presently obvious reason mutations of genes and chromosomes are more frequent during gametogenesis than during most or all other cell divisions (Chapters 21 and 25).

Spermatogenesis. The details by which a diploid primary spermatocyte of the testis becomes two secondary spermatocytes and finally four haploid sperm are summarized in Figure 2-4. The two cell divisions are designated meioses I and II, or maturation divisions I and II. The phases are also numbered, i.e., metaphase I, telophase I, prophase II, etc.

Preparation for meiosis involves growth of gonial cells of the testis to greater than usual size. Then the enlarged cell is recognized as a *primary gametocyte* or *meiocyte* which embarks upon a long prophase, the most specialized part of meiosis. During *prophase I* the two longest chromosomes pair, the two next longest pair, and each chromosome of the set pairs or synapses with the chromosome most like it in external appearance and internal genes. Even the heteromorphic X and Y synapse along part of their length. Each pair of chromosomes, a *bivalent*, soon shows the results of previous chemical replication into a four-stranded association called the *tetrad*. In man 23 tetrads are formed in each primary spermatocyte. The tetrad contains enough of each and every kind of chromosome for each of four eventual sperm cells. Each such strand of the tetrad is, of course, a chromatid. Unless exchange between two chromatids takes place (crossing over), two of the chromatids are derived from the paternal chromosome of each pair and the other two chromatids of the same tetrad are derived from the maternal chromosome. Toward the end of prophase I each tetrad moves toward the equator of the spindle which has formed typically. *Metaphase I* is brief but important to the final consequences. The still single maternal and paternal kinetochores become oriented randomly toward one or the other pole of the spindle. Their metaphase arrangement in a particular cell is purely random, like the toss of 23 coins, and it essentially determines two opposite assortments of homologues destined to pass to the secondary spermatocyte for final separation. During *anaphase I* and beyond it the two assortments of chromatids move apart with spindle attachments advancing toward the poles of the first maturation spindle. By this motion the grouping into tetrads has disappeared, and the components of each tetrad are now present as two *dyads* (two chromatids attached to the same kinetochore) each retreating from its opposite dyad. The beginning and completion of a cytoplasmic furrow across the primary spermatocyte mark the beginning and the end of *telophase I*.

The two daughter cells thus produced are *secondary spermatocytes*, and maturation division II proceeds rapidly to divide these two cells into a total of four. During *prophase II* the dyads turn one way or another as they approach the equator of the second division spindle. Their orientation in respect to the poles at *metaphase II* at last determines the assortment of chromatids which will reach each gamete. By the end of metaphase II the

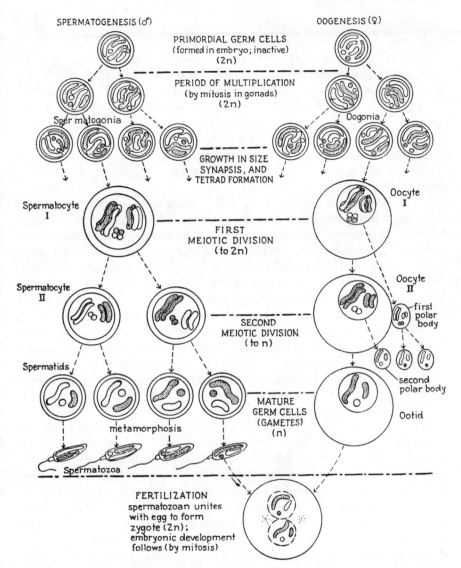

FIGURE 2-4 Meiosis. Simplified diagram of the origin and maturation of gametes in a species having as its diploid (2n) complement only six chromosomes. The three received previously from the mother are shown white; the three received from the father are shown stippled. Nuclear events in the two sexes are similar; cytoplasmic events differ markedly. Human oogonia complete their meiotic multiplication before birth. From *General Zoology*, 3rd edition by Storer and Usinger. Copyright 1957. McGraw-Hill Book Company. Used by permission.

kinetochore of each dyad finally divides and the two parts seem to repel each other and proceed during *anaphase II* with their respective chromatids to opposite poles. The *telophase II* cytoplasmic furrow finishes the cell division of each secondary spermatocyte into two *spermatids*. Thus one diploid primary spermatocyte has given rise to four haploid spermatids. By a drastic change of shape each spermatid next metamorphoses into one sperm consisting of interphase nucleus, centriole adjacent to it in the mid-piece, and a very long whip-like tail. Throughout the adult testis millions of primary spermatocytes are commencing meiosis and many billions of sperm are produced in a few days. Their variety is almost as great as their number.

Oogenesis. Meiosis in the ovary differs from the above in cytoplasmic behavior, but the nuclear events are closely similar. The two maturation divisions of oogenesis produce only one functional gamete, a large ovum, and three (or merely two) abortive cells, the *polar bodies*, with a minimum of cytoplasm around the nuclei of the latter. In size the mature ovum is virtually as large as the secondary oocyte and primary oocyte from which both it and the polar bodies are descended. Thus the large capital supply of food materials stored in the cytoplasm in advance of oogenesis is preserved in an amount adequate for one embryo rather than being subdivided into four equal but presumably inadequate amounts. The tremendous increase in volume of cytoplasm of the future egg takes place in one oogonial cell of an egg nest as it is slowly becoming a primary oocyte. Although the growth preparatory to oogenesis is slow, it takes place very early, during fetal life of both the human and mouse female.

The total number of eggs which these females can produce in a lifetime are present at birth as large but immature cells. Thus there will be no multiplication of oogonial cells during childhood or in the adult woman, whereas continuous and rapid multiplication of spermatogonial cells by mitotic cell division is a necessary part of reaching and maintaining the fertility of the male. After the female reaches sexual maturity, one or a few of the waiting primary oocytes are matured at a time. If a woman releases two eggs at the same time and becomes pregnant, fraternal twins would be the usual result. Mammals which have larger litters ovulate a larger number of maturing eggs from the ovary at the same day or hour. These separate eggs regularly become genetically different sibs and are not usually involved in identical twinning, although some sets of triplets and quadruplets may include individuals who are from one egg.

The nuclear behavior in oogenesis is the same as was described for gametogenesis in the male. *Prophase I* of oogenesis is long and allows the synaptic pairing of homologous chromosomes. Each such bivalent configuration becomes a tetrad consisting of four chromatids, and the tetrads (23 in humans) move toward the equator of the first division spindle, some with their undivided kinetochores of maternal origin oriented toward a certain pole, other tetrads with their paternal kinetochore pointed that same way. Thus the assorting of genes which pass through the parent from grandparents to child is under way. *Metaphase I* persists for different times in different species of mammals as a dormant period depending on whether the stimulus of sperm entrance is needed for the completion of division. In *anaphase I* the chromatids of the tetrads are pulled apart to form two groups of dyads which are normally equal in all respects except for the difference of paternal or maternal genes. The nuclear events so far have taken place with one pole of the maturation spindle near the cell membrane. Consequently in *telophase I* the cytoplasmic furrow seems to pinch off the outer group of dyad chromatids with hardly any cytoplasm into *polar body I* leaving a qualitatively opposite group of dyads in the voluminous cytoplasm of the *secondary oocyte.* Further division of polar body I usually is lacking, and this is a minor departure from the nuclear behavior of spermatogenesis, but occasionally it does divide (Figure 1-1).

The second maturation division of oogenesis forms a new spindle from the inner end of the old spindle and rearranges the orientation of the dyads during *prophase II*, forms an equatorial plate in *metaphase II*, and separates the chromatids of each dyad in *anaphase II*. Thus the cell is able to discard a haploid set of chromatids into the diminutive *polar body II* while retaining a haploid set in the cytoplasm-rich and now mature *ovum.* The chromatids of the haploid set may now be called chromosomes. Each chromosome has been *segregated* from its opposite partner in the former tetrad, and one *assortment* from among millions of possible genetic assortments has been achieved.

The number of pairs of chromosomes in a species sets a minimum number on the kinds of assortments made during gametogenesis in either sex. The minimal number rests on the assumption that whole chromosomes are assorted without there being any crossing over or exchanging of segments between maternal and paternal chromatids (Chapter 11); wherever that may occur, the variety of kinds of gametes goes up many-fold. Minimum chromosomal assortments may be obtained by applying a power rule that the assortments equal two raised to the same power as the number of segregating chromosome pairs (Table 2-1). The apparent complexities of the assortments are no different in principle from Mendel's laws as illustrated in monofactorial and two-factor pair inheritance. The various aspects of monohybrid inheritance will occupy our attention for the next several chapters. Dihybrid and multihybrid transmission of genes and chromosomes is being postponed to Part Two of this textbook.

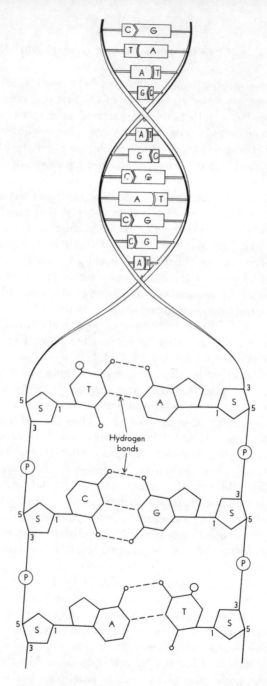

FIGURE 2-5 Part of a DNA molecule, diagrammatic. Above, generalized double helix. Below, detail of nucleotides and cross bonding. A = adenine; C = cytosine; G = guanine; T = thymine; P = phosphate link; S = 2-deoxyribose (see Figure 2-6). From David M. Bonner and Stanley E. Mills, *Heredity*, 2nd edition. (C) 1964, by permission of Prentice-Hall, Inc., Englewood Cliffs, N.J.

Sugars

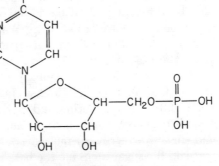

ribose

2-deoxyribose

Purines

adenine

guanine

Pyrimidines

cytosine

thymine

uracil

Nucleoside

Nucleotide

cytosine riboside

cytosine ribotide

FIGURE 2-6 Components of nucleic acids. Purines bond to sugars at the lower NH position, as do pyrimidines. Carbons in the pentose sugars are numbered from the left counterclockwise. Deoxyribose loses O from the carbon 2 position. Ribose and deoxyribose bond to phosphate first through carbon 5. Phosphate may bond again to carbon 3 of an adjacent nucleotide.

TABLE 2-1   Minimum possible number of assortments of whole chromosomes

Number of pairs segregating, n	Kinds of gametes, 2^n	Examples
0	1	homogametic sex
1	2	heterogametic sex
2	4	*Ascaris* (a worm)
3	8	*Cyclops* (a crustacean)
4	16	*Drosophila melanogaster*
5	32	*Drosophila azteca*
10	1,024	*Zea maize* (corn)
20	1,048,576	*Mus musculus* (mouse)
23	8,388,608	*Homo sapiens* (man)
40	1,099,511 million	*Salmo alpinus* (fish)

THE CHEMICAL COMPOSITION OF CHROMOSOMES

Our interest in chromosomes as constant structures visible in the dividing cell is heightened by the knowledge that the chromosomes are bearers of the hereditary information. For some time it was thought that the chief component of chromosomes would have to be protein because of the great variety of protein structure, but later it was discovered that they contained a large amount of simpler compounds called histones. Still later, by the use of the Feulgen reaction and other analyses, it was shown that long polynucleotide molecules of *deoxyribonucleic acid*, called DNA, were intimately associated with chromosomes and were found exclusively in chromosomes. DNA is now known to exist in forms varied enough to embrace the multitude of kinds of genes which we had previously thought could be specified only by different protein beads linked together on a chromosomal chain. The model of DNA proposed by Watson and Crick provides an adequate basis for the coding of gene differences. Its structure has a likeness to a spiral staircase (Figure 2-5).

The DNA molecule is made up of repeatable units of only four kinds arranged, as Watson and Crick so brilliantly formulated it, in cross-linked pairs of two *bases*, purine and pyrimidine, between oppositely directed strands of a long double helix. The helical spiral is made up of phosphate and sugar (deoxyribose) molecules alternating regularly, and to a certain place on the sugar molecule the base is attached as a side chain. The combination of a purine base (or pyrimidine) to deoxyribose is called a *nucleoside*. Complete repeatable units (phosphate plus sugar plus base equal one *nucleotide*) are formed every 3.4 Angstroms of length; the helix makes one complete turn for every ten nucleotides, therefore every 34 Angstroms.

About 10,000,000 of these submicroscopic turns are contained in one visible chromosome of representative size. Furthermore, it has been estimated that there are as many nucleotide pairs in one cell as there are individual letters in 133 unabridged English dictionaries.

The repeatable units in the DNA model are of just four kinds: adenine-thymine, cytosine-guanine, guanine-cytosine and thymine-adenine. Together either of these two pairs, A-T or C-G, can just bridge the distance between the oppositely trending sugar-phosphate helices whereas the size of two purine bases, adenine and guanine, would be too much for the distance, and the size of the two pyrimidine bases together would be too little for the space. The adenine completes the crosstie by forming only two chemical bonds with thymine rather than to the other base of the same size, and guanine bonds regularly to cytosine by three cross linkages. Biochemical analysis of DNA within one species of animal shows that the total of adenine molecules equals the thymine total and that the numbers of cytosine and guanine molecules are the same. Yet the ratio of the A-T pairs to the C-G pairs is different in DNA from different species, a fact which, of course, correlates with there being genetic differences between species. The relation of the information coded in the nucleotide sequence to enzymatic and genic action in the cytoplasm will be considered further in Chapter 15.

The double stranded nature of the DNA molecule provides for its replication. Thus if the two halves of the double helix start pulling apart, as in opening a zipper, surrounded by a medium rich in purines and pyrimidines or their nucleotides, each half of the DNA molecule can selectively reconstruct its opposite half. For instance, when a cytosine unbonds from the guanine of the opposite helix its three hydrogen bonds appear to be highly attractive only to the hydrogen bonds of another guanine and not to available thymine, adenine nor other cytosine. Conversely, the removed guanine will soon bond with another cytosine in preference to another guanine, thymine or adenine. Thus each separated part of the double helix serves as a template for the reconstruction of exactly the same sequence of nucleotides which was opposite it before replication of the DNA molecule began. Currently the opinion prevails that another shorter and single stranded cellular chemical, ribonucleic acid, RNA, has among its other functions in the cytoplasm the movement of the necessary bases into the nucleus, perhaps in subassemblies, for the reconstruction of the double helix.

Problems remain as to whether a coiled double helix of the length of a chromosome could unwind fast enough for replication in some rapidly dividing cells such as in embryos or in tissue which is forming erythrocytes. Therefore further ideas about the relation of the DNA molecule to the relatively great length of the visible chromosome (which somehow contains all of the DNA) may soon be emerging as research continues at biochemical and cytogenetic levels of organization. Our present ideas contrast sharply with older although reasonable beliefs. Once we thought that genes reproduced by accretion of the same kinds of protein followed by the splitting of gene and chromosome axis into smaller amounts of complete genic material followed then by thickening of the axis. Now it appears that the gene and the axis may be the same, in spite of the mechanical difficulties just mentioned above. With that view the splitting at the chemical level would come first, and the double stranded gene-chromosome would rapidly reconstruct to normal size. It is amazing that the replication process seems to depend on a temporarily single-stranded molecule, and yet reproduction of DNA is exact enough to keep mutations at a very low rate (Chapter 21).

SUMMARY

The importance of cell division by mitosis in the maintenance of the genetic constancy has been reviewed. The cells of a person have a constant number of chromosomes, usually 46. These chromosomes are of 23 distinct (but not always visibly distinguishable) kinds in regard to total length and to arm ratio (shape) occurring usually as two of each kind. Interphase, prophase, metaphase, anaphase and telophase of cell division were reviewed. Meiosis with two cell divisions following only one replication of chromosomes is the key to much of the variety of genetic data. The two chromosomes of a pair, one from each parent, synapse in prophase I of meiosis and also show a visible replication by this time. Such a tetrad of homologues contains one future chromosome for each of four sperm cells in males, or enough for one egg and three functionless polar bodies in females. Allelic genes of maternal and paternal origin are regularly segregated at this time. The direction of this segregation to the egg or to a particular sperm cell is random in respect to the direction of segregation of any other among the total of 23 chromosome pairs. This randomness is the basis for assortment and recombination of genes previously received from one's father and mother. The minimum number of kinds of gametes from one man is 2^{23} assortments of whole chromosomes. With the same number of possibilities a woman's 400 eggs must almost inevitably be different from each other.

The chemical composition of chromosomes includes histones, proteins and deoxyribonucleic acid. The last, DNA, is found only in chromosomes and is double stranded. The complementary nature of the two strands of DNA seems to provide for its exact replication during unzippering in a mixture of four nucleotides. Adenylic acid fits into place by weak hydrogen bonding with thymine. Thymidylic acid similarly bonds with exposed adenine.

Cytidylic acid joins through triple hydrogen bonds to the guanine part in an open strand of DNA, and guanylic acid likewise bonds with available cytosine. The sugar-phosphate parts of these incoming acids line up to form a new longitudinal half of the double helix. Within a species the ratio of A-T pairs to C-G pairs is constant, but among different species a variety of ratios of A-T to G-C is found. Further specificity along the length of a chromosome seems to exist in respect to the sequence of a four symbol code, namely the symbols A-T, C-G, G-C, T-A. The DNA code seems to be read by a messenger RNA, which is of single-stranded nature and composed of the A, C, G and uridylic acid nucleotides. Problems of untangling the tremendous length of DNA helix and of the manner of reading by the mainly cytoplasmic RNA are currently under intense investigation.

SUGGESTED READING

Mazia, Daniel, "Mitosis" pp. 77–412 in J. Brachet, and A. E. Mirsky, eds., *The Cell* Vol. III, New York, Academic Press, 1961. A modern treatise.

Mazia, D., *Sci. Amer.* **205**: 100–120 (1961) and reprint series *How Cells Divide*, San Francisco, Freeman, 1961, 15 pp. This short article includes electron micrographs and excellent drawings.

Mittwock, Ursula, *Sci. Amer.* **209** (No. 1): 54–62 (1963). Describes sex differences at the cellular level with diagrams, photographs and autoradiographs.

Ohno, S., H. P. Klinger, and N. B. Atkin, *Cytogenetics* (Basel) **1**: 42–51 (1962). Human oogenesis was studied from fetuses and from ovulating adults.

Painter, T. S., The Y-chromosome in mammals, *Science* **53**: 503–504 (1921). Reporting a range of total chromosome numbers from 45 to 48, the author says that his clearest figures showed 46 chromosomes in man.

Rhoades, M. M., "Meiosis" pp. 1–75 in J. Brachet, and A. E. Mirsky, *The Cell*, Vol. III, New York, Academic Press, 1961. Of special interest to geneticists.

Schrader, F., *Mitosis* 2nd ed., New York, Columbia University Press, 1953, 170 pp. An outstanding book on the mechanics of cell division.

Wilson, G. B., and John H. Morrison, *Cytology*, New York, Reinhold, 1961, 297 pp. A comprehensive and precise account of cytology and particularly the cytogenetics of the most instructive animals and plants.

PROBLEMS

2–1   Make from memory a large, clear diagram of the stages of mitotic cell division and then check your completed work with the text.

2–2   After reviewing meiosis draw from memory the behavior of one pair of chromosomes starting in a gonial cell of either sex and continuing through both maturation divisions into a mature gamete. After checking your work make a second series of diagrams to illustrate the maturation products from a gonial cell of the other sex.

2–3   How many assortments of the (maternal and paternal members of) different pairs of chromosomes could be produced by meiosis in a species
(a) Having 6 chromosomes in body cells?
(b) Having 12 chromosomes in body cells?
(c) Having 22 chromosomes in somatic (body) cells?

2–4   Briefly define:

adenine
thymine
nucleoside
nucleotide
DNA

2–5   If analysis of the DNA of a certain species showed 30 percent adenine and 20 percent guanine among the base residues what other bases would you expect and in what amounts?

chapter 3

Variations of Simple Ratios
in Small Families

Ideal ratios are not always encountered, as most people realize out of their own personal experience. Families of two children do not always consist of one boy and one girl; a true coin does not always fall heads and tails alternately in a sequence of flips, and a hand of bridge is not limited to containing six red and seven black cards or seven red and six black cards just because the deck from which it was dealt contained equal numbers of red and black cards. Yet these common observations are sometimes forgotten when one turns his attention to the laws of inheritance, whether they may apply to the sex ratio, the 3 : 1 ratio or other predicted mean ratios among two or more classes. Although we seek certainty and have a mental preference for the ideal expectations, the scientist must be prepared also to accept deviations from the ideal and sometimes very wide deviations. Conversely, it is said that nothing is impossible. Hence we need to unify these diverse statements by some suitable, comprehensive frame of reference. Such a unification may be obtained by knowing the probability of each and every outcome possible in small-sized families such as human sibships typically must be.

The methods discussed in this chapter are suitable and necessary for sibships of up to 12 and even 20 members, should such be encountered. A record number of 24 births has been claimed for Mrs. Orlean Hawks Puckett, who lived beside the present Blue Ridge Parkway in southern Virginia. Even such a number can be considered, statistically speaking, to be on the border zone between small and large numbers. Computations for larger numbers, or for convenient but less accurate treatment of small size samples, will be described in Chapter 7.

PARAMETER VERSUS EVENTS

A distinction must be made between the true parameter and the outcome of one or more samples. The *parameter* is the true expectation, known or unknown, as it exists in nature. It is assumed to be operating constantly during the course of a sampling period and therefore determining the overall expectation. One parameter might be a 1 : 1 expectation, as for the formation of males and females at fertilization, never changing with age or season. Another parameter might be the Mendelian expectation of 3 Dominant : 1 recessive among any and all offspring from certain kinds of parents. A parameter of 1 : 5 would be operating for the upturn of a specified face of a true die, say the six-spot side. Many other parameters exist; some of them are easily figured from strictly mechanical models, but other parameters must be estimated from samples taken under assumed uniform conditions. Thus in a biological situation where some circular reasoning is involved, it is well to pay careful attention to both parts of the cycle, the assumptions of uniformity and the methods of assessing variation as found in different small samples.

Biological differences which segregate as if influenced by 1 : 1 parameters are both numerous and convincing, and they are closely associated with chromosomal segregation. It seems fair to say that many of these estimated 1 : 1 parameters would be realized exactly if we performed the impossible feat of using all the sperm of an XY male. Then the resulting male and female offspring would be equal just as the red and black cards in a complete deck. Actually it is doubtful if as much as 1/10 of the sperm output of an insect may be used; more likely it is less than 1/1000. In mammals only 1/1,000,000 or even a smaller fraction of the sperm output is probably sampled by fusion with egg nuclei.

Incomplete sampling, and therefore the necessity of estimating the determining parameters, is also forced upon the observer or experimenter by the maturation of only one egg and the simultaneous loss of sister nuclei in degenerating polar bodies. Were it possible to sample completely the four nuclei produced in oogenesis, as it is in the mold *Neurospora* and in other kinds of Ascomycetes, exactly equal ratios from the simplest crosses would doubtless be obtained. Whether it be forced upon us by lack of time, lack of facilities or by the nature of the beast, sampling, as opposed to complete enumeration, brings us to a consideration of probability distributions, or simply to natural variation.

EXPECTED SAMPLES FROM A 1:1 PARAMETER

The full range of expression of an ideal ratio is easy to present for small-sized human families. For samples of size one it is obvious that the samples will be of two kinds, those with one class and those families with the other class. In the case of an equal expectation, these kinds of samples of one would occur with equal frequency. For samples of size two, both children could be of one class, or both of the other, or there could be one of each. For samples of size three, all could be of one class, all of the other class, or the sample could be two and one or one and two. These four samples comprise the complete distribution of outcomes in samples of size three, for no other kinds are possible. The kinds of outcomes as well as the relative frequencies of each are obtained simply by expanding the binomial $(a + b)^n$. In this formula a and b represent, respectively, the probability (parametric) of the first outcome and the probability of the other outcome, and together they must total one, which is the numerical equivalent of certainty. This binomial expression is to be raised to the nth power, where n is the number of independent individuals in the sample. Note that, for lack of independence, two identical twins would count as one of a kind and as one in the total sample size. Some examples of the full range of outcomes for samples of sizes 2, 4, 8, and 16 are presented in Figure 3-1 as illustrative of certain trends. These curves were computed by letting the parameter a equal .5, and therefore, in a binomial, b had to equal the remaining .5 chance.

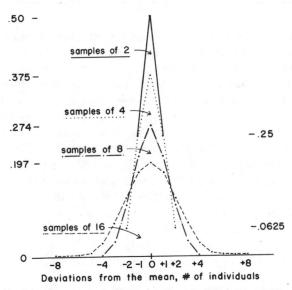

FIGURE 3-1 Random deviations from a mean expectation of 1 : 1 according to size of the sample, computed by the exact binomial expansion.

With increasing size of sample the probability of getting the ideal ratio, 1 : 1, 2 : 2, 4 : 4, and 8 : 8, in Figure 3-1 decreases even though each of these remains the most likely result, the *mode*, on its curve. Other outcomes of greater variety are possible in each larger sample as the height at the mode shrinks to a smaller percentage of the whole distribution. Similarly, the ease of realizing the extremes of distribution, 2 : 0, 4 : 0, 8 : 0, 16 : 0, and their opposite extremes, decreases with increasing sample size. For instance, 0 : 2 is expected $\frac{1}{4}$ of the time in samples of size two; 0 : 4 is expected in 1/16 of samples of size four; 0 : 8 is expected only 1/256 of the time among samples of eight having the assumed equal expectation of *a* and *b*.

TABLE 3-1   Pascal's triangle, or the numbers of orders of birth having the same ratio of classes

			1		1			1 child
		1		2		1		2 sibs
	1		3		3		1	3 sibs
1		4		6		4	1	4 sibs
1	5		10		10		5	1	5 sibs
1	6	15		20		15	6	1	6 sibs

To facilitate the computation of exact probabilities in small samples it is well to remember the distribution of numbers in what is known as Pascal's triangle (Table 3-1). These numbers give the number of ways, i.e., orders of birth, in which the same family total may be reached. For instance, in sibships of six there are 15 ways of obtaining four of kind *a* and two of kind *b*, and there are 20 different and mutually exclusive orders of birth which result in the 3 : 3 total. Pascal's triangle may be extended indefinitely by a simple system which is perhaps apparent to the reader. The symmetry of these figures has been called beautiful; and the usefulness of Pascal's triangle will be quickly grasped by those students who may prefer geometrical presentations to algebraic formulas. However, the latter students will obtain the same coefficients (i.e., number of orders of birth) for any one term of the expansion by using the expression

$$\frac{n!}{r!(n-r)!}$$

where *n* is the total number of individuals in the sample; *r* is the number of one kind; and *n* − *r* is the remaining number of individuals of the other kind. By adding horizontally across one line of the triangle one may obtain the number of different kinds of sibships and the total possible combinations in one sample size. Only when the alternate expectations are equal, when *a* equals *b*, are the mirrored outcomes (i.e., 4 : 1 versus 1 : 4) equal to each other. This may be verified by using the full formula for one term of the binomial

$$\frac{n!}{r!(n-r)!}\, a^r b^{n-r}$$

and substituting $\frac{1}{2}$ for a and $\frac{1}{2}$ for b. The relation of Pascal's triangle to Figures 3-2 and 3-3 is not very difficult to see. We shall continue to consider the variability of samples in the special case where the parameters a and b are equal.

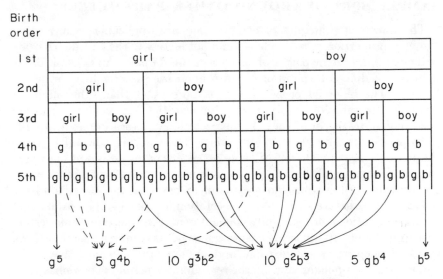

FIGURE 3-2 Distributions of girls and boys in small sibships.

A graphic illustration of the full range of expression of $1:1$ expectations in small-sized sibships may be presented. In Figure 3-2 the order of each birth is numbered from the top line to the bottom, and the proportion of sibships of each sequence is indicated by the widths of the boxes on any horizontal line. Thus, one-half of single child families have a girl born, one-half have a boy. One-eighth of three child families (line 3) have three girls born, and another one-eighth (just beyond the center) have the sequence of boy, girl, girl; and only one sequence of three can result in all boys, represented by the last one-eighth of line 3. Comparison of the several lines will remind one that with each additional child the number of different sequences of siblings is doubled, so that by the fifth birth there are 32 different possible sequences. Note that no one sequence is more likely than another as long as there are strictly equal expectations of g and b. If one wishes to know the final ratios rather than the alternative sequences which compose them, the accumulations to any level may be made from the figure, or they may be computed from the binomial expansion, which is perhaps easier. A reconciliation of the two methods may be made by comparing the bottom boxes of Figure 3-2 with the expansion of the binomial $(g + b)^5$ which has been written out just below the boxes with the multiple sources of certain of the final ratios shown by the arrows.

SAMPLE SPREAD AROUND OTHER PARAMETERS

The foregoing principles of computation are applicable to any other expected proportion between classes and not merely to the 1 : 1 distribution of the sex chromosome pair or of another dissimilar pair. An example of the influence of different values of a and b upon the samples to be expected follows. The binomial probabilities are more exact than other methods especially for samples up to 20 when intermediate parameter values are operating, or to almost 30 for a 3 : 1 expectation and for samples up to 100 when parameters like 19 : 1 are operating. The unifying rule is that where the product npq (equal to nab of Table 3-2) is five or less, it is best to employ the binomial probabilities. Tables for this purpose have been published by the Bureau of Standards and are found in many of the larger libraries.

Let us take the Mendelian 3 : 1 expectation in small samples as our first example of ratios more generally encountered. Assume that from certain parents a Dominant-appearing offspring is to be expected $\frac{3}{4}$ of the time and a recessive offspring $\frac{1}{4}$ of the time and assume, furthermore, that these parameters do not change during the reproductive period. Thus sibships of one Dominant will comprise $\frac{3}{4}$ of all sibships of size one, and recessives will comprise the remainder of sibships. Birth of a second child will divide the former two kinds into four kinds of sibships: (1) those with two Dominants, (2) those with Dominant followed by recessive, (3) those with recessive followed by a Dominant and finally, (4) those sibships with two recessives. Birth of a third child will again divide each two-child sibship into two kinds of three-child sibships. The sequence is visualized in Figure 3-3 for a sequence of three births in which, at each birth, the likelihood of having a Dominant is three times the likelihood of having a recessive. The diagram carefully reflects this independence of each birth from what has resulted in previous pregnancies.

The binomial method will give the same answer more efficiently. One now substitutes $\frac{3}{4}$ for a and $\frac{1}{4}$ for b as the parameters for the outcome of one Dominant or one recessive, respectively. Line 2 of the figure is distributed

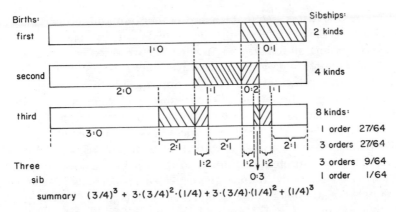

FIGURE 3-3 Distributions of Dominant (white) and recessive (shaded) phenotypes in small sibships.

according to the terms $(\frac{3}{4})^2$ and $2(\frac{3}{4})\frac{1}{4}$ and $(\frac{1}{4})^2$. This comes out to be 9/16 of sibships with two successive Dominants, 6/16 with one of each, and 1/16 of sibships with two recessives. Therefore sibships of two will tend to occur in the three proportions .56, .375, and .06 for all possible outcomes based on the 3 : 1 overall expectation. The expansion of $(\frac{3}{4}$ Dominant and $\frac{1}{4}$ recessive$)^3$ gives rise to the proportions used in line 3 of Figure 3-3 and to the algebraic sums written just below it.

For larger sized samples from unequal ratios it is obvious that the graphic method will rapidly become tedious, and so the algebraic method should be employed. Thus to get the expansion of $a + b$ to a higher power, n (where $n = 4$), one may multiply the expansion of it to a lower power, such as 3, by the expansion of the remaining lower power, $4 - 3$ or 1. For instance, one may take the distribution from Figure 3-3 and express it in ratio form for multiplying as follows

$$
\begin{array}{r}
27\ DDD\quad +\quad 27\ DDd\quad +\quad 9\ Ddd\quad +\quad ddd \\
3\ D\quad +\quad d \\
\hline
81\ DDDD\quad +\quad 81\ DDDd\ +\ 27\ DDdd\ +\ 3\ Dddd \\
27\ DDDd\ +\ 27\ DDdd\ +\ 9\ Dddd\ +\ 1\ dddd \\
\hline
81\ \text{of}\ D^4\quad +\quad 108\ \text{of}\ D^3d\ +\ 54\ \text{of}\ D^2d^2\ +\ 12\ \text{of}\ Dd^3\ +\ 1\ d^4
\end{array}
$$

The sum of all coefficients is 256, and hence that many sibships would be required to show in whole numbers the ideal distribution of sibships of size four where the constant parameters are $\frac{3}{4}$ for D and $\frac{1}{4}$ for d. Computation by direct expansion of the binomial to the desired power is of course easier.

From the above it is seen that a family of four from suitable parents would contain no recessives 81/256 of the time, whereas at the opposite extreme a sample containing all four recessives would be expected only 1/256 of the time. Furthermore, a majority of recessives may be expected 12/256 of the time, while the representative 3 : 1 mode appears only in some 42 percent of the samples. The expectation for the frequency of each possible outcome under this 3 : 1 parameter in sibship sample sizes from one through nine is given in Figure 3-4, after the birth orders have been grouped.

The point of being conversant with these distributions is to know what results are to be expected in addition to the outcome closest to the ideal. Furthermore, one needs to know the expected proportions of near misses and of not-so-near misses. Finally, one needs to know what outcomes are so little likely as random variables that he might profitably seek to formulate hypotheses which would set up new expectations nearer to an observed result. Thus one would expect to encounter a 1 Dominant : 3 recessive distribution, in spite of an overall expectation of 3 : 1, only .047 of the time among families of size four, and this particular sample result should be considered both as a rare but possible deviation from 3 : 1 and as a possible result of some other unnamed influences. Discoveries are made by considering alternate explanations of rare events. Arbitrarily we are guided by the rule that events are "rare" or "exceptional" when they would occur less than 5 percent of the time as mere random deviations under the stated assumptions.

SECONDARY SEX RATIOS

A ratio studied longer than any other and sampled perhaps more extensively than any other is the ratio of males to females at the time of birth. It is called the secondary sex ratio to distinguish it from the primary ratio at fertilization, which is usually assumed to be one to one. The vital statistics of several European countries and the United States have included these data since before there was a science of genetics, and today it is possible to make large scale studies on certain geographical groups or on other subdivisions of the population. In most large samples of the secondary sex ratio there is a slight excess of males to females. Among North American whites this is around 106 males : 100 females; among other populations the excess of males is even greater, and it ranges from above 111 down to the very slight margin of 101 : 100 in favor of the males.

The reason for the consistent excess of human male births has been sought in terms of differential selection during implantation of the fertilized ovum and during pregnancy. Two general possibilities exist: (a) early selection

Number of recessive offspring from two heterozygous parents

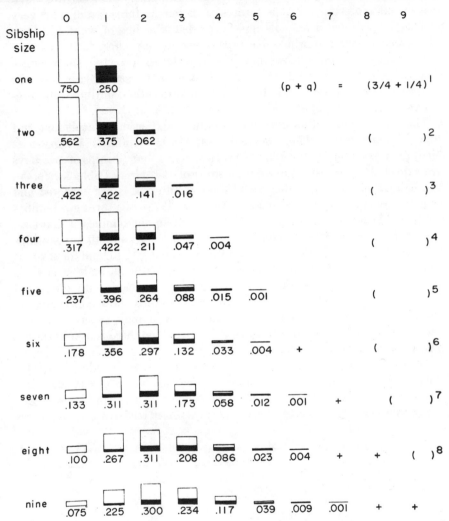

FIGURE 3-4 Distribution of sibships of various sizes by totals of recessive and dominant individuals regardless of order of birth. Figures (and height) show proportion of that kind among that size of sibship. Black denotes the recessive fraction, white the dominant fraction within sibship.

might be against female zygotes and later selection against males, but not as severely, or (b) the primary sex ratio might be higher than any later sex ratio as a result of preferential fertilization by Y sperm, followed by somewhat higher mortality of males than females *in utero.* There is direct evidence that more human male fetuses than female fetuses die; and very recently experimental animals have provided evidence of what has been called *meiotic drive,* by which one type of sperm may effect fertilization in as much as 90 percent of the offspring of a testcross in certain tailless mice studied by Dunn and in several other animals and insects. However, the action of meiotic drive seems to be of limited duration, until one allele replaces another in a population.

The consequences of an unequal sex ratio might seem slight at first, but they are cumulative. The observation of .515 males and .485 females at birth (corresponding to the 106 : 100 ratio) means that sibships of two boys are expected more often than are sibships of two girls (Table 3-2 for an approximation, line 2). Likewise sibships of three boys are expected and usually encountered with frequency $(.515)^3$, or .137, while three girl families are found with lower frequency $(.485)^3$, or .114, among families of that size. With even more children the disparity between all girl and all boy sibships increases so that for sibships of six the ratio is about 19 : 13, and for sibships of 12 : 0 versus 0 : 12 the disproportion in favor of the all male sibships is more than 2 : 1. Comparisons of the binomial expectations with the actual observations of the sex distribution in large sibships show consistent excesses of predominantly male and predominantly female sibships, so that one is led to question the basic assumption, whether there is a uniform expectation for each birth and/or for all families.

The best evidence for mixed expectations as to the secondary sex ratio comes from experiments with animals rather than from observation and statistical study of data on humans, even though the available census data are voluminous. By consistently selecting rats from sibships with an excess

TABLE 3-2 Distribution of random samples of two, according to $(a + b)^2$

Parameters	Both *a*	One of each	Both *b*
$a = .50 = b$	.25	.50	.25
$a = .52,\quad b = .48$	.27	.499	.23
$a = .75,\quad b = .25$	.56	.375	.06
$a = .90,\quad b = .10$	.81	.18	.01

of males in one line of descent and in a parallel line selecting for an excess of females in a colony, Weir has bred two lines of rats in which the expected proportion of males in the high line is 52.8 percent and in the low line is 41.8 percent. The establishment of these two separate and different lines by selection in opposite directions from the same source shows that there are genotypic differences with respect to sex ratio among mice. These differences were doubtless present as a mixture in the colony from which the experiment began.

A rather common and very persistent belief is that during times of war the human secondary sex ratio rises slightly. The increases found have been so small that it is a surprise that the idea ever got started unless one remembers that samples can vary, that variations toward more males might get more public attention and that variations toward more females might receive less notice in wartime. Careful studies for changing expectation have been made in a manner useful also in studying the incidence of other genetic conditions such as twinning, Down's syndrome of mongolism and other phenotypes. The sex ratio was found to vary with *parity* (or birth number) such that the first birth was more apt to be that of a boy than would the second birth. The relation of this to war seems to be that there was a greater than usual number of first pregnancies (*primiparae*) during the early year or so of a war. However, the age of the mother might be more closely associated with sex ratio differences than would birth order, and this has also been studied by statistical methods. It is less obvious that the age of the father might influence the sex ratio among his children, and although all the subtle differences in the secondary sex ratios remain slight, a recent large study by Novitski and Kimball shows that there is a relatively greater influence of paternal age than of the mother's age or order of birth upon the human sex ratio at birth.

SUMMARY

Three general conclusions may be drawn from this chapter. First, single human families and even small collections of sibships may exhibit ratios with extremely wide departures from the parameter which is actually operating. Second, the expected distribution of small samples around the ideal is best figured by the method of expanding the binomial. Third, a mixture of parameters, or a changing parameter, will lead to the observation of more sibships being in the extremes of the distribution than the binomial expansion predicts on the usual assumption of uniformity.

SUGGESTED READING

Levene, Howard, "Statistical Inference in Genetics" in E. W. Sinnott, L. C. Dunn, and T. Dobzhansky, *Principles of Genetics* 5th ed., New York, McGraw-Hill, 1958, 459 pp. Paragraphs 1 to 8 are very pertinent at this point. Has handy chart of confidence intervals on page 395.

Mosteller, F., R. E. K. Rourke, and G. B. Thomas, Jr., *Probability and Statistics*, Reading, Mass., Addison-Wesley, 1961, 395 pp. A handy introduction. Has useful tables on normal curves and binomials.

Novitski, E., and A. W. Kimball, Birth order, parental ages, and sex of offspring. Amer. J. Hum. Genet. 10: 268–275 (1958). Describes the very small changes in sex ratio detectable in large totals.

Weir, J. A., Hereditary and environmental influences on the sex ratio of PHH and PHL mice. Genetics 47: 881–897 (1962). Describes strain differences between selected lines of high blood pH and low pH.

Handbook of Mathematical Tables 1st ed., 579 pp., supplement to *Handbook of Chemistry and Physics*, Cleveland, Chemical Rubber Publishing Co., 1962.

Tables of the Binomial Probability Distribution, National Bureau of Standards, Applied Mathematics Series No. 6.

PROBLEMS

3–1 Briefly define:

> parameter
> mean
> mode
> sample
> primiparae

3–2 State an assumption necessary to the use of formulas in this chapter for the computation of the proportion of families of five which contain five boys.

3–3 (a) Approximately how do the numbers of families of three containing three boys compare with the number of that size family containing three girls?
(b) Would your answer still be true for families of nine children?

3–4 How often would the 3 : 1 ratio be realized exactly
(a) In sibships of four from heterozygous parents?
(b) In sibships of eight?

3–5 From memory make a Pascal's triangle to cover all possible sex distributions of seven sibs and express the last line in complete algebraic form ready for the substitution of parameters a and b.

chapter 4

Segregation in Monohybrid Inheritance

Whenever we deal with the effects of a single gene pair, we are concerned with the simplest of all genetic situations, monohybrid inheritance. Practically all complex determinations in genetics are influenced by the behavior of one or more gene pairs; it was part of the genius of Mendel that he sought to explain *unit differences*, as he called them, rather than the whole gamut of differences between inbred strains of peas. After mastering the fundamentals of monohybrid segregation, he clearly showed how two pairs and three pairs would segregate and assort, and he predicted the higher orders of diversity which have subsequently been well substantiated. In the remainder of Part One we shall concentrate on all of the main aspects of monohybrid inheritance, such as the development of simple phenotypic differences, population ratios and effects of consanguineous matings. Then we shall proceed to dihybrids and multihybrids in Part Two.

PHENOTYPIC SEGREGATION WITHOUT DOMINANCE

The M-N Antigenic Blood Type Difference. This clearly defined difference in the blood of humans shows that it is determined by a single pair of genetic factors. Human beings differ in respect to antigens on their red blood cells by having an M substance, an N substance or both. The steps in demonstrating the types are fairly simple. One starts with an injection of the cells from a person of known blood type, such as M, into a rabbit. Then after several days a sample of blood plasma of the rabbit may be diluted and used to test samples of whole blood from many people. Cells from a type M person are quickly clumped (*agglutinated*) by the test rabbit serum, while cells without M remain normally dispersed in anti-M serum. All humans tested fall clearly into three phenotypic classes, those having antigen M only, those having another antigen called N and finally persons having both M and N on their red blood corpuscles. The antibody against N cells is obtained from the plasma of other rabbits which have been injected with some red blood cells from a person without any M antigen (Figure 4-1).

Blood from   Sera containing   Phenotype shown

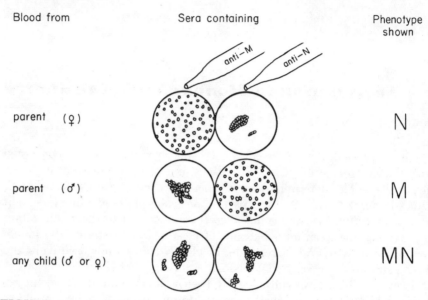

FIGURE 4-1 Agglutination (clumping) of red blood cells by serum which contains a specific antibody. All persons are in one of these three blood types.

Within a family the members may all be of one class or may divide among two or even three types depending on the kinds of parents. By serological tests combining a drop of human blood with each of the two kinds of anti-sera from the rabbits it has been shown repeatedly that the children of type M father and type M mother are also of type M. Likewise the children of N by N parents are all of type N. However, marriages between type M and type N parents result in children all of one intermediate type, MN. When an MN person and an N person have children, each child resembles one parent or the other in respect to the M-N contrast; likewise the children from type M and MN parents segregate into type M and type MN off-spring. When a type MN woman and a type MN man have a family each child belongs to one or another of the three kinds, M, MN, or N blood type. In this last kind of sibship it is noteworthy that MN individuals are twice as numerous as are the type M individuals or the type N sibs separately. These facts lead to an explanation in terms of one pair of genic differences located on one pair of homologous chromosomes.

Here the three kinds of phenotypes correspond to three different genotypes, and we have no complication by any dominance. The M phenotype person has two genes of the same kind which we shall call $L^M L^M$, the N person differs in having two genes of the opposite kind making the genotype $L^N L^N$, and the MN phenotype has one of each of these genes and therefore the genotype $L^M L^N$. The L^M and L^N forms of the gene are called *alleles* of each other because they are not identical genes and because observation shows that they *always segregate* from each other in reproduction. The L^M and L^N are said to occupy corresponding *sites* or *loci* on homologous chromosomes, and therefore when meiosis separates the two chromosomes of a pair the two $L^M L^M$ genes (or the two $L^N L^N$ genes or the L^M and L^N genes) are carried to opposite cells in their respective chromosomes. Thus each parent will hand on to any one offspring only one of the two genes which he or she possesses at the L locus, or at any locus. The symbol L honors the name of Landsteiner who discovered blood antigens of another kind in 1900 and then with Levine in 1927 demonstrated the M-N antigenic difference.

We may elaborate usefully on the definitions above by saying that a *homozygous* individual arose from the union of two gametes containing identical genes of the pair under discussion and that the homozygote can produce only one kind of gamete. By contrast, the *heterozygous* person arose from the union of an egg and a sperm containing allelic forms rather than identical forms of a gene pair, and the heterozygote will produce two kinds of gametes if it is monohybrid, more if it is dihybrid (Chapter 10). In the genotypes of parents and child shown below it will be noted that parents both of whom are homozygous will produce only one kind of child in each family, because each parent forms only one kind of egg or one kind of sperm in respect to the L gene.

$$L^M L^M \quad \text{by} \quad L^M L^M \quad \rightarrow \quad L^M L^M \text{ offspring}$$

$$L^M L^M \quad \text{by} \quad L^N L^N \quad \rightarrow \quad L^M L^N \text{ offspring}$$

$$L^N L^N \quad \text{by} \quad L^N L^N \quad \rightarrow \quad L^N L^N \text{ offspring}$$

The possibilities increase if one or both parents are heterozygous and can form two kinds of gametes. The three combinations of parents and offspring shown below in genotypic form correspond to three different kinds of crosses in animal or plant experiments, namely, the backcross, the testcross and the F_1 by F_1 cross. In human genetics the *backcross* type of mating would be between a heterozygote and a homozygote (MN either to an M spouse or to an N spouse). The backcross would be expected to produce only two kinds of children in equal numbers, homozygotes like the one parent and heterozygotes like the other (see the first and third families). Such a 1 : 1 sibship may be called a backcross sibship although it is preferably called a *testcross generation* if dominance is acting.

$$L^M L^M \quad \text{by} \quad L^M L^N \quad \rightarrow \quad L^M L^M \quad \text{and} \quad L^M L^N \qquad \qquad \text{offspring}$$

$$L^M L^N \quad \text{by} \quad L^M L^N \quad \rightarrow \quad L^M L^M \quad \text{and} \quad 2L^M L^N \quad \text{and} \quad L^N L^N \text{ offspring}$$

$$L^M L^N \quad \text{by} \quad L^N L^N \quad \rightarrow \qquad \qquad \qquad L^M L^N \qquad \quad L^N L^N \text{ offspring}$$

Parent pairs of the F_1 by F_1 type, or better *heterozygote by heterozygote* (see the middle family above) may have among their offspring three kinds of genotypes and therefore three kinds of M-N phenotypes. These are homozygous M children, heterozygous MN children and homozygous N blood types in the ratio of 1 : 2 : 1, respectively. This ratio corresponds to the segregation ratio in the F_2 generation of a typical laboratory or greenhouse experiment for any pair of genes which are expressed without the intervention of dominance of one phenotype. Examples of 1 : 2 : 1 ratios in the F_2 generation are numerous and widespread among plants and animals but not common as we presently observe and classify people. The use of more refined methods of classification, chemical and otherwise, will doubtless reveal more gene pairs in which some aspect of the phenotype of the heterozygote will differentiate it from that homozygote which it may more closely resemble.

Other Examples.   The *singing voice* has its characteristic range set by a single pair of genes, according to a theory of F. Bernstein. Women are either sopranos, mezzo-sopranos, or altos according to the segregation of a single pair of genes, and young boys also have the same genetic determination of their childhood voice ranges before the voice lowers in the teen years. Thus sopranos include females and young boys with two doses of the same allele; altos are homozygous for the opposite allele; and mezzosopranos are heterozygous for the two alleles. With the arrival of sexual maturity the alto voices of boys become only moderately lower and are tenor voices; the mezzo-soprano voices of childhood become the baritones of maturity; and the high soprano voices of young boys become deep bass voices of adulthood. Obviously, the genotype of any of these individuals does not change during growth by mitotic division, but the hormonal background has changed; therefore it should not be surprising that the phenotype might change, and this is such an example. In this illustration the modifiability of the phenotypes has not been such as to hide or to override the underlying genic differences between persons. Such recognition of several separate influences is not always the case.

A rare one of the several forms of freckling shows an intermediate phenotype for the heterozygote and extreme expression in the homozygote. In this example the heterozygote for the *xeroderma pigmentosum* gene shows a rare pattern of heavy freckling which is accentuated by exposure to sunlight, like the commoner types of freckling. Heterozygotes of the same scarce kind very seldom are married to each other, and so there are not many individuals known who have a double dose of the rare allele. However, the gene locus is known and the allele is named by the skin condition of the rare homozygote. A double dose of this gene results in the skin condition called xeroderma pigmentosum, in which the freckling is very heavy, and numerous small cancerous growths in the skin lead to an earlier than normal death.

COMMON PHENOTYPES INVOLVING DOMINANCE

In monohybrid genetic studies it is frequently found that only two phenotypes appear instead of three, and this may mean that the heterozygotes are mixed in the same phenotypic class with one of the homozygotes. Whichever phenotype includes both the heterozygotes and homozygotes is called the *dominant phenotype;* by contrast the *recessive phenotype* is pure and not a mixture of genotypes. A gene which in single dose produces as much phenotypic effect as two doses is fully dominant or, simply, *dominant.* The use of a capital letter in the symbol for the Dominant allele is a preferred usage. This leaves lower case letters for the recessive allele where only two alleles are known for a gene site. The name of each Dominant phenotype will be capitalized in this text.

The ability to taste the chemical PTC (phenylthiocarbamide) as bitter or not divides people, both male and female, into two different phenotypes. It is fortunate that PTC is no longer used in making plastic ice-cube trays. Two *nontaster* parents have only children like themselves in this respect, and this is the indication that the nontasters are the recessive phenotype. Conversely, PTC *Taster* parents may have among their offspring one or more nontasters. Any nontaster child from two Taster parents shows that both of the parents were heterozygotes from among the mixture of Dominant phenotypes. Thus all nontasters breed true whereas some Tasters do and some do not. Contrasting results from phenotypically similar matings demonstrate the complication introduced by dominance (Figures 4-2 and 4-3).

Handedness has genetic as well as social determination. In many families of right-handed parents two or more left-handed children are known, and this has been interpreted by some geneticists to mean that there is a simple

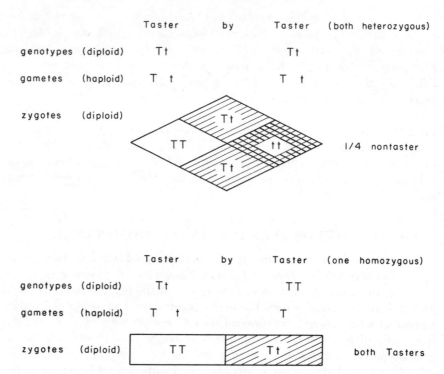

FIGURE 4-2 Inheritance of PTC-tasting ability. Phenylthiocarbamide seems distinctly bitter to some persons, yet may be without taste to some of their offspring.

mode of inheritance in which left-handedness is recessive to right-handedness. On this hypothesis two left-handed parents would be expected to have only left-handed children, but there are many exceptions to this. Recently Falek has found that left-handed mothers have more left-handed children than do left-handed fathers or the other two combinations of kinds of parents. Although some 5 percent of college students are left-handed, our information about the inheritance of handedness is inconclusive for at least two major reasons. Environmental pressures from parents and teachers to make children become right-handed are strong in some instances and weak in others, so that large numbers of children cannot be easily studied under the uniform environmental conditions of growth so necessary to the scientist before drawing inferences as to genotypes. It would not even be easy to measure the degree of environmental pressure on different children because of the varying ways in which encouragement and discouragement are

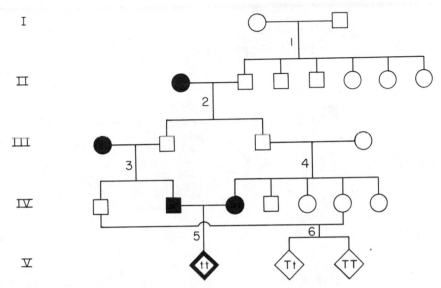

FIGURE 4-3 Hypothetical pedigree to illustrate genetic types of crosses. Circle, a female; square, a male; diamond, sibs of either sex. Darkened symbols are for the rarer genetic phenotype, here recessive nontasting. 1, inbred Dominants with no genetic segregation; 2, outcross and no segregation; 3, testcross from which a recessive (male) results; 4, outcross by chance producing a recessive (female); 5, inbred recessives produce only recessives (*tt*); 6, inbred Dominants in a cousin marriage, also a backcross type producing no phenotypic segregation but only Dominants of the *Tt* and *TT* varieties.

applied. The second reason is that handedness may not be a monofactorial trait in more than a few pedigrees. The collaboration of several gene pairs may safely be assumed, with some pairs having modifiable effects and other pairs leading to phenotypes which develop more inevitably.

A less modifiable phenotypic difference is that between the presence of *Free earlobes* and their virtual absence (see Figure 4-4). The Free earlobes are the more common form. Persons who do have attached lobes, those which merge into the side of the head, are frequently found to have both parents Free-lobed. This indicates that attached earlobes may be recessive to Free earlobes, but the question deserves further study, preferably within large pedigrees.

An often cited unit genetic difference is eye color, whether the *iris* is *pigmented* or unpigmented. Eye color is certainly a genetically determined trait as shown by many close resemblances within families and by differ-

Recessive attached earlobes

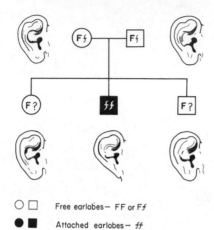

FIGURE 4-4 Earlobe inheritance according to a simple monohybrid hypothesis.

O ☐   Free earlobes— F F or F*f*

● ■   Attached earlobes— *ff*

ences between races, but it is an oversimplification to say that blue eyes are recessive to brown eyes. Rather it is a general rule that the unpigmented iris, whether blue or hazel or gray, seems to be recessive to the various shades of brown caused by the deposition of brown pigment in melanophore cells. However, the distinction is not always a sharply defined one, for the degree of pigment may be so light that a person is classified in the unpigmented "blue" phenotype although he or she may be genotypically able to transmit a gene or genes for unmistakable dominant iris pigmentation. Even though the genetic determination of eye color is not well-enough established for exact genetic studies, such as for chromosomal linkage, a fundamental distinction between dominance and prevalence of a phenotype may be pointed out.

A recessive phenotype is not necessarily rare in a population, but only within certain categories of families such as testcrosses and F_2 types. For instance, the blue eyes which tend to show recessive inheritance where testable are very common among Scandinavian peoples, a little less common among the English and rare among southern Europeans. Conversely, the Dominant phenotype happens to be the prevalent phenotype within certain kinds of sibships, those where one parent is a homozygous Dominant and where both parents are heterozygous monohybrids. Yet the question of dominance receives only an indicated answer by noting the relative numbers within a collection of data; the question of dominance is really settled by examination of the phenotype of known hybrids, that is, of F_1 offspring from homozygotes of contrasting phenotypes.

RARE PHENOTYPES DOMINANT TO THE NORMAL

Some of the genetically well-known Dominant phenotypes are so rare that the homozygous Dominant is not formed or remains unidentified. If the homozygote is phenotypically like the heterozygote, the examples which follow would behave genetically like the PTC Tasters discussed above. If, however, the homozygotes should be more extreme than the heterozygote, inheritance would then follow the pattern illustrated earlier by the M-N blood type difference. Examples of rarer homozygotes extreme enough to cause death long before the end of pregnancy will be described in Chapter 5. Thus examples of individuals homozygous for many not-so-rare genes having some dominant phenotypic effect in the heterozygote may be missing at the age when surviving members of a sibship are being classified. Therefore information about sibships of grown children may be considered incomplete unless it includes the numbers of juvenile and infant deaths and also the numbers of pregnancies which did not produce a live birth. Such information is not always easy to obtain.

Polydactyly, the presence of a sixth finger or toe, runs in many pedigrees as if determined by a single dominant gene. Each Polydactylous person usually has one affected parent, and the children of a Polydactylous individual and a normal spouse segregate in the testcross ratio with a 1 : 1 expectation. Both of the above statements indicate the heterozygous nature of the individual with the extra digits. Exceptions to the expectation of a Polydactylous parent in each generation of the six-digit pedigrees are explained by two other considerations. The origination of the rare allele for Polydactyly has occurred somewhere by mutation (Chapter 21) from the normal allele in a parent with the normal number of fingers and toes. Hence the Polydactylous part of a pedigree may begin with a single case who has two normal-fingered parents, four normal grandparents and so on among normal ancestors. Another cause for exceptions, to be described more fully in Chapter 17, is that Polydactyly has a wide range of expression, ranging from large extra digits on both hands and both feet to smaller sixth fingers and toes to merely a single extra finger or toe. When this range of variation extends to no extra digits whatever, a person may be classified as normal phenotypically and yet later prove, by a Polydactylous offspring, to have been a dominant heterozygote with chance failure of expression (Chapter 17). Polydactyly is common in cats as a "double-pawed" condition, and it is known in guinea pigs, mice and other animals.

A short-fingered condition known as *Brachydactyly* is similarly inherited. The overall condition of short fingers may be achieved in several different

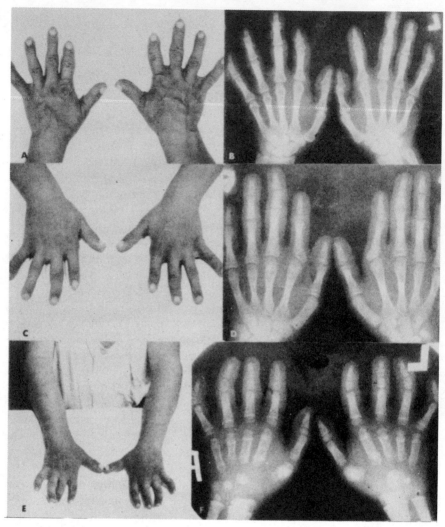

FIGURE 4-5 Brachymesophalangy in a child, mother and grandmother. Some fingers are short because of shortened middle phalanx. Finger tips are normal in X-ray pictures. From Margolis, Schwartz and Falk, J. Hered. **48**: 24 (1957).

ways but is achieved consistently one way within most pedigrees where it is present at all. Thus X-rays may show a shortened middle phalanx of fingers and toes in several persons in one line of descent (Figure 4-5). Another pedigree may show shortness due to a shorter finger tip (Figure 4-6). Only rarely do sibs show both kinds of Brachydactyly (Figure 4-7). Still

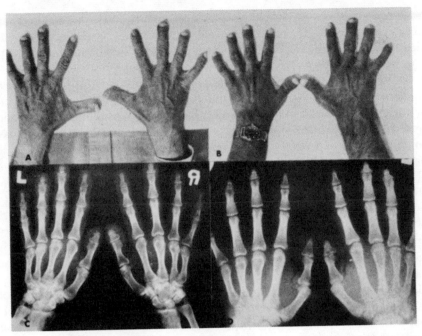

FIGURE 4-6 Brachytelephalangy in father and son. Finger shortness is due mainly to shortness of phalanx bone of finger tip. From Margolis, Schwartz and Falk, J. Hered. **48**: 22 (1957).

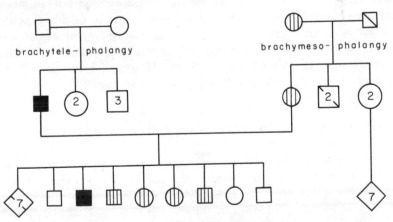

FIGURE 4-7 Short fingers of two different kinds in the same pedigree each due to a different dominant gene. Finger length was not reviewed in seven older members of the largest sibship marked with one diagonal. After Margolis, Schwartz and Falk, J. Hered. **48**: 21 (1957).

other pedigrees may have the fingers shortened in the basal segment. Each form is inherited as if a single abnormal allele within a pedigree were sufficient to cause the development of its own particular kind of dominant short-fingered phenotype.

Kinky hair form is common enough among many Negro peoples, and a similar form, *Woolly hair*, appears independently in a few Caucasian pedigrees. In a Scandinavian family Woolly hair develops as though determined by a single gene which is rare in that part of the world and is therefore easy to trace in lines of descent. When some siblings have Woolly hair and some have straight hair, only the Woolly-haired individuals transmit the effective allele to the next generation; straight-haired segregants breed true for the straight-haired condition, as recessive phenotypes are expected to do.

White forelock, when not acquired from a bottle of bleach or dye, is a part of a genetically determined phenotype which is manifested on widely scattered parts of the body. Small or large areas of skin as well as the hair growing from each such area are completely without dark pigment. The name "white forelock" or "white blaze" suggests the comparison with the diamond-shaped forehead marking of some horses and on the heads of other mammals. The general name of "piebald spotting" infers a comparison with white-spotted rabbits, dogs and other mammals. The causes of white spotting in mammals might be the same in terms of the kind of gene differences involved, or the white spotting in various animals might represent changes of slightly different color genes in the various species. If Brachydactyly, above, is slightly different in unrelated human sibships, then more remotely related species have less chance of having exactly the same kinds of abnormal genes. Yet the phenotypic comparisons among animal species are often close enough to suggest the possibility of similar or identical causes of parallel abnormalities. However, Francois (1961) lists five kinds of white spotting within the human species.

RARE PHENOTYPES RECESSIVE TO NORMAL

The foremost example of a rare recessive trait in man is the usual form of *albinism*, characterized by a complete absence of dark pigment in the skin, hair and iris of the eye. The classic studies of Pearson located numerous pedigrees of recessive albinism in the different races of mankind, and recessive albinos among mammals are familiar as examples of simple Mendelian inheritance in mice, rats, guinea pigs and other animals. The typical albino is pink-eyed, due to the lack of pigment granules in the deeper layer of the iris and the consequent rosy reflection from the blood in the capillaries of the choroid layer of the eyeball. Albinos frequently avoid strong sunlight and peer through partly closed eyelids.

Three principles of recessive inheritance are illustrated among the many pedigrees in which albino persons appear. First, because albinism is recessive to pigmentation, two normally pigmented parents can have an albino child. Second, because the responsible recessive gene is rare, few or no relatives may be found who are also albino, although the larger the pedigree the greater is the chance of finding another albino. Third, because the condition is recessive, two albino persons have only albino offspring. This last is an example of "recessives breeding true"; they breed true because they are not heterozygotes, as some among their dominant brothers and sisters most likely are.

Phenylketonuria, a formerly unsuspected metabolic defect leading to one form of idiocy, is now both diagnosable and remediable if treatment is instituted in early infancy. Normal individuals metabolize phenylpyruvic acid without delay, but children who are homozygous recessive for the rather rare phenylketonuria gene and who eat the usual diet excrete this chemical in the urine. Its presence can be readily detected by the simple test of putting a drop of 10 percent ferric chloride solution on a moist diaper. The spot remains orange in the presence of normal urine, but it turns to a deep blue-green color if the ferric chloride is reduced by the presence of phenylpyruvic acid. The acid has come to the urine from the blood, in which it has been circulating to all parts of the body. This acid is damaging particularly to the normal development of the cells of the brain, and its continued presence results in retarding mental growth so that the child becomes feeble-minded and then idiotic in a few years, if not given a special diet. The fundamental difficulty in the phenylketonuric individuals is an inability to metabolize the amino acid phenylalanine, which is a widely found component of our usual foods. Instead of oxidizing it completely these recessive individuals metabolize it only part of the way along the normal path, and the intermediate product piles up in the tissues and, in the brain at least, acts as a slow poison.

However, phenylketonurics need not develop into idiots if a diet appropriate to them is substituted for the normal foods of infancy and childhood; hence an early diagnosis of the urine content is important. Diets are now available with a very low content of phenylalanine and with substitutes for this usually necessary amino acid. Although these diets were very expensive at first, they are now obtainable at only a modest increase over regular food cost. The appropriate diet should be begun during the first year of life of phenylketonurics and preferably during the first month or two. Thus the full impact of an inherited condition need not be realized in the adult phenotype; the situation is somewhat analogous to cultivating different varieties of a garden plant in different ways.

The above is an excellent example of important, and perhaps general, relationships between heredity and environment in the mutual determination of the phenotype. Sibs having the same normal diet may be of normal intelligence or idiotic, depending on gene segregation. Conversely, two genotypically identical phenylketonurics may later be either idiot or normal in intelligence, with the final difference being attributable to diet and time of dietary adjustment (Figure 4-8). From the standpoint of ex-

FIGURE 4-8 New diet for phenylketonuric babies. Younger sister (left) diagnosed in early infancy and raised on a special diet, low in phenylalanine, and older sister (right) raised on a normal diet. Both have the same rare recessive genotype. From *Life* Magazine © 1962 Time Inc. All rights reserved.

plaining the final phenotype, a geneticist without full information would be hesitant to attribute a normal adult phenotype to the possession of normal genes or to the joint action of abnormal genes and compensating diet.

Similarly, the explanation of an adult idiot could be due to two alternative sequences, either a subnormal genotype without further injury or a normal genotype followed by some later environmental accident like carbon monoxide poisoning. The situation is summarized in Table 4-1. Other recessive genotypes leading to idiocy have also been well identified, and still others doubtless remain to be described.

Juvenile amaurotic idiocy is another well-defined phenotype which is differentiated from normal by yet another recessive gene pair. The rare homozygotes are normal at birth and during infancy but begin to fall behind the norm in mental development during their early teens. This genetic condition differs from the above in that there is a fatty deposition in the cerebellar part of the brain, vision is slowly lost, and the juvenile amaurotics have an early death and leave no progeny. Hence new cases of the homozygous recessive arise from two heterozygous parents. Juvenile amaurotics are not found uniformly around the world but are more common in some groups (for instance among Swedes).

Infantile amaurotic idiocy, also called *Tay-Sachs* disease, is still another phenotype recessive to the normal. It leads to blindness and death earlier than in the previous kind, and it has an onset during infancy as the name implies. The defect is in part differentiated by fatty deposition in the cerebellum and incomplete branching of the ganglion cells of coordination there. Although it is very rare, the disease can be located more readily among Hebrew families and among the Japanese than elsewhere.

TABLE 4-1 Alternative pathways to different phenotypes

Genotype	Environment	End phenotype
phenylketonuric	normal diet	idiot
	special diet	normal I.Q. range
normal metabolic	no poison	normal I.Q. range
	monoxide poisoning	lowered I.Q.

The enumeration and brief description of three genetically different forms of recessive idiot phenotypes have been presented early in this book for several useful purposes. Although these three phenotypes could be carelessly grouped as idiots and spoken of together, they exhibit three different times of departure from the normal, three different lengths of life expectation, two or more chemical pathways different from normal and at least one successful therapeutic procedure.

The general phenotype of *deafness* may have various causes, and these include obvious injury or infection after birth, fever in the third month of pregnancy or earlier genetic causes. Hereditary deafness is known to behave as if differentiated from normal by recessive genes. It is usual for genetically deaf children to have hearing parents and hearing brothers and sisters, as many pedigree studies show. Even where one parent is deaf, normal and deaf children are both possible as in a testcross generation. When pairs of deaf people have children the results may at first seem surprising in that the rule of "recessives breeding true" sometimes seems broken. In particular, some pairs of deaf parents have only deaf children, as expected, whereas other pairs of deaf parents, each of whom has near relatives who are deaf, have only hearing children. Because parallel data have long been known from studies of other animals and of plants there is a ready hypothesis that we must consider. Two different causes of hereditary deafness, each recessive to normal hearing, might be involved.

True breeding of recessive phenotypes is found only where the parents are recessives both with the same genotype and not one with a *mimic* phenotype. Parents *dd* by *dd* would have only *dd* offspring who would be deaf. Similarly, parents who are deaf and are *ee* by *ee* would have only deaf children, those differentiated from normal by the *ee* part of the genotype. An opposite result appears in the immediate generation of offspring from marriages of two deaf parents who are not of the same genotype, for all of their children are hearing children although they carry two different recessive deaf genes. It must be pointed out that because these genes for deafness are rather rare the *dd* deafened parent is usually homozygous *EE*, and the *ee* parent is usually homozygous for the normal pair *DD*. Thus each such homozygous parent will contribute a dominant gene which will cover up the phenotypic effect of the recessive from the other parent, so deaf father *ddEE* and deaf mother *DDee* will have only *DdEe* hearing children. Although these children have escaped hereditary deafness themselves, each may be expected to transmit genes for recessive deafness which might show in either homozygote of some later generation. Such possibilities will be discussed in full in connection with dihybrid inheritance (Chapter 10). At the present time let it be emphasized that all similar phenotypes do not have to be genotypically the same; one can mimic another. Examples from the recessive category are presented in Table 4-2.

The term "deaf-mutism" often appears in print as if to distinguish congenital complete deafness from other forms of deafness (acquired or genetic developing later in life). The term tends to overlook the fact that deaf persons can be taught to speak to a certain extent by very special teaching with the use of visual aids and even oscilloscopes. The basic problem is that the completely deaf young child who has not previously learned to talk has not been able to correct his voice by auditory trial-and-error. As a

TABLE 4-2   Mimics of some recessive phenotypes by other genes[a]

---

adrenal hyperplasia, four forms separable biochemically

albinism, two or more forms separable statistically and by pedigree data

amaurosis congenita I, II (blindness), separable by complementation

amaurotic familial idiocy, at least two, separable by age of onset

corneal dystrophy, one congenital, another later, still others doubtfully genetic

cystinuria I and II, phenotypically different, allelism not tested

deafness (complete), 6 to 12 or more forms distinguished anatomically, by population calculations and by normal children from deaf parents

disaccharide intolerance I, II, III, separable enzymatically

factors I, II, V, VII, X, (XI) XII deficiencies of blood clotting (factor VIII deficiency and factor IX deficiency are sex-linked hemophilias)

glycogen storage disease I, II, III, IV, V

hyperbilirubinemia, onset either in childhood or in infancy

hyperlipidemia, two forms

hypoadrenocorticism, alone or with other symptoms

keratosis palmo-plantaris, two or three forms

mental retardation, part of nine pleiotropic phenotypes

microcephaly, alone, secondary, or as a phenocopy (see Figure 19-2)

mucopolysaccharidosis I, III, IV (type II is sex-linked)

muscular atrophy, two or three forms by times of onset

muscular dystrophy, two or more autosomal types (one other is sex-linked)

retinitis pigmentosa, part of six different syndromes

thrombocytopenia, two forms, one without radius bones

thyroid hormogenesis defect, five forms enzymatically different

---

[a]After McKusick, unpublished data.

partial substitute for this, the visual imitation of lip and tongue positions and the tactual imitation of vibrations felt through the neck modify the "deaf-mute" possibility to a deaf-but-limited-speaking phenotype. A further difficulty with the venerable term "deaf-mute" for deafness present at birth is that congenital deafness may be either genetic from the *dd* or *ee* recessive pairs or acquired during a certain period of pregnancy. A further consideration of prenatal and postnatal modifications will be found in Chapters 19 and 20.

SUMMARY

The fundamentals of monohybrid genetics have been set forth in this chapter. Examples of segregation into three phenotypic classes in the ratio of $1:2:1$ for the first homozygote, the intermediate heterozygote and the other homozygote were given, including the M-N blood antigen contrasts.

Other examples involving a dominant phenotype and its contrasting recessive gave a 3 : 1 ratio among the offspring of heterozygous parents. A distinction was made between dominance in a known heterozygous individual and prevalence in a population or among sibships. Sibships in general were named as F_1 type, backcross type, testcross type and F_2 type even though backcrosses and the inbreeding of F_1 sibs are rare among people. The category of rare Dominant genes is provisionally set off from incompletely Dominant genes for lack of information about the even rarer homozygotes. Different genes may act by different routes to produce similar or mimic effects in the phenotype. Some phenotypes are changed in known ways by hormones, other phenotypes are changed to variable degrees by training or by diet, and still others seemingly remain unchanged. Both genetic variety within mankind and apparently similar genetic types among remotely related mammals have been pointed out.

SUGGESTED READING

Francois, Jules, *Heredity in Ophthalmology*, St. Louis, C. V. Mosby, 1961, 731 pp. References for the specialist.

Hutt, F. B., *Animal Genetics*, New York, Ronald Press, 1964, 546 pp. A textbook profusely illustrated with examples from mammals and birds.

Scheinfeld, A., *The New You and Heredity*, Philadelphia, Lippincott, 1950 ed., 616 pp. A cursive book which is also well referenced.

PROBLEMS

4–1   Compare and contrast the following pairs of terms:
        backcross and testcross types
        inbreeding and outbreeding
        F_1 and F_2
        heterozygous and heterogametic
        homozygote and homogametic
        agglutination and clotting (of blood)

4–2   What kinds of blood types would you expect among children from parents
  (a) Both of type M?
  (b) Both of type N?
  (c) Both of type MN?

4–3   In a diagram using genotypes and gametes explain the kinds and proportions of children to be expected from parental pairs MN by N?

4-4   (a) If two parents have a phenylketonuric child, what are their genotypes?
      (b) What are the chances that the next child will be a PKU child?
      (c) What are the chances that one more child would not be of type PKU (and would therefore not require a special diet)?

4-5   Name five different and specific causes of subnormal I.Q.

4-6   Name two or more genetic conditions which are mimicked by phenotypes resulting from other causes either genetic or environmental.

4-7   Which of the following ratios are typical of an F_2-type distribution: $3:1$, $1:1$, $1:2:1$?

chapter 5

Early and Delayed Appearance
of Genetic Traits

Not all of the examples of monohybrid differences used in the previous chapter may be distinguishable at the time of birth, yet they were inherited. The presence of five or six fingers is easily seen at birth. Likewise, the distinction between the normal male and the normal female is recognizable in the newborn child, although still other differences between them will develop later, especially at the time of puberty. At birth the albino can be distinguished from the nonalbino normals by the pink iris, but the various other shades of pigmentation cannot be recognized for several days even among babies of Negro parents. From one to six weeks are required before phenylketonuria can be detected by the ferric chloride test (page 59). It takes more time for some other genetically determined differences to show phenotypically. Right-handedness versus left-handedness cannot be observed until the infant begins to grasp things, to hold toys and to manipulate them in diverse ways; and the earlier a diagnosis of handedness is made, the more often it is incorrect. Throughout infancy and for several years a child who will develop juvenile amaurotic idiocy seems as normal as his sibs in respect to intelligence; the difference begins to show after approximately age six, and the diagnosis is usually certain before the attainment of age 12. Muscle dystrophy, some behavioral characteristics, certain gastric ulcers and certain duodenal ulcers appear in persons previously considered normal and healthy. Even the length of life may be genetically determined, although not simply so.

Inherited phenotypes which are recognizable at birth, such as the possession of six fingers and toes, are said to be *congenital* abnormalities, but among persons who seem normal at birth there may be genotypic differences which only later develop their respective phenotypes. The term "congenital" is merely a convenient descriptive term for the phenotype visible at the time of birth; it does not include all inherited conditions, nor does it exclude those alterations which result from fevers or from the physiological influences of certain drugs, such as cortisone or thalidomide, during the course of pregnancy. In this chapter we shall pick out some examples of monohybrid differences which make their appearance at a variety of times, some of them before birth and others of them afterward. The time for differentiation of each, however, is at a rather definite age. Hence these well-analyzed examples may serve as models for the understanding of the limits of the range of expression of other phenotypes involving more complicated means of determination such as adult intelligence.

Knowledge of just when unit gene differences in humans become expressed is difficult to obtain, but the situation among other mammals is much better known because of extensive investigations on the genetics, embryology, endocrinology and physiology of mice and other experimental animals. In 1952 Gruneberg listed some 85 gene loci known in mice as compared with perhaps 30 to 40 monohybrid differences known in man at that time. At the present writing some 200 gene loci are known in mice. Careful experimentation on mice has determined the time of onset of visible symptoms in some 40 different genotypes. From the variety listed by Gruneberg we may pick out five types which become differentiated from the normal at some specified time between the 5th and 14th days of pregnancy; doubtless many other genotypes become differentiated in the last week of pregnancy and therefore would add to the list of congenital anomalies. A similar spread of the times of departure from the more normal steps of embryonic and fetal development may eventually become known for the human species.

GENETIC DIFFERENCES IN THE EMBRYO

At the time of implantation of the blastocyst in the uterine wall of the mouse, on the sixth day of pregnancy, homozygous Yellows shrivel in the blastocyst stage and fail to multiply their cells. On the following day they are dead and being resorbed. The Yellow gene, designated a^Y (Chapter 8), which kills so early when present in double dose, results in bright yellow fur on a heterozygous individual, and it has long been known to mouse fanciers. The fact that Yellow mice never would breed true, followed by the observation that the litter *size* of Yellow females averages smaller when sired by Yellow males than when sired by nonyellows led eventually to the realization that homozygous $a^Y a^Y$ zygotes were forming the usual one-fourth of the potential offspring of Yellow by Yellow heterozygotes but were lost somewhere along the way. Apart from this omission the remaining expected ratios are realized. Thus a 2 : 1 ratio is a sign that a gene with *recessive lethal* effect has segregated. Testcrosses of Yellow by nonyellow mice, made with either sex as the heterozygote, result in a 1 : 1 ratio of Yellow and nonyellow. The living offspring of two Yellow parents are distributed around the monohybrid expectation of 2 Yellow : 1 nonyellow furred. In later life Yellow mice tend to become obese and they are more susceptible to pulmonary tumors, but they show a decreased incidence of mammary carcinoma as compared with their normal siblings. Other genotypes doubtless act earlier than homozygous Yellow, but they have not yet been identified.

The growth and maintenance of the notochord, the very important first structure of the vertebrate embryo, is under the control of the Short-tailed genes, T, of the Brachyury series in the mouse. One dose of the gene causes a pinching off of the notochord of a heterozygous embryo partway down the tail, followed by the loss of the distal part of the tail. Two doses of the T gene cause the homozygous embryo to fail to develop any notochord and to be so deficient in development of the allantois that the blood vessels to the placenta fail to develop and the homozygote quickly dies. The early development of all embryos in a litter from $T/+$ by $T/+$ matings proceeds apace for approximately the first $8\frac{1}{2}$ days, when two or three pairs of somites begin to show. As more somites form on the following day, the neural tube becomes slightly irregular and small blebs appear near the tube, only to disappear the same day. By the tenth day the T/T embryos are markedly abnormal in having no hind limb buds, a loss of distinction between what few somites have developed, a slowly growing allantois and no umbilical arteries and vein. Death occurs before the 11th day, and the homozygote is quickly resorbed. Hence the litter size from two Short-tailed parents is about $\frac{1}{4}$ smaller than the number of live young in normal litters.

GENIC EFFECTS IN THE FETUS

The $T/+$ heterozygotes continue developing in gross appearance like their normal sibs for a longer time. Tails are growing rapidly in both genotypes by the tenth day, but then a deep constriction appears in the tail of a future Short-tailed mouse. Behind the constriction the tail of the fetus is resorbed, and in front of it caudal vertebrae and sometimes even sacral vertebrae will become irregular in shape. The first sign of these changes histologically is the irregular development of the notochord in the tail region, which departs from the normal plan by $8\frac{3}{4}$ days of pregnancy. Table 5-1 compiled by Gruneberg illustrates the monofactorial behavior of the dominant Short-tailed gene and its recessive lethal action among embryos halfway through the period of pregnancy.

The contrast between these fundamental changes which take place in the skeleton under genic control and changes in color or hair form may serve as

TABLE 5-1   Embryos from $T/+ \times T/+$ matings[a]

Author	+/+	T/+	T/T
Dobrovolskaia-Zavadskaia and Kobozieff (1930)		28	10
Chesley (1935)		432	125
Ephrussi (1935)		126	38
Kobozieff (1935)	53	91	42
Total		730	215

[a]From H. Gruneberg, *The Genetics of the Mouse*, 2nd edition, The Hague, Netherlands, M. Nijhoff, 1952.

a reminder that genic differences are not limited to minor aspects of the phenotype. A minor role for heredity was once hastily concluded from a survey of the multitude of gene loci with small effects as known in rats, mice and insects. Early embryonic lethals have also been demonstrated in *Drosophila*, and the number which awaits analysis there and among mammals is known to be large indeed.

Among the rare but widely occurring white vertebrate animals many but not all white individuals are albinos. True albino specimens among mammals and even birds and reptiles are distinguished from other white animals by the possession of pink eyes. The eye color is due to the hemoglobin of the blood showing through the unpigmented iris, and iris pigmentation is laid down earlier in the mouse than in man. By the 11th day of prenatal life albino mice can be distinguished from normals by looking at the iris.

Hydrocephalus occurs in human babies, but such phenotypes are much better understood in the mouse. At least three different kinds of hydrocephalus have been recognized and carefully studied in mouse strains now lost. The times of death were the same for two genetically different strains, and in congenital hydrocephalus, *ch/ch* homozygotes die at birth from inability to inflate the lungs. These recessives are born with a foreshortened snout, open eyelids and a Pekingese-dog-like appearance in facial profile—consequences of a general difficulty in cartilage formation which does little permanent damage elsewhere in the skeleton, but which is crucial in the development of the brain case. The *ch/ch* homozygotes develop in the same manner as their other two kinds of siblings during the first $12\frac{2}{3}$ days of embryonic and fetal life, at which time the mesenchyme begins to form separate *cartilages*, prechordals and parachordals, at the base of the brain.

Failure of fusion of the parachordals and prechordals and concomitant failure of their lengthening result in compression of the brain, which becomes more spherical than elongated. This change of shape compresses an important foramen through which secreted cerebrospinal fluid normally escapes without building up hydrostatic pressure within the brain cavities. In the hydrocephalic mouse continued pressure in all directions changes the shape of the head and the function of the brain. Elsewhere in the body a similar delay in the formation of cartilage produces no later skeletal change except that the sternum ossifies into only one or two sternebrae or else there are no breastbones at all. The reason for death by suffocation right after birth is surprising in comparison with the longer lives of three other genetic strains of hydrocephalic mice.

One other mouse gene recognized by the short ear aspect of its phenotype also affects cartilage growth beginning noticeably at the 14th day of uterine life, just a little later than the above example of an early-acting gene. Green and Green have shown that as the various cartilages become critically active at specific times before or after birth the abnormalities appear in several of those cartilages with the result that many structures are affected. The whole picture of the associated departures from the normal represents the pleiotropic effect of the *se/se* genotype. Although the basal cartilage of the ear deviates from normal in midpregnancy, the support for the main part of the ear remains normal until a few days after birth. At another definite time the xiphisternal cartilage begins to develop abnormally and becomes bifurcated or is absent. At from 5 to 25 days after birth kinky tails appear in the short-eared strain due to the action of muscles and nerves, but the kinks may disappear later in many individuals. Still other manifestations of the pleiotropic short ear recessive gene are less regular in their appearance, but when they do show up, they do so during predictable times of growth.

POSTNATAL GENIC EFFECTS IN MAMMALS

Although the period of birth is very important physiologically and sometimes is even hazardous to offspring or mother, it does not close the book on the development of hereditary differences. Not all parts of some of the mutant phenotypes named above are present congenitally; hence it should not be surprising that other mutants may not appear in any form until later in life and thus be included among the category of individuals classified as normal at birth. All of the hair form differences and all of the minor differences in distribution of pigments within the hair are hereditary but not congenital phenotypes because mice are born naked, except for the vibrissae, and require a week to grow a coat of hair, which may then prove to be rough, smooth, angora or some other phenotype.

The widely known waltzer mouse, homozygous recessive v/v, behaves normally and has normal internal ears at birth. Soon the organ of Corti of the inner ear begins to degenerate, and waltzer mice become deaf. Their unusual circling and whirling movements begin in the second week after birth and become very persistent. The original waltzer strain of mice has a long history. The genetics of waltzing was studied and reported in Germany even before the rediscovery of Mendel's publication. It was noted that none of 28 F_1 offspring of outcrosses to normal strains showed waltzing, yet the inbreeding of these F_1 produced eight waltzers out of 44 F_2 offspring. This 1898 report by von Guaita is entirely consistent with simple monohybrid inheritance showing dominance of normal behavior over waltzing in the first generation and showing 3 : 1 segregation in the F_2. Two other phenotypes known as shaker-1 and shaker-2 appear similar to waltzer in many but not all aspects of the phenotype, but the three are shown to be genetically different by simple tests described in the chapter on dihybrid inheritance (Chapter 10). These three may be said to be duplicate phenotypes of each other, just as are several genetically different forms of deafness in humans.

The Trembler gene, Tr, dominant over its normal allele, causes spastic paralysis and convulsions in young mice beginning in the second or third week after birth and continuing during the juvenile period. Growth of the young is delayed during the juvenile period, and many Trembler mice die then. Those which survive the period of convulsions retain a distinctive tremor as adults. The Trembler gene in mice is somewhat unusual in that two doses of this abnormal allele make no more change in the phenotype than does one dose; thus it is completely dominant over its wild allele (Table 5-2).

TABLE 5-2   Segregation of Trembler[a]

MATING		OFFSPRING	
Male	Female	Trembler	Normal
$Tr/+$	$+/+$ (testcross)	54	48
$+/+$	$Tr/+$ (testcross)	217	272
$Tr/+$	$Tr/+$ ($F_1 \times F_1$)	42	13
$+/+$	Tr/Tr (P_1)	71	0

[a]Data of Falconer, J. Genet., **50**: 194–195 (1951).

A recessive dwarfism phenotype in mice, due to the substitution of *dw* for its normal allele, has been traced to postnatal malfunction of the master endocrine gland of the body, the *anterior pituitary gland.* Homozygous *dw/dw* mice do not fall behind their normal littermates in any conspicuous way until two weeks after birth. In the third week they may be identified from normals by their shorter snout, ears and tail (see *se* and *T*, above) and by an actual loss of weight in many individuals. Upon more intensive investigation of litters from proven F₁ parents the lessening of normal growth and the slower growth of bones can be detected by the end of the first week. Histological examination of the endocrine glands reveals that the anterior pituitary is abnormal at this early time. Not only is growth reduced or reversed in *dw/dw* mice, but body temperature may drop at weaning, a critical time. Both sexes may be sterile; in the male the testes fail to descend, and in the female the vagina does not open.

Certain treatments which alleviate or correct the abnormalities of the *dw/dw* mice demonstrate the accuracy of the name as pituitary dwarfism and, furthermore, indicate wide possibilities in coping with some genetic diseases in man. Injection of whole pituitary glands from rats into these dwarf mice corrects the deficiencies and changes in all other glands, but it does not correct the primary defect, the absence of acidophilic cells in the pituitary of the host. Injection even results in fully fertile males and in irregular functioning of the female estrus cycle. Treatment which avoids the weight loss may involve the administration of thyroxin to the very young dwarf mice, or as an alternative, incubation at a 33 degree temperature during the critical weaning period. This is a remarkably well analyzed example of the interplay of genes, hormones of several kinds and the external environment in the control and development of different phenotypes which all emerge within a range of possible expressions of the *dw/dw* genotype. It should be a model for human thinking about human genetics.

The period of weaning is also especially critical for the recessive gray lethal mice, *gl/gl.* Again as in the above dwarf, stationary weight before weaning time and loss of weight are symptoms. If the gray lethals are weaned rapidly at 21 days of age, the decline in weight is rapid and death comes early. If weaning is prolonged, the weight loss is slower and the gray lethal may live to age 30 days. On a special liquid diet the life of a *gl/gl* mouse may be stretched to 42 days but without gain of weight. Because the teeth do not erupt, the weaned gray lethals starve to death; yet something else is wrong with those kept alive on a liquid diet. Their tolerance of parathyroxin is very high, and the bones of the skeleton show a general failure of secondary bone resorption by the osteoclast cells. Thus many of the bones become heavy, and the characteristic large marrow cavities of normal long bones do not develop. The failure of bone resorption seems to impede the eruption of the teeth of the gray lethals. The coat color is the result of lack of deposition of yellow pigment in the hairs.

A temporary genetic effect is shown by one among several hairless genes in the mouse; only the juvenile fur coat is reduced. Recessive hypotrichosis juvenalis mice, *hj/hj*, are born appearing normal, but by the juvenile period the phenotype varies from almost complete nakedness to a coat differing from normal only by a slight fuzziness. Some of the more hairless mice lag behind their sibs during the juvenile period, but at about five weeks of age a normal coat of fur grows, and these mice soon catch up in weight also. In making up their lost weight they are like the more successful of the Tremblers above. This is in contrast to the more permanent damage of many other known abnormal genes.

POSTNATAL DEVELOPMENT IN MAN

A few human genes are well enough analyzed so that we may reliably describe the late differentiation of certain phenotypes from the normal. One of the several forms of muscle dystrophy (see mimic genes listed in Table 4-2) is not usually detected until the boy or girl is between 10 and 17 years of age. During that time muscles which had previously seemed healthy and of normal size are no longer maintained and shrivel to uselessness. This autosomal muscle dystrophy affects both males and females equally often, and it does not shorten the length of life conspicuously. These two statements distinguish autosomal muscle dystrophy from two other kinds of hereditary muscle degeneration. At first thought it might appear paradoxical that much effort is going into research to prevent the hereditary disease of muscle dystrophy, but if the biochemistry of the maintenance of muscle integrity can be worked out, "cures" comparable to the "cure" of phenylketonuric idiocy in advance of its full development may confidently be expected even for an inherited "disease."

The development of a single genetic phenotype ranges over a much larger period of time in the case of the *Lawrence-Moon-Bardet-Biedl syndrome*. Recessive homozygotes for the differentiating gene show some of the constellation of signs early and others at later times. At birth most of these *LMBB syndrome* individuals have an extra digit on one or both hands or feet, and in this respect they are somewhat similar to individuals of the dominant polydactyl phenotype. During growth persons with this syndrome soon show hypogenitalism, obesity and subnormal mental development. One more aspect of this recessive phenotype is the excessive pigmentation of the retina, and this alteration of the eye is phenotypically not yet distinguished from dominant Retinitis pigmentosa. Until most of these phenotypic manifestations have appeared, it is not at all easy to diagnose whether one is dealing with a homozygote for the Lawrence-Moon-Bardet-Biedl syndrome gene or with another genotype.

The discovery and description of the *Gardner syndrome* began about 1950 with the recognition of the last and most severe manifestation of a dominant gene, death from carcinoma of the large intestine, and has now progressed to signs recognizable in young children. Several persons in the same kindred in Utah died in this manner, but some of their sibs have survived after surgical removal of parts of the intestine having numerous polyps. (See generations I, II, III of Figure 5-1.) It was recorded in the years shortly following the first description of the dominant phenotype that several of

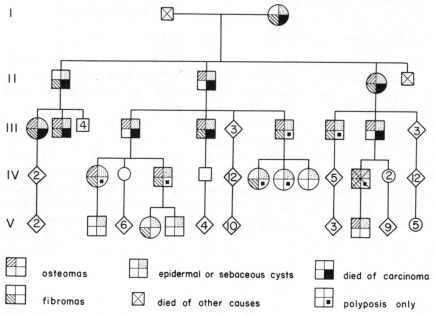

FIGURE 5-1 Gardner's syndrome, inherited as a dominant. It originally came to attention as death from carcinoma, quickly was recognized as preceded by intestinal polyposis, more recently found to be preceded by other pleiotropic effects in connective tissue and skin. Large squares and circles, Syndrome males and females, respectively. Small squares and circles, nonsyndrome males and females, respectively. After Gardner, Amer. J. Hum. Genet. **14**: 377 (1962).

the affected members had bony outgrowths (osteomas) of the jaw and often of other facial bones such that false teeth were required in early maturity.

A few of the persons lacked the osteomas, for instance in generation IV the three sisters; and the last male in generation V had the osteomas but no polyps. Individuals free of polyps were also free of osteomas of the face. Thus effects of the dominant gene formed a syndrome usually expressed in two diverse tissues, the intestinal mucosa and the bones of the face. In further studies within the kindred, Gardner and his associates noticed that fibromas and sebaceous cysts also tended to be found in persons with intestinal polyposis and to be absent in persons and in lines of descent lacking the intestinal carcinoma. It is known now that the first signs of the syndrome are the sebaceous cysts or fibromas and often both. In generation V four children of parents who have had polyposis are already showing epidermal cysts, while none of the first cousins from normal parents do. Obviously, the first kind will certainly be watched by their doctors for the appearance of intestinal polyps at a later age. If these are surgically removed in time such syndrome individuals may readily escape the death by carcinoma which five of their direct ancestors have already suffered.

The late average age of appearance for the phenotype of *Huntington's chorea* is another example of the delayed detection of a dominant abnormal human gene. The affliction is a nervous disorder at first involving muscle twitching, then the loss of coordination and later the loss of mental powers followed by invalidism. Very few persons with the Huntington's chorea gene show any abnormality during youth and early maturity. Most of them remain normal while producing a family. The median age of onset of symptoms in $H/+$ persons has been estimated in several studies to lie in the 30's and as late as age 40. Yet the range of onset is great, and the muscle twitchings may not appear until after age 60. Hence this gene has been spread far and wide in certain kindreds by persons who did not know they were genetically sick. The need for earlier diagnosis of Huntington's chorea is certainly great, and some help in this direction may result from the study of electroencephalographs or of other physical or biochemical signs.

The early or late times of appearance of the various phenotypes will obviously affect the recorded number of segregants of each kind. Classification at birth may be too late to detect any of the embryonic lethals, and it will be too soon for the separation of some inherited differences of adults. Consequently, the age at which each person still appears normal in a study is a very important part of the geneticist's record. An individual apparently normal at one age may not turn out to be genetically normal at another age.

SUMMARY

All inherited differences in man may not appear congenitally; many become first noticeable in various intervals after birth. Children who later show one of the genetic forms of muscle dystrophy in their teen years seem normal at birth. Huntington's chorea appears in adults who have passed through ages at which muscle dystrophy or other genetic differences develop overtly. Therefore the age of each normal person is an important part of the geneticist's record. Parts of the phenotype of the Laurence-Moon-Bardet-Biedl syndrome appear at birth and other pleiotropic effects become evident at several later times. Single gene effects in mice also are known to appear each at a rather definite age postnatally, among them the waltzer activity, pituitary dwarfism and the gray-lethal phenotype.

The origin of congenital defects is more readily studied in other mammals than in humans. In mice genes are known which lead to obvious abnormalities of the fetus such as hydrocephalus, tail shortening and defective development of one or another area of cartilage formation. Genes acting upon the notochord can lead to abnormalities either in the embryo or some fetal stage. Homozygosity for the gene named originally for its yellow fur effect in single dose acts as a recessive lethal gene and regularly kills the blastocyst before it develops into an embryo.

SUGGESTED READING

Glucksohn-Waelsch, S., Lethal genes and analysis of differentiation. *Science* 142: 1269–1276 (1963). On numerous studies in mice. Well-illustrated.

Gruneberg, H. *The Genetics of the Mouse*, 2nd ed., The Hague, Netherlands, M. Nijhoff, 1952, 650 pp. A standard reference on the genetically best known mammal.

Hadorn, E., *Developmental Genetics and Lethal Factors* (translated by Ursula Mittwolk), New York, Wiley, 1961, 355 pp.

PROBLEMS

5–1 Define the terms:

congenital
inherited
lethal
dominant
syndrome

5–2 (a) If the young mice from Short-tail by Short-tail matings as given in Table 5-1 had not been observed until the time of birth, what segregation ratio would have been approximated in Kobozieff's data?

(b) Define dominance and recessiveness in this example.

5-3   Among the mice raised by Ephrussi and summed in Table 5-1, how many do you suppose would have grown up
(a) To be normal-tailed mice?
(b) To become Short-tailed mice?

5-4   Falconer reported the offspring of numerous litters from two heterozygous Trembler parents to consist of 42 Tremblers and 13 normals.
(a) Would you expect either of these phenotypes to breed true?
(b) Upon crossing all those of one kind to normals, how many such pairs of mice would you expect to produce only Trembler offspring?
(c) How many pairs would you expect to produce both Trember and normal offspring?

5-5   In Figure 5-1 what is the apparent segregation ratio
(a) Among the members of generation III?
(b) Among the members of generation IV from a Gardner syndrome parent?
(c) Among all possible testcross sibships shown?

5-6   In Figure 5-1 why do the numbers of normal persons seem to be increasing in each generation?

chapter 6

Population Gene Frequencies and Segregation Ratios

The gap between animal experimentation and the study of human genetics may seem large. However, the principles of population genetics permit the scientific study of species in nature without the handicaps of small family size and lack of experimentally planned marriages. Study of a whole population is, in fact, often superior to the collection of large pedigrees, because the latter are often reported in the scientific literature for their oddity interest rather than for their representativeness. To put genetic segregation into proper perspective, it is well for the investigator to proceed stepwise from (a) large-scale sampling of individuals within a population, to (b) collection of parent-offspring data within that same population, and optionally to (c) the study of kindreds in case there has been evidence of mimic genes, as in deafness (page 62). Alternatively, he may proceed from (a) directly to (d) a similar study of individuals from a geographically different population which usually has a slightly different distribution of genes.

Within many populations an equilibrium of genotypes prevails. This was first pointed out in 1908 independently by the mathematician G. H. Hardy and the physician W. Weinberg, whose several contributions laid the foundations of the genetic study of natural populations of wild animals and including man. A population *isolate* is considered to be that group of persons within which individuals choose their partners. Such an isolate is also called a *Mendelian population*. Ideally the population isolate inhabits an island, a mountain valley, a peninsula like Spain or Scandinavia or even a whole continent. If the isolate is not changed by natural selection, nor by mutation, nor by migration, and if the population size is large and if individuals are not mating assortatively, then the isolate is said to be in equilibrium. The monohybrid genetic phenomena in a Mendelian population isolate will be examined in the main part of this chapter followed by a preliminary discussion of the limitations and extensions of the equilibrium idea.

HARDY-WEINBERG EQUILIBRIUM

The Hardy-Weinberg equation allows for the mixtures of all nine possible kinds of matings: male Dominants, heterozygotes, and recessives with females of the three similar types. Since the pairs involved in the choice often are blissfully unaware of their phenotypes in respect to M-N blood types, Taster of PTC or other examples, the choice of a partner indeed appears to be random and not assortative. Such a population, Mendelian in respect to the gene difference under consideration, is found to contain the genotypes RR, Rr and rr in the proportion $p^2 + 2pq + q^2$, where p is the proportion of R alleles and q the proportion of r alleles among all loci of the population. This is a general formulation, and it includes the familiar $1 : 2 : 1$ ratio characteristic of the F_2 generation in a controlled experiment of crossbreeding and inbreeding. In a deliberate monohybrid experiment the gene frequencies of the two kinds of alleles in the F_1 and in the F_2 generations are each .50 of all alleles at that locus in the totality of individuals. This is a special proportion, and so the F_2 generation has .25 RR, .50 Rr and .25 rr genotypes (Population B of Figure 6-1).

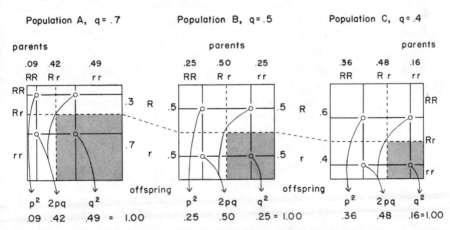

FIGURE 6-1 Constancy of proportions of recessives (dark area) from parental generation to offspring in each of three populations which differ only in the recessive allele frequency, q.

Populations with unequal allele frequencies are more representative, such as two of the examples symbolized in Figure 6-1. Note in that illustration that the genotypic frequencies in the parental generation directly determine the gene frequencies of their gametes. These gametes in turn establish the frequencies of the three genotypes among the offspring. Because the offspring and the parents have the same numerical distributions, the population is in equilibrium for any number of successive generations.

Genetic equilibrium at five other levels of gene frequency can be most conveniently illustrated with examples from the M-N blood types, where there is no masking effect of dominance (Table 6-1). Suppose that in a certain town in central Europe a random sample of several thousand in-

TABLE 6-1   Frequencies of M-N blood types, and L^M and L^N genes in various populations[a]

NUMBER AND POPULATION	GENOTYPES AND PHENOTYPES BY PERCENT			ALLELES FREQUENCIES	
	M	MN	N	L^M	L^N
569 Eskimos	83.5	15.6	0.9	.913	.087
398 Finns	45.7	43.2	11.1	.673	.327
91 Basques	23.1	51.6	25.3	.489	.511
504 Ainu	17.9	50.2	31.9	.430	.570
200 Papuans	7.0	24.0	69.0	.190	.810

[a]From *Genetics and the Races of Man* by William C. Boyd, Copyright 1950, by William C. Boyd. Reprinted by permission of Little, Brown and Company, publishers.

dividuals revealed that .3025 of them were of type M and that .2025 were of type N and that the remaining .4950 were heterozygotes. Here one may count up the L^M genes as all gametes forming the first group and equal to $\frac{1}{2}$ of the gametes of the heterozygotes, or an additional .2475 for a total of .55 L^M alleles. Similarly $\frac{1}{2}$ of the alleles of the heterozygotes are L^N alleles and all of the genes at this locus in the type N homozygotes also are, so the total of .2475 and .2025 gives .45 as the frequency of L^N alleles. Because the .55 L^M and .45 L^N alleles total all of the alleles possible at the locus, and because $(.55)^2$ is .3025 $L^M L^M$, as observed, and $(.45)^2$ is .2025, as observed, and $2pq$ is .4950, as observed, the three blood types in this population are found to be consistent with an interpretation based on monohybrid inheritance. Confirmation within other populations may now be sought.

The whole world is a laboratory with many independent tests under way if the proportions of the several genotypes are viewed according to the

principles of population genetics. The frequencies of the genotypes of the
M-N system have been sampled at many places around the world, and in
each population the homozygotes and the heterozygotes were distributed
according to the expanded binomial $(p + q)^2$. If the hypothesis were incorrect that a single pair of alleles is differentiating the phenotypes, or if
some of the conditions for equilibrium were not met (such as by premature
death of one homozygote), then the Hardy-Weinberg equilibrium prediction would not match the observed results. A small listing from among
dozens of populations which show an equilibrium distribution of their
Landsteiner M and N alleles among the three genotypes is given in Table
6-1. Evidently an assumption which provides accurate predications in
populations of such diverse gene frequencies has much to commend it.

The repeatable distributions of phenotypes allow a simplification of
viewpoint. One may test the distribution of individuals within one generation under the assumption of monohybrid inheritance, by seeing whether

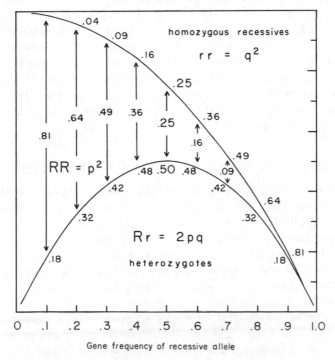

FIGURE 6-2 Proportions of recessive, heterozygous and
homozygous dominant persons in populations with any gene
frequency. Compare with Figure 6-1.

observed fractions of the three genotypes agree with the calculations from the observed allele frequencies. As a model for these calculations Figure 6-2 may be consulted. Vertically in the center of the figure the outcome of a special situation, the typical F_2 generation of an experiment, may be read off above the .5 on the scale of gene frequency. Equilibrium for such a population is 50 percent heterozygotes, 25 percent homozygous RR and 25 percent homozygous recessives. Note in the graph that the sum of the alleles at a locus, here just a monohybrid, equals one. Furthermore, note that the vertical distances, which represent the proportions of the three genotypes, also add up to one no matter what the gene frequency may be. Thus if dominant alleles are nine times as common as the recessives ($p = .9$ and $q = .1$) then homozygous dominants are .81 or p^2, heterozygotes are .18 or $2pq$ and recessives are .01 or q^2 of the genotypes in the population. The R and r alleles may be found in different proportions in different population isolates. Note in Figure 6-2 that the heterozygotes are never expected as the majority of a Mendelian population, rather their maximum is .50, found in populations where $p = .5 = q$. Recessives become a plurality of individuals when $q = .67$ or more of the alleles, and recessive individuals comprise a majority of the population whenever the recessive allele is slightly above .70 in frequency. On the other side of the curve homozygous dominant individuals are more common than heterozygotes in populations where the dominant allele frequency is above .67, and they become more numerous than the sum of the other two genotypes at slightly higher dominant allele frequencies.

EQUILIBRIUM ATTAINED IN ONE GENERATION

The existence of equilibrium in large populations in any generation may be better appreciated by considering several parental generations which are not in equilibrium. Such mixtures may be obtained from sudden extensive migration between two Mendelian populations, or they may be created artificially among experimental animals, or they may be made as hypothetical mixtures. Suppose that a group of colonists leaving London to found a new colony a century ago consisted by rare chance of $\frac{1}{3}$ each of blood types M, N, and MN. The colony has in its *gene pool*, as the totality is called, equal numbers of the L^M and L^N alleles. Consequently, the offspring of these colonists in the days before blood typing, and probably even so today, should be 25 percent each of types M and N and 50 percent of type MN. This equilibrium according to the formula $(p + q)^2$ in one generation of impartial choice of mates has been confirmed many times in animal experimentation.

For an opposite starting point, one may suppose that all of the parental generation was of type MN and therefore the gene frequencies again would be equal at .5 for each allele. A 1 : 2 : 1 distribution of genotypes in the next generation would be predicted, and such has been confirmed innumerable times experimentally in breeding F_1 mice to form an F_2 generation. For a third example generalized from other animal species, if one should place equal numbers of *RR* males and females into a suitable environment with equal numbers of *rr* males and females, then by chance *RR* parents together would produce 25 percent *RR* offspring, *rr* parents together would produce another 25 percent of *rr* offspring and pairs of opposite parents would result in 50 percent heterozygotes in the next generation. Thus in one generation of Mendelian choice of mate, i.e., without regard for phenotype or cryptic genotype, the equilibrium proportions of the F_2 (and later) generations are achieved whether the beginning is from (a) 100 percent heterozygotes, or (b) no heterozygotes at all, or (c) an arbitrary fraction of heterozygotes.

Populations in nature very rarely contain opposite alleles in equal frequencies, but the same principles apply whether a certain allele is the more common or the less common allele. Certain other representative possibilities are included in Figure 6-2, and they represent, in round numbers, some of the variety of equilibria already enumerated in Table 6-1. The same population may have a high frequency of the recessive allele of one pair *J-j*, an intermediate frequency in another pair *K-k*, a low frequency of the recessive member of a third pair *L-l*, and so on. In this chapter, however, we are concentrating on the monohybrid situation.

DILUTION OF F_2 AND TESTCROSS RATIOS

Parent pairs within a population which is segregating for a completely recessive phenotype are of only three kinds. These are two recessives, recessive and Dominant as a phenotypic testcross, and both parents Dominant. However, the testcross parents as phenotypically recognized do not have 1 : 1 ratios among the totality of their offspring. Neither do the recessive children from Dominant by Dominant parents come up to the unadjusted 25 percent expectation. Yet the observed frequencies of the recessives from phenotypic testcrosses and from Dominant parent pairs have predictable relations to each other and to the frequency of the recessive individuals from all three sources in the population.

The dilution of the 3 : 1 and the 1 : 1 ratios is greater where the Dominant allele frequency is greater. In a population where the ratios are about .67 Dominant genes to .33 recessive alleles at one locus the proportions of

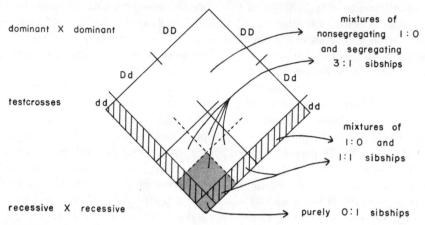

Offspring of pairs by phenotype

dominant X dominant

DD   DD   mixtures of
                        nonsegregating 1 : 0
                        and segregating
                        3 : 1 sibships

Dd   Dd

testcrosses dd   dd

                        mixtures of
                        1 : 0 and
                        1 : 1 sibships

recessive X recessive   purely 0 : 1 sibships

FIGURE 6-3 The relative abundance of the kinds of parental pairs by genotype and the effect of phenotypic grouping on ratios among offspring.

Figure 6-3 obtain. This or any isolate consists of parent pairs which are testcrosses or else resemble one of the two kinds of inbreeding, phenotypically speaking. Testcrosses are shown in Figure 6-3 as diagonally barred areas, the area representing the proportion of all offspring produced from Dominant by recessive parent and reciprocally from recessive by Dominant. The inbreeding of two recessives will occur with the frequency proportional to the smallest square of the figure. Similarly, inbreeding among those of Dominant phenotype will be in the proportion shown by the remaining large blank square which is partly subdivided by solid lines, the areas of the subdivisions representing the marriage combinations $DD \times DD$, and $DD \times Dd$, $Dd \times DD$ and $Dd \times Dd$. Of the nine possible kinds of matings genotypically, five give rise only to Dominant phenotypes while the remaining four produce at least some recessives. The recessive offspring, in the proportion shown in gray stippling, come partly from one of the four kinds of incrossing among the Dominant parents, partly from two of the four possible testcrosses, and the remainder from all of the incrossing of recessive parents. In any population where the choice of marriage partner is random in regard to the D-d character, the proportion of recessive offspring from all four sources will correspond to the square of the frequency of the recessive allele in the previous generation. The dashed lines of Figure 6-3 are important summary lines in both parental and offspring generations. They simultaneously divide in half the amount of the margin allotted to the heterozygotes of the parental generation, and they intersect and go on to bound the square area which is proportional to the frequency of the recessive offspring. Although the gene frequencies may differ in different populations, the bisectors of the proportion of the heterozygous parents correctly predict the fraction of recessive offspring among the entire population.

The reasons for the dilution of the laboratory style ratios is re-emphasized and put in general quantitative terms in Figure 6-4. Inbred recessives involve no ambiguities, and all of their offspring are recessive homozygotes.

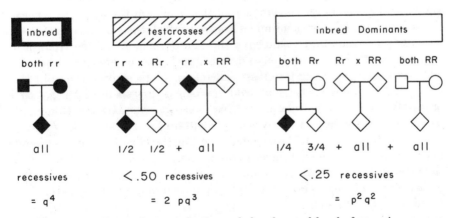

FIGURE 6-4 Types of parental pairs and the observed level of recessive proportions according to recessive gene frequency, q.

Phenotypic testcrosses include genetic tests of Dominant individuals some of whom are carriers of the recessive allele and may be expected to have 1 : 1 segregation among their offspring and others of whom are not carriers and hence will have only the Dominant phenotype among their children. Marriages of Dominant by Dominant will include four genotypic categories, three of which will not result in any but Dominant offspring. Only those Dominant marriage partners who are both heterozygotes may show a $3:1$ segregation of Dominant to recessive offspring. Other couples in which either the father or the mother or both are homozygous RR will produce no recessive rr children.

The effect of dilution may be stated by figuring the combined likelihood of just three kinds of marriages and the contribution of each marriage type to the total proportion of recessive offspring. We assume here that a parent pair in one category produces, on the average, the same number of children as does a parent pair in a different classification. Recessives may be expected to marry each other with the random frequency of $q^2 \times q^2$ (the proportions of recessives among males and recessives among females of the population), and since all of their children will have the same genotype, we may expect q^4 of the next generation to be recessive from genotypically similar parents. See the leftmost pair of Figure 6-4. From the testcross category recessive offspring may be expected among $\frac{1}{2}$ the children of true testcrosses, which would be recessive mother by Rr father and those between Rr mother and recessive father. These reciprocal pairs are shown by the second pair of parents, the Rr member being a white diamond to stand for either sex. Note that the third pair will contribute no recessive children. Here the recessive mother again is q^2 of the women in the parental generation whereas the heterozygous males are $2pq$ of the fathers in the population. An identical calculation would give the random chance of the reciprocal testcross, mother heterozygous and father recessive, a chance which is in addition to the preceding testcross. Therefore the recessives from all testcrosses will be $\frac{1}{2}$ of the two reciprocal kinds of $q^2 \times 2pq$ spouses, $2/2 \times 2pq^3$, or simply $2pq^3$. The calculation for recessives from among the Dominant parent pairs is similar. Recessives may result on the average among only $\frac{1}{4}$ of the children of two heterozygotes (the fourth pair of Figure 6-4) and nowhere else within phenotypically similar marriages as represented by the the fifth and sixth pairs. Therefore the calculation is $\frac{1}{4} \times 2pq \times 2pq$, or $\frac{4}{4} p^2q^2$, which is p^2q^2 recessives in the population coming from among the Dominant parent pairs.

ORIGINS OF RECESSIVES

Numerical examples of the proportion of recessives from the three contributing kinds of parents and the sum of all recessives in the population are given in Table 6-2. It will be noted that as the total of recessives in the population drops (fifth column) the contribution from recessive parents and testcrosses in columns two and three drops very fast. The recessive proportion from Dominant parents also decreases, once the recessive allele drops below .5 in frequency. Note that the sum of columns two, three and four on any line equals the total of recessives in that population, as given in column five. If the origins of the recessives are compared among themselves in Table 6-2 it may be correctly inferred that for q values above $\frac{2}{3}$ the largest contribution comes from two recessive parents. In other populations with

TABLE 6-2 Origin of recessives from recessive parents (q^4), from test-cross parents ($2pq^3$) and from Dominant parents (p^2q^2) in populations with medium and low gene frequencies, q.

Recessive allele, q	CONTRIBUTING PARENTAL PAIRS			Total recessives, q^2
	Recessive, q^4	Testcross, $2pq^3$	Dominant, p^2q^2	
.67	.2015	.1985	.0489	.4489
.50	.0625	.1250	.0625	.2500
.33	.0118	.0482	.0489	.1089
.05	.00000625	.000237	.002257	.0025
.025	.00000039	.000030	.000594	.000625

gene frequencies between $\frac{2}{3}$ and $\frac{1}{3}$ the largest of the three contributions is from the two reciprocal testcrosses. In still other populations with q values below $\frac{1}{3}$ the chief source of recessives becomes the pairs of Dominant parents; in fact, at very low frequencies the q^4 and the $2pq^3$ contributions of recessives are almost negligible.

At low gene frequencies of the recessive allele these quantitative relationships take on new importance, even of a qualitative nature. Notice first in Table 6-2 on the bottom two lines that from 90 to 95 percent of the total recessives, as given in the last column, come from Dominant parents, as given in the fourth column. One repercussion of this numerical fact is to be considered in the discussion of consanguineous matings in Chapter 9. Briefly, in populations with a gene frequency only a little below .025 the marriages of first cousins contribute a noticeably greater fraction of recessive offspring than the p^2q^2 portion arising from more distantly related parents. Another conclusion coming more directly from the same table is that recessive genes cannot be effectively prevented from entering the next generation by any barrier to the breeding of recessive individuals whether with each other or in testcross pairs. Such attempts at eugenics would be incomplete at first and even less effective the rarer the occurrence of the undesired recessive. For instance, phenylketonuric idiots rarely have children, but a new quota of these recessives arrives in the population each generation from normal parents. A fuller discussion is reserved for Chapter 26 on selection.

The proportional origins of whatever recessives a population may have are presented graphically in Figure 6-5 for use with populations having gene frequencies from .1 to .9 or so. The dilution of the 1 : 1 testcross ratio

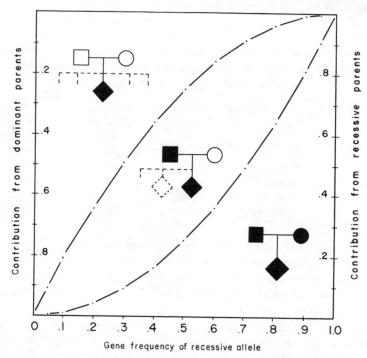

FIGURE 6-5   The distribution of parental origins of all recessives in a population with any gene frequency. Vertical distance shows proportion of observed recessives having (in center) one parent of each phenotype.

is indicated in the center of the figure by the representation of more than one Dominant symbol with the one solid recessive, and a dilution in the same direction is indicated by the suggestion of more than three Dominant siblings of the recessive offspring of two Dominant parents.

A series of numerical examples of the amount of dilution of the testcross and the F_2 ratios in populations is given in Table 6-3. The top line refers to a population with a high q value, one in which almost all phenotypic Dominants would be heterozygotes. Therefore the combined offspring from all testcross parent pairs would approach equality of recessive and Dominant

TABLE 6-3 Observed fractions of recessive offspring from groups of parents where only one or neither parent is recessive

Recessive allele frequency, q	$1 + q$	RECESSIVE PROPORTION AMONG CHILDREN	
		Of testcross parents, $q/(1+q)$	Of dominant parents $[q/(1+q)]^2$
.99	1.99	$<.50$	$<.25$
.8	1.8	.444	.1975
.6	1.6	.375	.141
.4	1.4	.286	.082
.2	1.2	.166	.0278
.1	1.1	.091	.00826

types. In the same population the pairs of Dominant parents would have almost 25 percent recessives among their total offspring. For exact expectations one uses the fraction $q/(1 + q)$ for the expected outcome of testcross parent pairs and the same value squared for the outcome of recessives among all children of all Dominant by Dominant parent pairs. Such computations have been made in the table. Note that in the column from testcross parents the recessive proportion goes down from its maximum of 50 percent with decreasing frequency of the recessive allele in a population. Similarly, the recessive proportion from two Dominant parents decreases from its maximum expectation of 25 percent even more rapidly in populations with successively lower recessive allele frequencies. Many different kinds of rare recessive alleles are carried in low frequency in a population because the sibships in which they have a possibility of being detected phenotypically are a small minority among all sibships from similar Dominant parents. Such sibships are formed by chance within the general population and by some couples among the marriages of cousins and other near relatives.

ASSUMPTIONS FUNDAMENTAL TO POPULATION ANALYSIS

All of the above calculations either aid or mislead according to the success of meeting the assumptions upon which the mathematics is based. In review, these assumptions, as pointed out by Hardy and others, are (1) random choice of partner, or *panmixis*, in regard to the possible genotypes being studied, (2) a large population to facilitate the above and to permit a larger sample in the next generation, (3) no differences in fertility among the genotypes for any reason including emigration and (4) no mutation from R to r or the reverse. These are stringent conditions.

It may aid the student to remember the conditions necessary for the application of population principles by considering the one or more effects of not meeting each condition. (1) Violation of the condition of panmixis, as the random or proportional choice of partner is called, may be in either direction. If opposite phenotypes attract each other in more than their joint occurrence in the population, then there would be too many heterozygotes, more than the $2pq$ term, at the expense of the other classes among the next generation. Such a choice of opposites is usually called *negative assortative mating*. The other form of departure from the requirement of panmixis is *positive assortative mating*. This takes the form of Dominant preferring Dominant, heterozygote preferring heterozygote and recessives choosing each other more often than at random frequency. The effect on the next generation would be the production of more than p^2 homozygous Dominants and more than q^2 homozygous recessives. This is a general effect of inbreeding within genotypes; increases in both kinds of homozygotes result at the expense of the heterozygous proportion. It does not change the allele frequencies, nor does negative assortative mating, but it does alter the distribution of the offspring away from the panmictic expectation of $(p + q)^2$.

(2) The smaller the population of parents, or of offspring, the greater the sampling variations can be. This statement about the behavior of small numbers applies in two ways, to chance deviations from random choice of mate in one generation and to chance deviations in the gene frequencies in the next generation. The latter will be discussed later under the heading of *genetic drift* (random fluctuations of gene frequencies which become greater in smaller populations and may go all the way to 0 or to 1). Genetic drift is sometimes spoken of as the "Noah's ark" effect, and the idea is very helpful. A pair of animals on the ark and coming from a population having a certain recessive allele present with frequency .40 might within reason have that allele present in the pair with frequency .50, .25, .75 or 0 or even 1. Extreme but not at all impossible changes of gene frequency of an allele from .25 to 1.00 or from .75 to 0 frequency can occur. The smaller the population the greater is the opportunity for the vagaries of genetic drift. Thus heterozygosity may give way to homozygosity for one or more loci.

(3) Selection against any genotype in one generation would alter the gene frequency among the offspring. Adverse selection can take many forms, but they all have one thing in common — a lessened contribution of children to the next generation. Thus, premature death, sexual immaturity, or early emigration from the population can change the relative values of p and q slightly or profoundly even in one generation. The change will occur even if the heterozygote is selected against (see erythroblastosis, page 264),

except in the rare population where the allele frequency is exactly .50, a precarious balance point. Conversely, hybrid vigor will tend to pull gene frequencies toward .50 in successive generations of positive selection. Selection for one genotype or against another is routinely suspected when the observed proportions of individuals do not agree with the Hardy-Weinberg calculations.

(4) Ideally there should be no mutations between different allelic genes for the use of simple calculations of population equilibria. However, mutation rates for single gene loci are usually very low, and the mutations from common to rare allele are somewhat compensated in number by mutations of the rarer allele to the more common form. Therefore a more useful revision of the rule is that there shall be no net change of an allele frequency due to mutation, if the equilibrium expectation is to be approximated closely in an actual population.

The insights afforded by the simple calculations in this chapter have many extensions and applications, some of which will be encountered later. The interplay of net mutation and selection will be estimated against the background of simple Hardy-Weinberg equilibria. Again the effect of continued persistent selection of complete or partial degree can be predicted. Modifications may be made to conform with the special mode of inheritance of the X-chromosome from fathers to daughters, which causes a zig-zag approach over several generations to reach the new equilibrium. Especially interesting and historically important is the fact that equilibria can be computed for more than one pair of genes and for more than two alleles of a locus in a population. The analysis of the ABO and of the Rh blood groups rests upon foundations explained in this chapter.

SUMMARY

The viewpoint of population genetics includes all offspring and all parents within a genetic isolate, rather than merely pedigrees chosen for interest. Thus the scientist gets around the difficulty of small sibships and deals with large numbers of individuals or with the larger accumulations of several kinds of marriages. If men of two or more kinds choose women of the same or opposite kinds as individuals rather than favoring persons because of being the same or opposite phenotype as themselves, the population among whom the choices are made is said to be a panmictic population. In it the genotypes AA, Aa and aa are distributed according to the proportions $p^2 + 2pq + q^2$, respectively, where p is the frequency of the A allele and q the frequency of the a allele in the same population.

Although different populations have different gene frequencies out of their past history, the equilibrium discovered by Hardy and by Weinberg tends to be maintained within each population. Where there is no dominance, the equilibrium of three kinds of individuals is found among natural populations but is not approximated in artificial mixtures of data nor among people in an area with unassimilated immigrants. The Hardy-Weinberg equilibrium becomes possible in one generation in regard to any single pair of genes, provided it is on an autosomal pair. Where dominance exists between a pair of genes, the recessive proportion is the square of the recessive gene frequency, q, and from the latter one can make three testable predictions: (1) that inbred recessives will have only recessive children, (2) that crossbred Dominant-recessive pairs will have the recessives among their total combined offspring in the fraction $q/1 + q$, 0.5 as a special case, and (3) that inbred dominant phenotypes will have only $(q/1 + q)^2$ recessives among their total progeny, 0.25 as a special case. These predictions are not realized when a faulty hypothesis is under examination.

SUGGESTED READING

Dahlberg, G., "Genetics of Human Populations" pp. 69–98 in M. Demerec, ed., *Advances in Genetics*, Vol. II New York, Academic Press, 1948, 373 pp.
Li, C. C., *Human Genetics*, New York, Blakiston Division, McGraw-Hill, 1961, 218 pp. Most of the chapters are on population genetics. The mathematics is well explained.

PROBLEMS

6–1   Compare and contrast:
        positive and negative assortative mating
        Mendelian population and isolate
        gene frequency and population genotypic frequency
        segregating and nonsegregating marriages
        dominance and prevalence

6–2   Compare Figures 6-1 and 6-2 to see whether the distribution of the genotypes of parents agrees with the gene frequencies assumed for populations A, B and C.

6–3   What distribution of phenotypes would you expect in a Mendelian population where the frequency of the recessive allele is 0.6? 0.75? 0.90?

6–4   Compare each item of the appropriate line of Table 6-2 with the appropriate area or areas of Population B of Figure 6-1.

6–5 Where do the majority of recessive individuals come from in populations with
   (a) More than .67 recessive alleles?
   (b) Less than .33?
   (c) Gene frequencies between .34 and .66?

6–6 Compare Figure 6-4 and Table 6-3.

6–7 Why are Figures 6-1 and 6-5 so similar numerically?

6–8 What are the assumptions essential to the use of the Hardy-Weinberg equation?

6–9 Which of the following populations are in Hardy-Weinberg equilibrium?
   .50 AA and .50 aa .33 AA and .33 Aa and .33 aa
   1.00 Aa .16 AA and .36 Aa and .48 aa
   .25 AA and .50 Aa and .25aa .36 AA and .48 Aa and .16 aa

6–10 (a) If the gene frequency, q, is .50, what fraction of the offspring of all randomly chosen dominant pairs of parents will be recessive individuals?
   (b) If q is .90, what will be the fraction of recessive children among a collection of testcross type parents?

chapter 7

The Amassing and Use of Larger Numbers: X^2-tests

"Safety in numbers" is not guaranteed, but the chances of greater accuracy increase with larger totals. The wonderful usefulness of statistics is in their superior guiding ability, like a better gyrocompass or a better telescope, rather than in completely proving or completely disproving a relationship or a theory. The utility of numbers rests upon their proper use. Let us proceed with the study of some statistical problems, problems posed by biologists to mathematicians and to statisticians.

The basis of working with numbers is that they truly represent what they are alleged to represent, for instance, is this total all apples, or is it a mixture of fruits with different properties? The question can be partly answered by performing tests of *homogeneity* upon the subtotals of the proposed total. Such a convenient test is the Chi-square (X^2) test for homogeneity in a contingency table. It may be used for any number of sub-samples and any number of classes, but in its simplest form it is a 2 by 2 contingency table. An instructive example concerns the birth of more boy babies than girl babies during the year 1943 in a certain large hospital and the significance of the figures. It was stated in a newspaper article that the birth of 624 boys and 572 girls supported widespread belief that more boys are born in wartime than in peacetime. Whether the sex ratio does or does not vary under external influences will be discussed later (Chapter 19); at present we wish to gain some advice on whether we may add other available data to the above to increase our total observations, specifically, may we add in the data for the year 1944, also a wartime year? We wish to do this if there is no reason for not including the births of the next year. The births during 1944 were 456 boys and 474 girls, which is a numerical excess of girls and possibly reflects different causes at work; therefore we should test the data from the two years for homogeneity.

HOMOGENEITY CHI-SQUARE

A homogeneity test temporarily uses the marginal totals to set up uniform proportions among the boxes of each class of each sample, and then the deviations from the several expectations are used to compute a value, called Chi-square, which is very small when only small deviations are encountered but becomes larger in the case of larger deviations. The formula for Chi-square is the sum of the square of each deviation divided by the expectation for that category, or $X^2 = \Sigma(d^2/e)$. In the simplest homogeneity test there are four such terms summed to obtain the value of Chi-square. The interpretation of Chi-square is made by consulting tables showing the probability, P, of obtaining by mere chance Chi-square values as large as or larger than a certain computed sum of (d^2/e) terms. In standard practice the judgment is made that Chi-square values that can be exceeded 70, 50 or 20 percent of the time by chance alone are hardly worth worrying about, i.e.,

TABLE 7-1 Homogeneity test in a 2 by 2 contingency table. Data are on sex ratios among babies born in a certain hospital in two different years. Steps in the computation are numbered (1), (2), (3) . . . (7)

Sample		Males	Females	Totals (step 2)	Fraction in sample (3)
1943	observed (1)	624	572	1196	.563
	expected (4)	607.56	588.44		($\times$ 1080), ($\times$ 1046)
	deviation (5)	16.44	−16.44	0	
1944	observed (1)	456	474	930	.437
	expected (4)	472.44	457.56		($\times$ 1080), ($\times$ 1046)
	deviation (5)	−16.44	16.44	0	
Totals	(2)	1080	1046	2126	1.0
	(6)				

$$\text{Sum}\left(\frac{d^2}{e}\right) = \frac{270.5}{607.56} + \frac{270.5}{588.44} + \frac{270.5}{472.44} + \frac{270.5}{457.56} = \text{Chi-square}$$

(7)

$$= .443 + .461 + .572 + .591 = 2.067$$

Degree of Freedom in 2 by 2 is 1   Probability is between .20 and .10

the data observed are consistent with the expectation employed. For lower probabilities of reaching or exceeding a certain computed Chi-square, judgments differ somewhat. It is customary to say that a Chi-square value is "significant at the 5 percent level" as in much biological work, or "significant at the 1 percent level" as in more demanding biological work and in much research in physics. The reasoning is merely that if deviations this great occur by chance only 5 or 1 percent of the time, the experimenter or observer can apply other laws or principles that will lead to a different expectation around which the observations already in hand will deviate less. All large Chi-squares do not induce scientists to finding those laws which lead to better expectations, but the opportunity or need to explain events by new hypotheses is increasingly greater where Chi-square values are higher. Something other than mere chance may be making the deviations so far from those expectations which were employed at first.

The computation of a 2 by 2 contingency table may be made with as few steps as are shown in Table 7-1. (1) Observations are set down in two columns and two rows. (2) Totals of columns and totals of rows are obtained, together with their grand total. (3) The proportion of the grand total represented by each of the marginal totals is computed for one of the margins, here the right-hand sample totals. (4) The fractional proportion of each row (or column) is multiplied by the total number of each column (or row) to obtain the number expected from an ideally homogeneous distribution of the total observations according to the source of the observations; these expectations may be conveniently expressed to the fraction of an individual and are thereby never to be confused with the observed whole number in the steps to follow. (5) The deviation of each observation from each expectation is written; some deviations will be positive, some negative, so the row total of deviations will be zero or a fraction away from it, and the column totals of differences will also be zero. Note that in a 2 by 2 test for homogeneity the four differences, plus or minus, are numerically the same. (6) Square each difference; they are $(-16.44)^2$ or $(+16.44)^2$ and conveniently the same in this size contingency table. (7) Divide each squared difference by the expectation for its box in the 2 by 2 contingency table; each of these is called a "contribution to Chi-square." Finally, complete the computation by adding the contribution from each cell or box to get the Chi-square for the entire pattern of observations and expectations.

The interpretation of a Chi-square value requires that a table be consulted showing how common or how unusual chance Chi-square values happen to be. Table 7-2 is such a reference work. At the top of this table it should be noted that the probabilities of (equaling or) exceeding a certain Chi-square will be listed in the table. Thus on the left are low Chi-square values that have a high probability of being exceeded. In the column under P .50 are median Chi-square values, those that are exceeded half of the time that random variations from expectation are observed. To the right are

TABLE 7-2 Table of Chi-square[a]

N'	P = PROBABILITY OF A GREATER VALUE					
d.f.	.99	.50	.20	.05	.02	.01
1	0.0002	0.455	1.642	3.841	5.412	6.635
2	0.0201	1.386	3.219	5.991	7.824	9.210
3	0.115	2.366	4.642	7.815	9.837	11.341
4	0.297	3.357	5.989	9.488	11.608	13.277
5	0.554	4.351	7.289	11.070	13.388	15.086
6	0.872	5.348	8.558	12.592	15.033	16.812
7	1.239	6.346	9.803	14.067	16.622	18.475
8	1.646	7.344	11.030	15.507	18.168	20.090
9	2.088	8.343	12.242	16.919	19.679	21.666
10	2.558	9.342	13.442	18.307	21.161	23.209
..						
20	8.260	19.337	25.038	31.410	35.020	37.566
30	14.953	29.336	36.250	43.773	47.962	50.892

[a]The probability level (P) that merely chance deviations from a true expectation will produce Chi-square values (body of table) as great or greater than the sum of all d^2/e terms. Note that the number of degrees of freedom (left margin, and see text) influences the size of Chi-square and the corresponding P level.

Table, abridged from Table IV of Fisher and Yates: Statistical Tables for Biological, Agricultural, and Medical Research, published by Oliver & Boyd Ltd., Edinburgh, and by permission of the authors and publishers.

columns of Chi-square values that are exceeded by chance among only 5, 2 or 1 percent of random samples. In the body of the table are separate lines of Chi-square distributions (cumulative from the left) for each of several *degrees of freedom*, d.f. In any 2 by 2 contingency table there is only one degree of freedom; in a 3 by 2 homogeneity table there would be two degrees of freedom, and in a 4 by 3 table there would be six degrees of freedom. The general rule is that the degrees of freedom equal the product $(r - 1) \times (c - 1)$ or (number of rows minus one) times (number of columns minus one) = number d.f., often shown as N' in tables of X^2.

The resulting Chi-square in Table 7-1 on two samples of the sex ratio with one degree of freedom is interpreted with the aid of Table 7-2 to mean that such deviations from expectation would be expected well over 5 percent of the time. Therefore we see no reason for not adding together the annual totals of births in the two consecutive years. Incidentally, the sex ratio in the combined totals is not at all unusual. A direct test of whether the sample for either year differs from some ideal expectation not influenced by the present sample will be given later; it is more logical to begin here with tests for homogeneity, and it is more convenient to introduce the mathematics which cover the more representative uses of Chi-square before getting down to calculations so simple that they can be done in one's head!

The general effectiveness of large numbers, provided that the large numbers are made up from homogeneous subtotals, is well known. How rapidly do larger numbers build up toward more certain conclusions? For example, let us consider two samples containing two kinds of individuals in the numbers 16 : 15 and 19 : 10. To the unsophisticated these might not seem to be the same, but the Chi-square computation in Table 7-3, upper part, leads to the conclusion that fluctuations in two samples of this size

TABLE 7-3   An effect of sample size on homogeneity Chi-square calculation and its interpretation

	Kind j observed and (expected)	Kind k observed and (expected)	Total	Diff.	Diff.^{2}/expect.	
Sample A	16	15	31	−2.1	4.41/18.1	.244
	(18.1)	(12.9)	(31)	2.1	4.41/12.9	.341
Sample B	19	10	29	2.1	4.41/16.9	.261
	(16.9)	(12.1)	(29)	−2.1	4.41/12.1	.364
AB Total	35	25		1 d.f.	$X^2 = 1.210$ $P < .30$	
Sample C	160	150	310	−21	441/181	2.44
	(181)	(129)	(310)	21	441/129	3.41
Sample D	190	100	290	21	441/169	2.61
	(169)	(121)	(290)	−21	441/121	3.64
CD Total	350	250		1 d.f.	$X^2 = 12.10$ $P < .01$	

may deviate this far or farther from the expectations based on homogeneity of the sampled material in some 30 percent or more of samples. Conversely, chance deviations will produce a smaller Chi-square most of the time, 70 percent or less. Hence while the given sample deviates more than one would expect samples in general to depart from expectation, the observed deviation cannot be called rare, and we may tentatively consider that sample A and sample B have been drawn from a homogeneous mixture of the two kinds of individuals, j and k. Now suppose that two samples ten times as large as A and B were appropriately obtained and suppose further that exactly the same ratios were represented, namely the 160 : 150 and 190 : 100 samples called C and D of the same table. The differences from expectation (based on homogeneity) are numerically 10 × the differences before, the squares are 100× greater, and after division by the larger expectations the Chi-square is 10× as great as in the similar but smaller samples.

A Chi-square of 12.1 with one degree of freedom is so large a value that it is exceeded by chance less than 1 percent of the time, or P is less than .01 in technical language. In this illustration samples C and D differ significantly from each other, whereas the smaller samples A and B although in the same ratio do not differ significantly. Considering all possibilities we may point out two extremes of interpretation: both pairs of samples, C-D and A-B, might indeed be mere chance departures from expectation, or both sample pairs might be from different sources with different expectations, the C-D pair clearly so and the A-B pair not at all clearly different. More often the truth will be found to lie between these extremes, such as in the statement that samples A and B could be from a homogeneous source and that samples C and D were probably not from a homogeneous pool.

X^2 TESTS OF EXTERNAL RATIOS

So far in this chapter we have not used expectations which come from information outside the sample totals; we have avoided using $3:1$ Mendelian expectations, or the theoretical $1:1$ expectation for chromosomal segregation among gametes, merely in order to emphasize testing for the basic assumption of homogeneity between subsamples. We are now ready to determine how likely is a certain sample of being a chance deviation from a $1:2:1$ ratio. Consider the sample of persons all of whom had MN blood type parents and consisting of $20:56:30$ of the three possible types, M, MN, and N. The computations recorded in Table 7-4 show that the ideal distribution on the $1:2:1$ hypothesis would be 26.5, 53 and 26.5, and that

TABLE 7-4   Offspring of MN parents tested for agreement with a 1:2:1 expectation by Chi-square computation

	M type	MN type	N type	Total
Observed	20	56	30	106
Expected	26.5	53	26.5	106
Deviation	−6.5	3	3.5	0
Deviation²	42.25	9	12.25	
Expected	26.5	53	26.5	
Chi-square =	1.594 +	.179 +	.462 =	2.226
2 d.f.				$P > .20$

the differences between observed and expected numbers are -6.5, 3 and 3.5, which sum to 0. After each difference is squared and that product is divided by the expectation for that category, there will be three contributions to the value of Chi-square. Because we are comparing three classes against a fixed ratio (1 : 2 : 1) there are two degrees of freedom associated with this Chi-square.

A Chi-square with two degrees of freedom will naturally tend to be larger than a Chi-square with only one degree of freedom, and the appropriate figures are given on the "d.f. 2" line of Chi-square tables. For our example, a Chi-square of 2.226 is not as high as that Chi-square value of 2.41 which is found or exceeded by chance in 30 percent of samples having two degrees of freedom. Therefore our observed 20 : 56 : 30 is found not to differ significantly from the ideal numbers to be expected under a 1 : 2 : 1 ratio in a sample of size 106. If the Chi-square had been near or beyond 5.99, we would have been increasingly suspicious that some influence other than chance might have been involved in producing our sample.

Two precautions must be emphasized in computing Chi-square values: actual numbers must be used in measuring the deviations, and the expected numbers must not be too small. The first point cautions against recording percentages in the body of the table of observations. Percentage deviations do not reflect the greater variability of small samples as compared with large samples. Table 7-5 has been prepared to illustrate this by giving the Chi-square and P values for samples with the same relative deviation from 12 : 12 and from 48 : 48 expectations on corresponding lines. The second precaution is also emphasized in the same table, where one of the expected classes is too small. Unless the value pqN is 5 or greater, it is considered better to use the binomial expansion (Chapter 3) instead of Chi-square, which is merely a convenient approximation designed for use with larger numbers. Thus, the 3 : 1 ratio in a sample of 24 has $pqN = .75$ (.25) 24 = 4.5 individuals in the smaller class which is too small to be used as a divisor. Yet a 1 : 1 ratio in the same total gives $pqN = 6$ individuals, a number above the recommended 5 for any expected class. The smaller class is well above the minimum 5 if the total individuals in the sample are quadrupled as in Table 7-5. Note that for testing a 9 : 1 expectation even a total of 55 would be too small for the accurate application of the Chi-square method, and the binomial expansion $(.1 + .9)^{55}$ would be a more reliable guide.

Statistical decisions among alternative hypotheses are usually guided by the Chi-square calculations and probability tables. If we wish to be alerted to oddities at the 5 percent level we would say, with the aid of Table 7-5, that we will accept the distributions 12 : 12 through 16 : 8 as merely chance deviations from an expectation of equality, but that we would reject the sample of 17 : 7 as having too small a chance (less than .05) of being a

TABLE 7-5

SMALLER SAMPLE $N = 24$						LARGER SAMPLE $N = 96$					
Expected 12 : 12						Expected 48 : 48					
obs.	d	d^2	d^2/e	$\Sigma d^2/e$	P	obs.	d	d^2	d^2/e	$\Sigma d^2/e$	P
12 : 12	0	0	0	0	$=1.0$	48 : 48	0	0	0	0	$=1.0$
13 : 11	1	1	.08	.17	$<.70$	52 : 44	4	16	.33	.66	$>.3$
14 : 10	2	4	.3	.6	$>.3$	56 : 40	8	64	1.33	2.66	$>.05$
15 : 9	3	9	.75	1.50	$>.20$	60 : 36	12	144	3.00	6.00	$>.01$
16 : 8	4	16	1.33	2.66	$>.05$	64 : 32	16	256	5.33	10.66	$>.001$
17 : 7	5	25	2.08	4.16	$>.02$	68 : 28	20	400	8.33	16.66	$<.0001$

Expected 18 : 6

$pqN < 5$ (see text)
(Chi-square is not suitable)
Use $(\tfrac{3}{4} + \tfrac{1}{4})^{24}$

	Expected 72 : 24						
obs.	d	d^2	d^2/e_1	d^2/e_2	$\Sigma d^2/e$	P
60 : 36	12	144	2.00	6.00	8.00	$<.01$
64 : 32	8	64	.889	2.667	3.556	$>.05$
68 : 28	4	16	.222	.667	.889	$>.3$
72 : 24	0	0	0	0	0	$=1.0$

random variation. Among larger size samples the rule of rejection at the 5 percent level takes effect at smaller proportional differences; the 56 : 40 sample would be accepted and the 60 : 36 sample would, for example, be rejected as deviations from the expected 48 : 48. To facilitate comparisons in the table note that on horizontal lines the proportional distributions are the same. If deviations from a 3 : 1 ratio are considered in the same total of observations, 96, Chi-square values rise more rapidly. This is mainly because the smaller expectation, $e_2 = 24$ (lower part of Table 7-5), results in a larger contribution to Chi-square, a contribution not balanced by a sufficiently smaller contribution from the larger class. In general, the larger contributions to Chi-square come from the smaller of two mutually exclusive classes. This is the reason for remembering the rule of "pqN greater than 5" being necessary for the above use of Chi-square. In testing against a fixed ratio or within a 2 by 2 table the *Yates correction* for continuity is used in whatever box the expectation is fewer than five items.

Yates' correction simply reduces the deviation closer to zero by one-half an item before squaring and dividing. Thus an expected 4.5 and an observed 7 would give an uncorrected difference of 2.5 but a corrected difference of 2, $(2.5 - 0.5)$, and therefore $2 \times 2/4.5$ as a contribution to Chi-square. Also an expected 3.5 and an observed 0 would mean that $(3.5 - 0.5)^2/3.5$, or $9/3.5$, is the contribution to Chi-square from this term using the Yates correction. It is conservative to use this correction when looking for significant differences from expectation or for departures from homogeneity.

A further example of making decisions at the 5 percent probability level may be pointed out in Table 7-5. For making decisions at a lower level other tables would be needed but would be similarly used. Suppose we raise the question whether a 16 : 8 sample was drawn from a population with a 2 : 1 expectation, a 1 : 1 expectation or a 3 : 1 expectation. Although it is numerically a perfect fit to the 2 : 1 expectation, the sample differs by only 2 from a 3 : 1 expectation, and it differs by 4 from equality. Are the differences negligible or large? The Chi-square computation summarized in the table shows that there is more than a 5 percent P value that a chance deviation from the 12 : 12 expectation this great or greater may be encountered. Hence no decision among the three alternatives may be made on statistical grounds. A decision is facilitated against one hypothesis if we consider a larger sample which came out 64 : 32. This has less than a 0.1 percent P value of being a random deviation from 48 : 48, so we may with considerable confidence rule out on the usual statistical grounds that this is a wide but acceptable deviation from a 1 : 1 ratio. It would require a larger sample, say 70 : 35, to differentiate itself from both 3 : 1 and 1 : 1 expectations at the 5 percent probability level. (See Table 7-6.) For a more cautious decision, a sample of 120 : 60 would be required to differentiate between a 2 : 1 and a 3 : 1 expectation at the 1 percent probability level. Thus the diagnosis of a 2 : 1 ratio among the living offspring of parents having $\frac{1}{4}$ of their zygotes dying in utero (Chapter 5) may be difficult but not impossible, provided that the collection of data is done with due care.

TRUNCATED COLLECTIONS OF DATA

The manner of collecting data will of course influence the distributions being accumulated. We may consider determining the sex ratio in a town or city by three different methods, following Stern: (A) by a *complete census*, or (B) by asking all girls, a *truncated census*, for the sex ratio totals in their sibships or (C) by asking only a few girls, an incomplete and *truncated sample*. The results of collections by methods B and C differ depending on the sizes of the sibships of each person sampled for information, but the direction of the trend is very apparent in the simplest sibships, all sibships of size two. The contrasting results are diagrammed in Figure 7-1. On the assumption of equality of boys and of girls in the population the totality of sibships of two would include sibships of two boys and sibships of two girls equally, and it would include boy-girl sibships of size two twice as often as either alone. Therefore we are seeking information about a population in

TABLE 7-6 The limited ability of a sample of 96 to discriminate among three simple hypotheses

					range of variation around a 2 : 1 expectation in 95 percent of samples						
Dom.	40	44	48	52	56	60	64	68	72	76	80
rec.	56	52	48	44	40	36	32	28	24	20	16

in this range lie 95 percent of samples from a 1 : 1 ratio

variation within this range expected 95 percent of the time with 3 : 1 parameter operating

which the sibships of this size are in the ratio of 1 : 2 : 1, the ratios of the uppermost areas in Figure 7-1. Determination of the sex ratio by method A (a complete census) would record boys and girls in equal totals, which we may express as 12 : 12 for convenient comparison with what follows. In

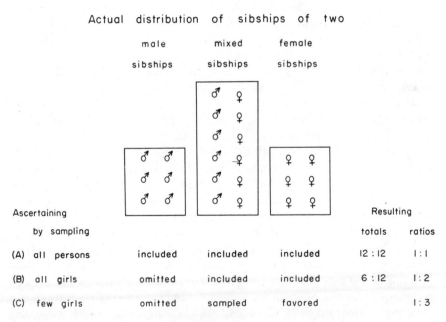

Actual distribution of sibships of two

male sibships	mixed sibships	female sibships

Ascertaining by sampling				Resulting totals	ratios
(A) all persons	included	included	included	12 : 12	1 : 1
(B) all girls	omitted	included	included	6 : 12	1 : 2
(C) few girls	omitted	sampled	favored		1 : 3

FIGURE 7-1 An influence of the method of ascertainment on the ratios shown within accumulated data. After *Principles of Human Genetics*, 2nd edition, by Curt Stern. San Francisco: W. H. Freeman and Company, 1960.

accumulations by method B (asking all girls about the total of girls and boys in their sibships) those sibships of all boys will be missed, and the collection of data will be truncated. Therefore among the remaining sibships of two we will still record 12 girls but only 6 boys, and hence a revised expectation of 12 : 6 would be used in calculations based upon this method of ascertainment. By the third sampling method, C (asking a small fraction of girls), the compiler will again miss all the boy-boy sibships, but he will also miss more of the girl-boy sibships than of the girl-girl sibships. The partial omissions occur because there is only one chance of finding the mixed sibships of two, namely, that the sole girl of the pair happens to incur the attention of the person doing the sampling. By contrast, the girl-girl sibships have double the chances of being found and recorded, because either the younger or the older girl may report the existence of a two-girl sibship to the recorder. Thus after adding the reports of an incomplete sampling of girls one will find in the sample something like 3 girls : 1 boy.

Similar reasoning about sibships of sizes three, four, five and up reveals the need of similarly modified expectations. This comparison of methods of ascertainment is applicable to cases of rare dominant phenotypes where the ratio of abnormal to normal is 1 : 1 within certain families but is far different from equality elsewhere. It would be less than 1 : 1 in the total population and greater in collections of affected sibships. As a direct consequence of multiple chances of ascertainment, investigators tend to discover those sibships with many or even two cases of rare Dominants more readily than sibships with only a solitary rare case.

The ascertainment of sibships via recessive index cases follows a similar course, and correction factors are necessary before an accumulation of large numbers can be interpreted in genetic terms. When a certain phenotype is completely dominant as, with our present knowledge, normal mentality is dominant over phenylketonuria, the heterozygosity of both parents is known only after they have had one recessive child. Thus the Mendelian segregation ratios expected in an F_2 generation are altered because there is known to be at least one recessive individual in each selected sibship. The numerical effect of ascertainment in various small sibships is given in Table 7-7. With larger numbers of births, i.e., above 10, the expectations rise toward 3 Dominants : 1 recessive, and the number of recessive children in sibships ascertained by at least one of the recessives subsides toward $\frac{1}{4}$ of the total. Because sibships are small in the human species, corrections are necessary — separate corrections for each sibship size. Only after the corrected expectations have been computed for the mixture of sizes of sibships in a body of data may a Chi-square test be appropriately computed based on the sum of the observations and on the sum of the expectations.

TABLE 7-7 Proportions of Dominant to recessive individuals to be expected among those sibships, of various sizes, ascertained by their having one affected recessive[a]

Children per affected sibship	Number of rr expected	Expected Dom. : rec.
2	1.143	0.75 : 1
3	1.297	1.31 : 1
4	1.463	1.74 : 1
5	1.640	2.05 : 1
6	1.825	2.29 : 1
7	2.020	2.46 : 1
8	2.222	2.60 : 1
9	2.433	2.70 : 1
10	2.649	2.77 : 1
20	5.016	under 3.00 : 1

[a]After *Principles of Human Genetics*, Second Edition, by Curt Stern. San Francisco: W. H. Freeman and Company, 1960.

A simple way to get around the bias introduced above in the inclusive sibship method is the use of the simple *sib method*. In it only the brothers and sisters of the person first contacted are tallied and added while the index member is omitted. Thus a truly representative sex ratio could be obtained either by scoring the numbers of brothers and sisters of girls in a private girls' school or of boys in a boys' club or the sibs of both in a predominantly male university class. The simple sib method can also be used where ascertainment has been made through a rare recessive case, but aiming for simplicity of total ratios in this manner greatly prolongs the search for a large total of cases secondary to the first found case in the sibship.

As a check on the influence of ascertainment, it is customary for geneticists when presenting a pedigree in print to show, by an arrow or otherwise, the *index case* or *proband*, the person through whom the investigation of the whole kindred began. A reviewer may then apply the simple sib method by omitting that proband.

TESTING GENETIC RATIOS IN POPULATIONS

The value of Chi-square calculations upon the large numbers of individuals obtainable with the use of gene frequency analysis should be obvious. It might be asked whether the offspring of testcross parents, one a Taster and the other a nontaster of phenylthiocarbamide, segregate in a monohybrid ratio or not. Large numbers of parents of this testcross category may be obtained, and the principles of population genetics discussed in Chapter 6 have shown how to calculate expectations. We may apply them here for a population in which there is random choice of mates in respect to PTC tasting and an observed frequency of .30 nontasters. Since the latter group consists entirely of homozygous *tt* individuals, the square root of the recessive fraction is the *t* gene frequency, namely, .55 of the alleles. The formula given in Chapter 6 for the recessive proportion from all testcrosses (of both heterozygous and homozygous Dominants represented in the equilibrium proportions) was $q/(1 + q)$, so in this population it should be .55/1.55 or .355 recessive offspring expected from apparent testcrosses. Thus we have an expectation according to the equilibrium mixture of genotypes in an existing population, but it is expressed in fractional terms, not in actual numbers. Suppose we have a tally of 400 unrelated testcross offspring consisting of 250 Tasters and 150 nontasters. We leave this ratio in the form of actual numbers and convert the .355 expectation into fractions of 400, which means an expectation of 258 Taster and 142 nontaster individuals. The differences, plus eight individuals and minus eight individuals, sum to zero as a check on our procedure thus far. The square of this deviation divided by the expected number of dominant individuals contributes .248 to Chi-square, and the other squared difference divided by the expected number of recessive individuals contributes a larger amount, .45, to the total of .698 for Chi-square. This value associated with one degree of freedom does not indicate a significant departure from expectation, in fact it does not approach the Chi-square value of 1.642 in Table 7-2 corresponding to deviations exceeded by chance more often than 20 percent of the time. Therefore the accumulated testcross data are not inconsistent with the assumption of a monohybrid difference with the Taster phenotype being dominant over nontasting. Both observations and computations allow for some of the Taster parents being *TT* and some *Tt* in the testcross category.

For large total numbers, such that the expectations in any separate box of the tabulation are more than five individuals, Chi-square has many uses. It can test for the significance of departures from any given ratio between two classes. It may also be used where there are three or many more classes within a sample. And it can be used when there are many sources of samples. For instance, samples of the distribution of the three M-N blood types coming from six different schools within a city could be tested for homogeneity in a 3 by 6 table, and the degrees of freedom would be obtained by subtracting 1 from the rows and 1 from the columns and multiplying the remainder, 2 by 5, to arrive at 10 as the number of degrees of freedom. If the array of boxes is found to be homogeneous, then the marginal totals of type M, type MN and type N persons could be compared with the population equilibrium expectations for the discovery of possible differences from theoretical expectation. Finally, it should be remembered that statistical procedures provide intelligent guides to conclusions rather than guarantees.

SUMMARY

Fluctuating numbers mislead the excitable and scare the cautious calculator. Fluctuations become smaller percentagewise in larger bodies of data, but a first step in the accumulation of figures is to test the portions of it for homogeneity before comparing the sum totals with outside expectations. A homogeneity Chi-square in a 2 by 2 or larger table is a good procedural step. Chi-square in general is a measure of variation away from internal or external expectation, which assumes larger and larger values with less and less frequency. The latter as a probability level, P, gives a rather objective evaluation to usualness, unusualness or remoteness of an obtained deviation from theory. Chi-square calculations are used on larger totals in place of the more cumbersome but more accurate binomial expansion described in Chapter 3 for small numbers. A Yates correction to the difference is used for testing against a theoretical expectation or in a 2 by 2 table.

The manner of collection of data may bias the totals to various demonstrable amounts. A truncated census and a truncated sample were each compared with a complete sample in the simplest situation, sibships of two. In larger segregating sibships, applications of the idea of recessive ascertainment show the exact expression of a 3 : 1 segregation in sibships of many different sizes.

SUGGESTED READING

Bryant, Edward C., *Statistical Analysis*, New York, McGraw-Hill, 1960. Chapters 3 and 5 on statistical inference will be particularly helpful.

Dixon, Wilfrid J., and Frank J. Massey, Jr., *Introduction to Statistical Analysis*, 2nd ed., New York, McGraw-Hill, 1957, 448 pp. Chapters 4, "Universe and Sample" and 7, "Statistical Inference" are especially recommended.

Finney, D. J., R. Latscha, B. M. Bennett, and P. Hsu, *Tables for Testing Significance in a 2 × 2 Contingency Table*, Cambridge, Cambridge University Press, 1963. Handy for consultation.

Williams, J. D., *The Compleat Strategyst*, New York, McGraw-Hill, 1954, 234 pp. Humor, logic and mathematics interwoven.

PROBLEMS

7–1 Define briefly but adequately:

degree of freedom	proband
census	sib method
sample	homogeneity of samples

7–2 By Chi-square calculation, test for homogeneity the number of the genotypes at the Landsteiner locus shown by the Basques and the Ainu in Table 6-1.

7–3 (a) Take a census on the sex of all persons in the sibships represented by the members of the genetics class and test the total for the probability of its being a random departure from a 1 : 1 ratio.
   (b) Explain the outcome.

7–4 (a) Take a census of the sibs of the members of your class and test this total (omitting all probands) for agreement with a 1 : 1 ratio.
   (b) If the total of sibs is several hundred, test the observed ratio against a 106 male : 100 female expectation.

7–5 The number of Tay-Sachs cases (infantile amaurotic idiocy) in sibships of various sizes ascertained by their being at least one case per sibship is given below. See if the total is consistent with simple recessive determination knowing the way in which the data were collected.

Size of sibships	Number of sibships	Total	Total Tay-Sachs
1	6	6	6
2	5	10	7
3	8	24	11
4	5	20	9
5	3	15	8
6	4	24	6

chapter **8**

Multiple Alleles of a Locus

A *locus* may be defined as a place on a chromosome occupied by a single gene. When it is discovered that two phenotypes show regular segregation, the geneticist thereby recognizes that these phenotypes are differentiated from each other by allelic genes. One or the other of these alleles occupies a fixed position or locus on a certain chromosome of the diploid set; and the corresponding locus on the homologous chromosome is occupied by the allelic gene in a heterozygous diploid, or by the identical form of the gene in a homozygote. Because of this precise positioning the haploid gametes from a hybrid would contain only one allele or the other. Thus 1 : 1 gametic segregation, found repeatedly and invariably, constitutes evidence for allelism of the genes determining a phenotypic difference; contrarily, exceptions to this brought about by free recombination or by limited crossing over (Chapter 11) point to the involvement of two loci and thus deny simple allelism.

THE i LOCUS AND A-B-O ALLELES

Differences in the blood antigens and antibodies are determined by several alleles. The practice of transfusing blood from one person to another long ago demonstrated that humans may be divided among four blood groups. Transfusions are best made where both donor and recipient are of the same blood group. However, some transfusions between persons of different blood groups may be made slowly, and other combinations of donor blood and recipient may even be fatal to the recipient. The differences which are physiologically important here are found both on the red blood cells and in the blood plasma, as shown in Figure 8-1. The names of the four blood groups correspond to the kinds of antigens which a person has on his red blood corpuscles. Thus both of the antigens A and B are on the corpuscles of the AB person; antigen A is on all corpuscles of the group

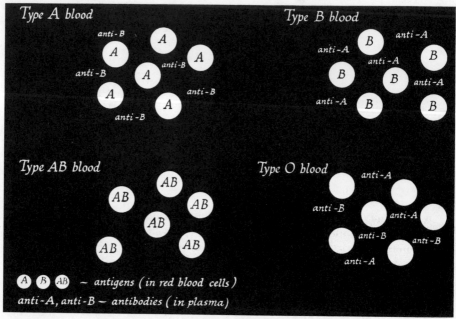

FIGURE 8-1 Diagram of whole blood of the four major isoagglutinating groups showing the relation of the A and B antigens of some blood corpuscles to their antibodies in the plasma of other blood groups. From A. M. Winchester, *Genetics*, Boston, Houghton Mifflin, 1951.

A person; antigen B is on the red blood cells of the group B person; and neither antigen is on the cells of the person of group O. The foregoing describes the phenotypes only half way; the plasma contains natural antibodies against the A or B which are not on its own red blood cells. Thus only the group AB persons have no plasma antibodies. Group A persons have anti-B circulating in their plasma, group B persons have anti-A, and group O individuals have both of the plasma antibodies, anti-A and anti-B, in their blood streams. The corpuscles and plasma differences seem at present to be dual outcomes of the same genotype and comprise a minimum example of pleiotropy.

The action of the plasma antibody is to cause a clumping together (*agglutination*) of the red blood corpuscles if the latter contain the corresponding antigen. Thus anti-A in the plasma causes corpuscles with antigen A to agglutinate, and B corpuscles are agglutinated into stacks or rolls by anti-B. In transfusions group O blood may be transfused slowly into any of the blood groups without having the donor O corpuscles clumped, but if the transfusion were to be made too rapidly the anti-A and anti-B in the group O plasma could cause some small number of the recipient's A cells or another recipient's B cells to be agglutinated.

Bloods are typed before transfusion, and for genetic studies, by obtaining plasma from a person known to be of group A and from another person known to be of group B and using these as sources of antibodies "anti-B" and "anti-A," respectively. If a drop of another person's whole blood is mixed with the anti-A test fluid (from type B blood) and the normally dispersed red blood cells clump together in a few minutes, it is thereby demonstrated that the person being tested has antigen A on his red blood cells, and he therefore belongs to group A or to group AB. The parallel test with serum containing anti-B (from a type A person's blood serum) would differentiate whether he also had antigen B on his red blood cells. Any person whose blood did not show agglutination of corpuscles when placed in the samples of anti-A and, separately, anti-B plasma would belong to blood group O.

When the above facts were first known, it was natural to think that one pair of genes might determine the presence or absence of one antigen on the red blood cells and similarly that a different pair of genes might determine whether the other antigen was on the cells. This plausible hypothesis was soon refuted by evidence from population genetics and from studies within families. It was observed that only those parent pairs which were one of group A and one of group B had offspring of all four kinds, and parents both of group O had only group O children. This demonstrated the homozygous recessive nature of the O individuals and made possible certain predictions about the offspring of AB by O marriages on two alternative hypotheses. If two pairs of genes were making the blood group differences, segregation for each pair should show up among the children of such a testcross type of marriage. Some children should be AB like that kind of parent, if an A-a pair and a B-b pair can assort; and there should also be some O children from some of the AB by O parents, if the dihybrid assumption were correct (see Chapter 10). However, only A children and B children are observed to result, and in approximate equality, from O by AB parents. This indicates strongly that only A gametes and B gametes are formed by the AB blood type person, and whatever genes invariably separate from each other in gametogenesis are, by definition, alleles of each other.

For the same reason, regular segregation, a third allele must be present in the pure-breeding O individuals. Many of the A by O marriages have only A children and O children in equal numbers, indicating segregation of an A allele from a not-A allele. Similarly, B by O couples have two kinds of offspring unless the B parent is homozygous, and the two types of children are B group and O group equally often after allowing for random sampling (Chapter 3). Therefore the genes *A*, *B* and *O* form a multiple allelic series, which it now becomes appropriate to designate by some uniform base letter, the locus symbol, to which may be added distinctive superscripts. Since the antigens and antibodies of the ABO phenotypes are developed within the human species, unlike the rabbit-formed antisera used to demonstrate the MN blood types, they are called isoagglutinogens and isoagglutinins. This has given rise to one of the most readable designations of the locus and of the alleles which may occupy the locus. The genotype ii indicates the homozygous recessive nature of the group O individuals. The monohybrid AB individuals are genotypically $i^A i^B$. Homozygous and heterozygous group A persons are $i^A i^A$ and $i^A i$, respectively; and group B persons are also either homozygous or heterozygous at this locus as $i^B i^B$ or $i^B i$ genotypes. Studies of siblings and their biological parents are consistent with the above genotypes, except for the rare occurrence of mutation (Chapter 21).

Gene frequency analyses on the two differing assumptions were historically instrumental in establishing that the multiple allele theory fitted the facts better than the two factor pair theory. The method of predicting population equilibrium proportions for the several phenotypes involving three alleles differs only slightly from the method already used for the presence of just two alleles. Let the proportions of the three alleles, i^A, i^B, and i be represented by the fractions p, q and r, respectively. The three diploid homozygotes will therefore be in the proportions p^2 of $i^A i^A$, q^2 of $i^B i^B$ and r^2 of ii as

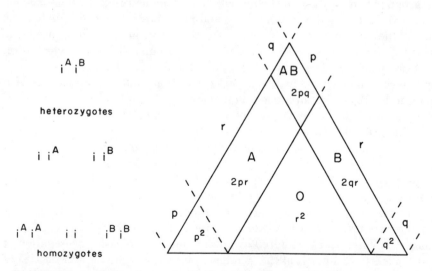

FIGURE 8-2 Proportions of phenotypes and genotypes in a population (English) with a certain proportion of three alleles at one locus. This represents a folded checkerboard.

in Figure 8-2, bottom. Furthermore, the three heterozygotes will be present in the proportions $2pq$ of $i^A i^B$, $2pr$ of $i^A i$ and $2qr$ of $i^B i$ hybrids as in the upper part of the same figure. The triangle form has nothing to do with the fact of there being three alleles; it is merely a checkerboard folded diagonally to superimpose in one area the $2pq$ areas and other paired areas for heterozygotes, which are separated in the usual checkerboard. The triangle may also be used for four or more alleles. All six genotypes will add up to frequency 1.000 of individuals, and the three allele frequencies will also add up to unity.

Conversely, the computation of the three allele frequencies from observed phenotypes may be guided by reference again to Figure 8-2. The gene frequency of the i^A allele may be estimated by taking the square root of the non-A-containing phenotypes and subtracting it from one. (It is possible to take the square root of the combined B and O classes because these are recessive in respect to being not-A.) Similar estimation of the i^B allele frequency starting from the frequency of non-B phenotypes may be made; and the i allele frequency may be estimated directly by taking the square root of the phenotypic frequency of group O individuals in the population. Thus

$$i^A \text{ freq., } p = 1 - \sqrt{B + O} = 1 - \sqrt{(q^2 + 2qr) + r^2}$$

$$i^B \text{ freq., } q = 1 - \sqrt{A + O} = 1 - \sqrt{(p^2 + 2pr) + r^2}$$

$$i \text{ freq., } r = \sqrt{O} \qquad\quad = \sqrt{r^2}$$

If the sum of these first estimates of allele frequencies does not add exactly to 1.000, then adjusted estimates may be made as described by Li (1961).

Studies in population after population around the world have shown that the observed frequencies of the ABO blood groups are in agreement with the equilibrium expectations based on the existence of at least three alleles of an i locus. Two such populations are shown in Figure 8-3. Furthermore, some of these same populations, the larger ones in particular, are significantly out of agreement with the older assumption of two factor pairs. Thus analyses of this blood group system by the methods of Hardy and Weinberg and by the study of kindreds mutually confirm each other.

Even more than three alleles are possible on general considerations and are already known for the i locus. Antigen A has been found in at least two and possibly three forms which are now called A_1, A_2 and A_3, with the phenotype A_1 dominant over either of the next two. These antigens are determined by the alleles i^{A_1}, i^{A_2} and i^{A_3}, respectively. This system of naming alleles may seem awkward, but it, like Topsy, just grew. For other loci

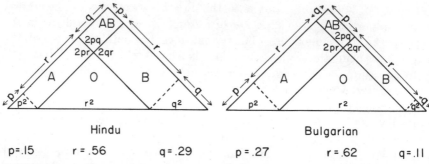

FIGURE 8-3 Equilibrium proportions of phenotypes and genotypes in populations with different gene frequencies. Compare with the previous Figure.

with many alleles somewhat different systems have been introduced, such as numbering each allele in turn with a superscript or by using the date of naming as a superscript. Each system has its advantages and disadvantages, and it does not yet seem possible to prescribe in advance that any particular system of naming alleles should be used.

The relation of *codominance* as well as simple dominance is found in respect to the ABO groups. The presence of the red blood cell antigens of the A phenotype is dominant over the O phenotype in the heterozygote, and likewise B shows phenotypic dominance over O in $i^B i$ persons. However, the A and B antigens in the $i^A i^B$ heterozygote are as fully expressed as A alone in group A persons or as B alone in group B persons, and this unhindered expression is called codominance between A and B. By contrast the O phenotype is recessive to A and also recessive to B. Note that we are here speaking of recessiveness and dominance of phenotypes rather than of genes. It is probable that as detailed knowledge of the processes of development accumulates, biochemists and physiologists will be able to detect the presence of each allele by an appropriate specific test; then there would not be any completely recessive genes, but rather some genes whose major phenotypic effect is recessive while other pleiotropic expressions of the same genotype might allow detection in the heterozygous individual.

ALLELES OF MS AT THE LANDSTEINER LOCUS

Additional alleles of the M and N pair of Landsteiner have been found. An antigen S is present in many persons and lacking in many others. Conversely, an antigen s has been found on the red blood cells of those persons whose cells do not have antigen S. The small s phenotypes never have S offspring when inbred, but inbred S couples may have s offspring in a recessive proportion. While it is true that type M persons can be S or s and that type N persons may also be of either kind, they are not impartially so. Family evidence and population data both indicate that a single gene locus with several alleles is determining. Within sibships which show segregation both for M-N and S-s differences there is observed only monohybrid segregation instead of assortment into four phenotypes. For example, the children in a testcross from a certain MNS parent receive an Ms chromosome or NS chromosome; another parent of the same phenotype might transmit only MS and Ns. Again, the recessive s phenotype is not found in more than one of the three M-N types from two MNS parents. The ss sibs are always N or always M or always MN; and the kinds of sibships depend on the genotypes rather than on the phenotypes of the MNS parents. While the above evidence was being accumulated, simple population studies were also indicating that one locus alone was the site of the several alleles.

The commonest alleles at the Landsteiner locus are L^{MS}, L^{Ms}, L^{NS}, and L^{Ns}, and their occurrence and segregation take us in one step to the same complexity as the A_1A_2BO series. Figure 8-4 shows the most common phenotypes recognized before 1965 and their genotypes. It may seem con-

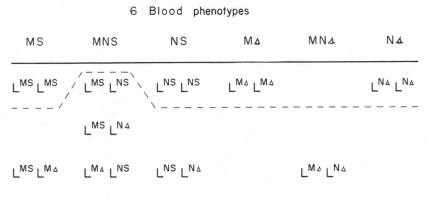

FIGURE 8-4 Correspondence of phenotypes and genotypes for the four most common alleles at the Landsteiner locus (M-N blood groups).

tradictory that the S antigen phenotype showed dominance over the s antigen detection while the M and N properties show no dominance, yet that is the result of early methods of recognizing phenotypes. Now an anti-s serum makes it possible to identify *Ss* heterozygotes, but the sera do not tell whether s is with M or N; only a genetic test does that. No diploid individual can have more than two *L* alleles, yet there was at first a variety of genotypes within the dominant S antigen group although not within the three phenotypic combinations with s. Now the hidden variety is reduced to two genotypes in the MNSs phenotype. The ten genotypes are found in varied frequencies within different populations because the frequencies of the different Landsteiner alleles are not the same. In some populations the *Ns* allele is the most frequent while the *NS* allele is by far the least frequent of the four. This great difference does not extend to the *Ms* and *MS* Landsteiner alleles, which occur approximately equally. This lack of independent distribution, i.e., the s : S ratio does not apply equally to the total of chromosomes carrying *M* and to chromosomes carrying *N*, is evidence from population studies that a single series of alleles is differentiating the phenotypes. The reasoning for this is elaborated in Chapter 10 on dihybrid assortment.

A population distribution for the ten genotypes at equilibrium is shown in Figure 8-5, which represents a checkerboard folded on one diagonal. The relative frequencies of the alleles of the *L* series are proportional to the space

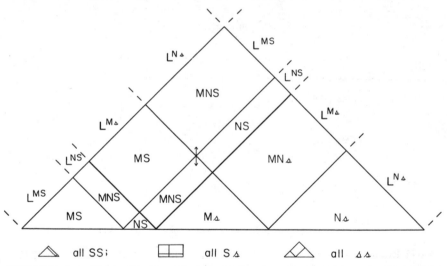

FIGURE 8-5 Example of equilibrium proportions of genotypes and phenotypes controlled by four alleles in a representative population (North American white). Note that the two alternative genotypes of MNS marked by the double arrow are usually unequal in multiple allelism (but equal in linkage, Chapter 11.)

used along the two marked margins to represent the proportions of the possible kinds of gametes, eggs along one margin and sperm along the other.

The allele frequencies may be designated by the fractions p, q, r and s which together must add up to 1. These values were .25, .08, .28 and .39, for the MS, Ms, NS and Ns alleles, respectively, in the Figure 8-5. It may be pointed out that the two rectangles denoting MNS phenotypes are not equivalent in ancestry, in proportion, nor in gamete formation. The effect of L^{Ms}/L^{NS} and L^{MS}/L^{Ns} on their offspring has been described in a preceding paragraph.

LOCI OF OTHER BLOOD TYPE ALLELES

Multiple allelic series at several other loci concerned with antigenic blood differences are known. The Kell locus has a common allele, k, (known also as the Cellano allele) and two different alleles, K and k^P, which show phenotypic dominance over the Cellano recessive. Similarly, there are already three known alleles of the P series designated P, p^1 and p^2. The Duffy locus became known when two different antigenic phenotypes were recognized by regular monohybrid segregation and attributed to the gene pair Fy^a and Fy^b, and later a third phenotype not showing antigenic reactions with the blood of either of the first two was discovered in West Africa, where this allele is very common. Its present gene symbol is simply Fy in the series of three Duffy alleles.

The blood differences occupy such a prominent position in genetics that a review of blood components will be helpful. Agglutination of cells by many kinds of surface antigens, as discussed so far, should not be confused with coagulation and hemophilia, which will be discussed soon in connection with sex-linkage. Serum and plasma differ by exclusion of some clotting proteins or by their inclusion in soluble form. In Table 8-1 this distinction is defined, and the location of many of the genetic differences to be found in blood are listed.

The structure of hemoglobin is differentiated by the action of many loci. At one of them three well-known alleles differentiate three kinds of hemoglobin, A, C and S, which can be separated by electrophoresis. The hemoglobin molecules migrate at a certain rate in the electric field depending on their mass and particularly on their charge. Those of a normal adult migrate more rapidly than do the hemoglobin molecules from a person with sickle-cell anemia, and both kinds migrate more rapidly than that from a person with a mild condition known as Hemoglobin-C disease. Other persons may have two of these kinds of hemoglobin. Individuals having both hemoglobin A and hemoglobin S are said to be heterozygous for the alleles Hb^A and Hb^S, and such persons have the phenotype of sickle-cell trait, a condition much less severe than the anemia of the homozygote $Hb^S Hb^S$. Other

TABLE 8-1   Components of blood and serum having hereditary differences

Components	Hereditary differences
CELLS	
leukocytes (WBC)	drumsticks on nucleus; Pelger anomaly
red blood cells (RBC)	hemoglobins A, C, F, S, etc.; surface antigens Rh, MNS, AB and many other agglutinogens
platelets (cell fragments)	coagulation factor
PLASMA (liquid separable from whole blood before coagulation)	
coagulation proteins	clotting factors I through XII
SERUM (liquid exudate from clotted blood)	
antibodies	against surface antigens of RBC
amino acids	aminoacidurias
fats	
globulins	beta-, gamma-globulin variants
glucose, other sugars	fructosuria, galactosemia
haptoglobins	1–1, 1–2, 2–2
salts	
transferrins	15 varieties of transferrins

heterozygotes having hemoglobins A and C are heterozygous $Hb^A Hb^C$ and show little gross difference from normal healthy individuals. Still other persons heterozygous for $Hb^C Hb^S$ have a type of anemia not as severe as the sickle cell disease. The differences among the three hemoglobins have been traced by V. M. Ingram to substitution of one or another amino acid at exactly the same place in the long and precisely ordered sequence of amino acids which comprise two of the subunits of the hemoglobin molecule (see Chapter 15).

SUMMARY

Although one person ordinarily has only two alleles at a locus, several persons may have three or more alleles from the population gene pool. Allelic genes such as i^A, i^B and i of the ABO phenotypes always show segregation and do not assort into more than two kinds of gametes. However, two parents may have four kinds of children, if they are each monohybrid for different alleles at one locus and therefore each forms two kinds of gametes. Genotypes in population equilibrium follow different distributions on one-locus and on two-locus assumptions. Phenotypes which do not occur in random combination with other phenotypes may be suspected of being determined by four or more alleles at a single locus. The gene frequency calculations for four or more alleles, as in the Landsteiner types, reveal unequal genotypic frequencies within a single phenotype such as MNSs. This with sufficient numerical evidence will differentiate adjacent loci from a single locus.

SUGGESTED READING

Li, C. C., *Human Genetics* New York, Blakiston Division, McGraw-Hill, 1961, 218 pp. Chapter 4 deals with the population analysis of the ABO and MNS systems.

Race, R. R., and Ruth Sanger, *Blood Groups in Man* 4th ed., Philadelphia, F. A. Davis, 1962, 456 pp. A separate chapter concerns each one of the blood groups mentioned above and other blood groups.

Sinnott, E. W., L. C. Dunn, and T. Dobzhansky, *Principles of Genetics*, New York, McGraw-Hill, 1958, 459 pp. Chapter 9 on allelism and pleiotropism is particularly helpful at this point.

PROBLEMS

8–1 (a) List all possible genotypes of persons in blood groups O, A, B, and AB.
(b) How would the phenotypes be subdivided and the genotypes extended by recognizing A_2, which is recessive to A_1?

8–2 (a) Can blood group O children come from parents phenotypically A by A?
(b) Can blood group O children come from parents phenotypically AB by AB?

8–3 A man accused of being the father of a certain AB M child is of blood type B N. The mother is B MN. How would you rule on this allegation?

8–4 Two babies brought home from the hospital as twins were later found to be of blood types O and AB.
(a) Could they have been sibs?
(b) Could they have been sibs if both parents were type B?

8–5 Pairs of MNS and Ns parents produce only two kinds of offspring within each family even when the sibships are large. Some sibships repeat the phenotypes of their two parents; other sibships consist only of MNs and NS individuals. Explain.

8–6 If a Mendelian population consists of 490 type O persons, 320 type A, 150 type B and 40 type AB persons, what are the allele frequencies of i, i^A and i^B?

chapter 9

Relatively Consanguineous Matings

Human beings are all remotely related. This truism is more often demonstrated in small communities than in large cities or countries. Yet it can be pointed out comprehensively that the population of the whole world was not large enough to provide separate ancestors for each of our 2^n bearers of chromosomes ten centuries ago. Merely ten generations ago each of us was foreshadowed in over 1000 ancestors, barring remote inbreeding. Twenty generations ago the theoretical number would exceed 1,000,000. The expected 2^{30} ancestors 30 generations ago would be over 1,000,000,000 without inbreeding, an impossible restriction, before the estimated world population reached 1,000,000,000. Only two generations earlier than that the potentially separate ancestors of a person living today, or 2^{32}, would exceed the present population of this crowded twentieth century world. Therefore many people are remote cousins although the average person may have very few first cousins.

Because there are several systems of naming the different degrees of cousin relationship, definitions become very important in applying the principles of this chapter. The legal usage in many countries is that shown in Figure 9-1. The children of sibs are first cousins of each other; the grandchildren of sibs are in the second cousin relationship; and greatgrandchildren of sibs are third cousins. The child of one's first cousin is a first cousin once removed; a grandchild of one's first cousin is a first cousin twice removed; and corresponding terms apply to the child or to the grandchild of one's second cousin.

GENETIC STEPS AND DEGREE OF RESEMBLANCE

The relationship between one parent and one offspring is defined as one genetic step, and it is clear that the intervention of meiosis has reduced genotypic resemblance to $\frac{1}{2}$ in this single step. A child receives only $\frac{1}{2}$ of his chromosomes and autosomal genes from one parent, and a parent can hand on only $\frac{1}{2}$ of his alleles by way of one gamete to any one offspring. Thus from grandfather to grandson would be two genetic steps and consequently an average $\frac{1}{4}$ genotypic identity. In like manner only $\frac{1}{8}$ of a person's genes reach any one greatgrandchild because of the three intervening genetic steps each having a meiotic reduction process.

A special genetic step exists between full sibs as a shortcut. Their similarity through their father involves two genetic steps so that their total resemblance for paternal genes is only $\frac{1}{4}$. In addition, full sibs have a second pathway of two more genetic steps through their mother and hence another $\frac{1}{4}$ resemblance for maternal genes. The sum total of resemblance between full sibs is $\frac{1}{2}$, and this fact allows one to take one genetic step horizontally between sibs, as in Figure 9-1, in tracing the total number of steps between more remote relatives. Therefore two first cousins are separated by three genetic steps.

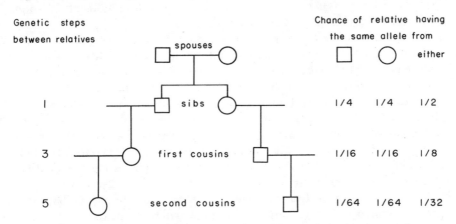

FIGURE 9-1 Definitions and degrees of resemblance of cousins (see text).

The degree of resemblance between relatives derives from the two parents, grandparents or other ancestors in common. The contribution of the male ancestor to two members of the same later generation simultaneously has been set forth in Figure 9-1 on the right with a numerically similar and independent column of contributions from the female common ancestor. Thus the total genetic resemblance is a summation amounting to $\frac{1}{2}$ for full sibs, $\frac{1}{8}$ for first cousins and $\frac{1}{32}$ for second cousins. This reasoning may be applied to other degrees of relationship. Between uncle and niece are two genetic steps, as there are between aunt and nephew, or between grandparent and grandchild. Half siblings also have two genetic steps between them. Three genetic steps connect first cousins, or connect great grand-parent and great grandchild, or intervene between great aunt and grand niece, for example. First cousins once removed have four genetic steps between them, and in each of these steps the chance of possessing the same allele of a pair is reduced to $\frac{1}{2}$ of whatever it was before that step. Identical twins, it may be noted, have no genetic steps between them and they therefore resemble each other fully in all of their chromosomes and genes.

GENOTYPES OF FIRST COUSINS

The methods of figuring resemblance in a monohybrid sense are similar between any two persons of known blood relationship, so examples con-cerning first cousins may be chosen for emphasis in this chapter. The reasoning as to the chances of a certain first cousin (such as a prospective bride or groom) having a certain rare and perhaps deleterious allele is apt to proceed from three different starting situations.

The first and easiest involves a person recessive in phenotype. There is certainty about the first genetic step from him toward his cousin; the chance is a full 1.0 that he has received one of his two recessives from that side of the family to which the cousin belongs. The uncertainties concern only the second and third steps to the first cousin. In the second step there is a $\frac{1}{2}$ chance that the aunt or uncle has the same allele known to be in the parent of the homozygote, and if that relative does have it, there is only $\frac{1}{2}$ of that chance that it will pass to the cousin. Therefore the first cousin of a recessive homozygote has a $\frac{1}{4}$ chance of possessing the identical recessive allele from their mutual grandparent.

If we figure this time from an assumed heterozygote (proven perhaps in a previous marriage to be a carrier) the three genetic steps to a first cousin each reduces by half the probability of presence of the hidden recessive allele. Therefore the probability of successful representation of the same allele in all three relatives — parent, his sibling, the latter's offspring — is $\frac{1}{2} \times \frac{1}{2} \times \frac{1}{2}$ or $\frac{1}{8}$. This is the chance that two normal first cousins will both be carriers of a recessive assumed to be in one of them.

The third starting situation is more often that in which no assumption is made about either of two cousins of normal phenotype. Rather the question is "What chance do these two cousins run of both having the same rare recessive gene which might be present in either of their mutual grandparents?" To reach both cousins the specified rare allele of a grand-parent must make four genetic steps successfully, and they might be called four hurdles. These are to one child and on to its child and similarly to and through the second child who is the parent of the other cousin. With only a $\frac{1}{2}$ chance of taking each genetic step successfully the four conjoint chances are $(\frac{1}{2})^4$, or 1 chance in 16 that two first cousins will have the same rare allele from one of their grandparents.

In a population the chance that the grandfather was a heterozygote is $2pq$, and the grandmother provided another such chance. The addition of these gives $4pq$ as the chance that a certain recessive gene was present in any of the four chromosomes of the normal appearing grandparents. After multiplying by $\frac{1}{16}$ for the genetic steps described above we get $\frac{1}{4}pq$ as the chance that two normal appearing first cousins will both be carriers of a grandparental recessive gene. For a small value of q this is approximately $\frac{1}{4}q$ that the two cousins will be heterozygous for the same rare recessive because of their cousin relationship. This stipulation omits the chance, usually smaller, that they have arrived at the same genotype without an assist from their common ancestors. Similarly to the above considerations the genotypes of nearer or more remote relatives than first cousins may be estimated starting from any person whether recessive, heterozygous or unspecified dominant.

CHILDREN OF FIRST COUSINS

It is the children of cousin marriages rather than the marriage partners who are the objects of special concern. With the aid of the foregoing descriptions of estimating the genotypes of relatives it is a simple matter to incorporate the testcross or F_2 type of segregation ratio, as appropriate. A child from the marriage of a rare recessive and his or her normal first cousin would be expected to be recessive with probability $\frac{1}{8}$ over the sum of many such cousin marriages. This would be composed of recessives expected among $\frac{1}{2}$ of the children from those $\frac{1}{4}$ of testcross cousin marriages in which the normal partner was heterozygous and none at all among the $\frac{3}{4}$ of phenotypically similar cousin marriages in which the normal cousin did not receive a copy of the rare allele. Thus the product, $\frac{1}{2}$ of $\frac{1}{4}$, would be $\frac{1}{8}$ of the whole collection of sibs from those first cousin marriages which were in the testcross category, one normal by one recessive.

In the above and in subsequent cousin marriages the prediction was made for the children of the group of such marriages, but the figure for a specific couple bears reinterpreting. Their specific risk is either a zero or else a $\frac{1}{2}$ chance of having a child who is recessive, more likely the former. However, once a couple has had a recessive child, it is thereby demonstrated that the dominant genotype is not homozygous, which would have prevented recessive offspring, but rather that the overall or average risk of $\frac{1}{8}$ in their phenotypic kind of cousin marriages has been $\frac{1}{2}$ in their instance. This half chance will apply to each and every child of this couple.

Similarly, the chance of a child being recessive from a marriage of two normal first cousins where there is reason to assume that one of the cousins is already of the necessary heterozygous genotype is 1 chance in 32. This combines the $\frac{1}{8}$ chance that the other cousin will also be a heterozygote and the $\frac{1}{4}$ chance that the child of two monohybrids will be a homozygous recessive. Here again this category of cousin marriages consists of a generous mixture of pairs who cannot have children of the recessive phenotype under consideration and a smaller number of couples who can. Yet the correct risk to be stated for each at the outset, or for the group of marriages as a whole at any time, is a $\frac{1}{32}$ chance of having a child (for example, the firstborn) being phenotypically recessive for the allele assumed to be in one of the married cousin pairs. As the many couples of this type proceed to have several children it will become slowly evident that some $\frac{1}{8}$ of these cousin marriages are heterozygote by heterozygote and have an actual risk of $\frac{1}{4}$ recessives at the birth of each child. And even more slowly and after the birth of many children in the sibships will it begin to appear that other parents are probably not able to have this kind of recessive homozygous child. The slowness of this information about parental genotypes inferred from a succession of Dominant offspring may be understood in the light of successive values of the term $(\frac{3}{4})^n$ in families where recessives are possible but by chance not formed (see Figure 3-4). Not only in cousin marriages but in most human marriages it is inherently difficult to demonstrate the lack of a recessive gene.

Most cousin marriages are between phenotypically normal persons where no assumption about one of them may be made, contrary to the case just considered. An application and a generalization will be made using this third and typical kind of cousin pair. Their mutual resemblance in having the same rare allele from a grandparent was shown to be $\frac{1}{16}$ (due to four genetic steps) so that their child would have a $\frac{1}{64}$ chance of being homozygous for that recessive allele. We now wish to generalize this description to cover all alleles, any one of which has only the population chance q of being in a chromosome of a grandparent. The two grandparents might have as many as four different alleles at the same locus from some multiple allelic series. We may now ask about the chances that a child from a cousin marriage between their grandchildren will be homozygous for any of their four alleles recessive or otherwise, and the answer must be four times the $\frac{1}{64}$ just computed for one allele of one of them. This means that children of first cousin marriages have a $\frac{1}{16}$ chance of being homozygous for any one allele of the locus and a $\frac{15}{16}$ chance of not being homozygous for any allele of a certain locus in either common grandparent. The $\frac{4}{64}$ and $\frac{15}{16}$ distribution may be advantageously viewed in another light.

Cousin marriages tend to produce more homozygous offspring and fewer of the heterozygous offspring than do marriages between unrelated persons. Some of this effect goes unnoticed because the homozygous Dominants are phenotypically like other Dominant persons and because common recessive phenotypes are not increased as conspicuously as are rare recessives from cousin marriages. Therefore let us concentrate our attention on the recessive class. At gene frequencies $q = 0.4$ or 0.3, recessive homozygotes from cousin marriages are imperceptibly more frequent than from random marriages (Table 9-1). If the gene pool has only 0.10 recessive alleles, the homozygous recessive offspring from cousin marriages are only about 1.5 times more frequent than those from unrelated parents. Where $q = 0.02$ the cousin marriages have recessive homozygotes for that allele four times as often as do marriages in general. For $q = 0.01$ the cousin marriages contribute recessives at a frequency over seven times that of random marriages.

TABLE 9-1   Genotypic proportions with and without inbreeding[a]

Gene frequency	CHILDREN FROM RANDOM PARENTS[b]				CHILDREN FROM FIRST COUSIN PARENTS			
q	D_o	H_o	R_o	$\frac{1}{16}pq$	D_I	H_I	R_I	R_I/R_o
.40	.3600	.4800	.1600	.0150	.3750	.4500	.1750	1.09
.20	.6400	.3200	.0400	.0100	.6500	.3000	.0500	1.25
.10	.8100	.1800	.0100	.0056	.8156	.1688	.0156	1.56
.04	.9216	.0768	.0016	.0024	.9240	.0720	.0040	2.50
.02	.9604	.0392	.0004	.0012	.9616	.0367	.00163	4.07
.01	.9801	.0198	.0001	.0006	.9807	.0186	.00072	7.19
.005	.990025	.009950	.000025	.0003	.99034	.00933	.00034	13.63

[a]From *Human Genetics* by C. C. Li.   Copyright 1961.   McGraw-Hill Book Company. Used by permission.

[b]H_o and H_I, heterozygotes from outcrossing and from cousin inbreeding, respectively; D_o, R_o, homozygous dominants and recessives, respectively, from outbreeding; D_I and R_I, from cousin inbreeding.

In cousin marriages the frequency of the man and wife both being heterozygous for the same allele is no longer merely the panmictic figure, $2pq \times 2pq$. The marriage of first cousins substitutes a $\frac{1}{8}$ chance that the spouse resembles one of these heterozygotes in having the identical gene from the common grandparent. Although that kind of marriage occurs with frequency $\frac{1}{8} \times 2pq$, or in $\frac{1}{4}pq$ of marriages, only $\frac{1}{16} pq$ of the children in the population will be recessive strictly because of consanguinity; in the remaining $\frac{15}{16}$ of the time, when a recessive child does not result from two inbred alleles, the q^2 or population chance meeting of two outside alleles will be operating, or one outside and one great grandparental recessive alleles will meet, When q is very small and hence p is nearly 1, the expression for recessive children for both reasons among all first cousin marriages becomes $\frac{1}{16} q + \frac{15}{16} q^2$. These two contributions within marriages of first cousins happen to be equal where the recessive gene frequency concerned is 6 percent. At this q value the frequency of recessive children from first cousin marriages is therefore twice as great as from marriages in the general population.

As the value of q becomes lower, the recessive offspring of first cousins owe their formation more and more to the fact of consanguinity. Thus cousin marriages may be said to be risky in regard to the bringing together of rare recessive alleles, and it may be added that we each tend to have a few such alleles among our many gene loci. Study of Table 9-1 will illustrate the magnitude of consanguinity effects on segregation at various low recessive gene frequencies. Note that the general effect of inbreeding is to reduce the proportion of heterozygotes from the population value H_o by the amount $\frac{2}{16} pq$ to H_I. Of this deduction, half is added to the homozygous dominants D_I on any one line of the table and half (or $\frac{1}{16}$ of the pq value) is added to the homozygous recessives R_I. As we have noted before, the addition to the recessive phenotype can become very conspicuous at lower recessive gene frequencies.

CONSANGUINITY AMONG PARENTS OF RECESSIVES

Now a constructive use may be made of the existence of cousin marriages, namely to gain evidence for or against a simple recessive mode of inheritance. If a certain rare phenotype of unknown causation is found to occur predominantly from random marriages and no more often from cousin marriages than cousin marriages occur among all marriages, then there is no evidence of a recessive mode of inheritance. If, on the other hand, cousin marriages (or other consanguineous marriages) are found more frequently among the parents of a certain kind of phenotype than among representative marriages in the same population, then this is evidence that by recent common descent two replicates of the same rare gene have been brought together by marriages between close relatives. Representative frequencies of cousin marriage lie between .001 and .02 of all marriages depending on the population size and customs.

An above-normal frequency of cousin marriages has been found among the parents of several rare phenotypes. The *Tay Sach's* form of amaurotic idiocy results from cousin marriage one-third of the time, from noncousins the remainder of the time. Parents of children with the rare skin condition *ichthyosis congenita* also are cousins much more often than are the parent pairs generally in that population. As an extreme example the majority of parent pairs of this congenital recessive were cousin pairs in another population. Many *albinos* have parents who are cousins or who are in some other consanguineous union. The extensive evidence of consanguinity among parents not only shows the recessive nature of the albino phenotype, but it allows further calculation as to whether all albino alleles are at the same locus by simple monohybrid segregation, a question which will be treated in a later paragraph. A similar problem concerns the parents of congenitally deaf children. Although some deafness is environmentally acquired through the mother having a high fever (from rubella fever) at about the third month of pregnancy, the parents of other children who are deaf at birth are closely related often enough to lead to the conclusion that there is at least one genetic deafness which is recessive to normal hearing.

It is obvious that the proportion of homozygotes deriving from cousin marriage will be influenced both by the recessive gene frequency, q, and by the frequency of cousin marriages, c. The ratio of cousin marriages, C_r, among all panmictic marriages producing the same recessive phenotype is

$$C_r = \frac{c(1 + 15q)}{16q}$$

when q and c are small. According to Dahlberg, therefore, a higher proportion of cousin marriages may be located via recessive offspring when cousin marriages are more common and/or when the gene frequency of the recessive allele is lower. If the population is not panmictic but has cousin marriages in excess of the mean proportion of cousins to noncousins among one's acquaintances, then the divisor should be $16\ (q + F)$, where F is the coefficient of inbreeding. Values of F for various populations are known up to 0.015, a figure found in a Brazilian village where almost 20 percent of 179 marriages were first cousin marriages.

The *coefficient of inbreeding*, F, devised by Wright for experimental animal work, takes on easily remembered values. For the offspring of sibs F is $\frac{1}{4}$. F for the offspring of half sibs, of uncle and niece, or of aunt and nephew is $\frac{1}{8}$. For the offspring of full first cousins the coefficient of inbreeding is $\frac{1}{16}$. For any child of first cousins once removed it is $\frac{1}{32}$. The general formula for F is $(\frac{1}{2})^N$ where N is the intervening number of relatives along the necessary genetic steps from the inbred individual through both parents and to the common ancestor (or through the equivalent shortcut directly from sib to sib). The coefficient of inbreeding becomes zero where there is no common ancestor of the two parents, and it could reach 1.0 if self-fertilization were possible, as it is in some plants. Some populations show inbreeding at the average level of children from second cousin marriage, where $F = .015$. The student should verify this value at this time.

Three examples of testing for the expected frequency of cousin marriages among parents selected by recessive index cases may illustrate the confirmation and extension of genetic hypotheses. The recessive condition of *alkaptonuria*, conspicuous because of the blackening of the urine upon exposure to air, is found in about one person per million (q^2) in a population where the overall frequency of cousin marriages is about 0.5 percent. Using Dahlberg's method (Table 9-2) one may estimate that for the corresponding gene frequency, $q = 0.001$, the cousin marriages should com-

TABLE 9-2   Percent cousin marriages among parents of recessive index cases in populations with various cousin marriage frequencies, c, and various q^2 levels

Frequency of index, *aa*,	FREQUENCY OF COUSIN MARRIAGES, c		
q^2	0.1%	0.5%	1%
.01	0.16	0.78	1.56
.0001	0.72	3.59	7.19
.000001	6.34	31.72	63.44

[a]Adapted from G. Dahlberg, *Mathematical Methods for Population Genetics*, New York, Interscience Publishers, 1948.

prise about 32 percent of all marriages giving rise to recessive alkaptonuric children. The observation of from 30 to 42 percent of cousin marriages among such parents in various parts of western Europe agrees with that estimate and is consistent with a simple monohybrid recessive explanation for alkaptonuria.

Albinism, considered as a single phenotype, occurs more often and therefore implies not nearly so high a contribution of recessives from cousin marriages. The albino phenotype has been observed with frequency 1/20,000 in a population where consanguinity at the first cousin level was encountered among 18 percent of the parents of albinos. It is difficult to reconcile these facts with the guidance of Table 9-2, which is based on the equation of Dahlberg (page 127) even if the highest of the three c values for cousin marriages is assumed. Thus the correctness of the simple monogenetic identity of all albino individuals is brought into question. Consistency is restored by the assumption that albinos, like genetically deaf persons, belong to either of two recessive genotypes, each with its own lower gene frequency (Figure 9-2). If we further assume that these two genotypes, at present not separable by direct observation or laboratory tests,

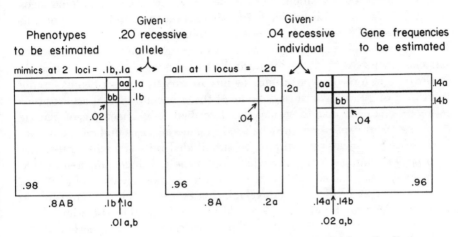

FIGURE 9-2 The effect of mimic genes in population genetics. Predictions on the one-locus model are numerically different from predictions based on two loci having equal recessive frequencies.

are equally abundant, then the gene frequencies for each would be lower and the proportion of cousin marriages among the parents of each genotype would be higher than on a monohybrid hypothesis. Thus two similar appearing kinds of albinos present with a frequency of 1/40,000 each would have a recessive allele frequency of 1/200. Such a gene frequency leads to the expectation of 13.4 percent cousin marriages among the parents of albinos of both genotypes, where by contrast all cousin marriages comprise 1 percent of marriages. Again for cousin marriages at the 2 percent level their estimated contribution becomes 26.9 percent of all parents of albinos. Because the observed 18 percent of cousin marriages among all couples having albino children comes within these reasonable estimates, there is no inconsistency with the present idea of separate but equally abundant recessive kinds of albinism.

Independent but scanty evidence supporting such an hypothesis comes from a very small pedigree study and from population data on a larger scale. It is recorded that two albinos once had three children of normal pigmentation. Many pairs of albino parents breed true for the phenotype, indicating that their recessive genes are at the same gene locus.

A population study of the testcross type of marriage, where one parent is recessive and the other is not, would be a further independent test. Among these couples most of the normal persons will be homozygotes, but a small proportion, $2pq$, will be heterozygotes and therefore able to have one or more recessives among several offspring. On the single albino locus hypothesis $2pq$ would be about 1/70, whereas on the two locus hypothesis it would be 1/100 for each. Therefore albinos would appear more often from testcross marriages if there were two loci concerned than if there was only one locus for recessive albinism.

Deafness as a phenotype of humans has already been described as having multiple but alternative causes. Some of the congenitally deaf are environmentally changed, and these may be described as phenocopies of genetic deafness. This expression must be used in general terms and with caution, because genetic deafness can also be subdivided into different forms, and so a person cannot readily say which genotype is being mimicked by the phenocopy. Among mice there are many known genetic causes of deafness, some present at birth, others developing later. It should therefore be no surprise that deafness in humans would have several different origins.

In a recent study of all children born deaf in a ten year period in the Belgian province of Antwerp some of the forms of congenital deafness could be sorted out. Of 111 persons deaf from earliest observation (deaf-mutes) 61 seemed to have an acquired (although prenatal) deafness and the remainder were differentiated from normal in one or another genetic manner. A majority, 45, of these (including a pair of monozygotic twin girls to be counted as one recessive zygote) were of the recessive type and were the subjects of further investigation. The proportion of first cousin marriages among their parents was too high to go with a recessive gene frequency as high as that computed from monohybrid assumptions and Hardy-Weinberg equilibrium. The relation of cousin marriages to population gene frequencies came into better agreement on the revised assumption of two different loci, each with a lower recessive gene frequency and therefore pointing toward a higher proportion of cousin marriages among the parents of deaf children. The assumption of only two mimic gene loci for deafness is probably conservative, partly in view of the many kinds of deafness in mice and partly in view of estimates by Chung, Robison and Morton that a minimum of 12 independently acting loci might be determining the population picture of deafness in Northern Ireland. This latter study not only subdivided recessive deafness into many genetic kinds, but it estimated that Dominant deafness was present among 22 percent of pedigrees because of an excess of occurrences within sibships above what recessives in sibships would be after correcting for sibship size (page 104).

In the same study in Northern Ireland the remaining sporadic cases, pheno-copies and unanalyzed genetic types, comprised only 9 percent of the study. Thus infections such as rubella fever seem to vary from place to place, and they may occur on the same genetic background or on differing gene frequency levels. Needless to say, it takes a large and carefully collected body of data to undertake such comparisons and to form profitable hypoth-eses in the absence of the methods usual in experimental genetics.

Muscular dystrophy appears as a recessive autosomal character in some kindreds although it is sex-linked recessive in others to be described in Chapter 12. The autosomal recessive variety is distinguished from other kinds of inheritance by the affected sibs being equally of either sex and by an excess of consanguineous parental pairs. Many cases of the autosomal kind of muscular dystrophy are shown on a *path diagram*, an abbreviation of a much larger kindred, in Figure 9-3.

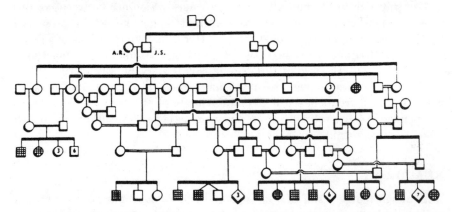

FIGURE 9-3 Autosomal muscular dystrophy (cross-hatched males and females) in many persons resulting mainly from consanguinity of their parents (marriage lines shown double). Several normal sibs are represented by totals within a single unshaded symbol. From Hammond and Jackson, Amer. J. Hum. Genet., **10**: 61 (1958).

RANDOM EXPECTATIONS OF CONSANGUINITY

The random frequency of cousin marriages to be expected is obviously related to the average number of cousins and to the circle of one's social acquaintances. In turn the average number of cousins will depend on average sibship size. In a stationary population where the mature children per family are reckoned to be two, the average number of aunts and uncles would be two, and the total of first cousins would be four, presumably divided equally between the sexes. For average sibships of size three during the last two generations, one's total of aunts and uncles would be four and of one's first cousins would be 12, of which only six would be of the opposite sex. For larger sizes of sibships the average number of aunts and uncles goes up linearly, but the number of cousins increases at a rapidly rising rate, i.e., exponentially. Where a person has many cousins and lives in a small community limited either geographically, because of language restrictions, for religious reasons or for maintaining the royal blood of monarchy, cousin marriages are apt to be more frequent than in other population isolates. The *population isolate* may be defined as that group of persons among whom mates are chosen panmictically. In these days of more travel, more frequent changes of residence and smaller families, genetic isolates are tending to break down and a person is much more likely to marry a nonrelative. Figures which relate the size of the genetic isolate and sibship size to the percent of all marriages which are between cousins or between either uncle and niece or aunt and nephew have been presented by Dahlberg and may be studied there. After direct compilations of sibship size and of frequency of these two degrees of consanguineous marriages have been made, the size of the genetic isolate may be estimated. If the population is large enough to have many uncle-niece and aunt-nephew marriages their frequency will give an estimate of effective population size independent of the estimate from cousin marriages. Naturally these will tend to agree within broad limits.

SUMMARY

Although marriages of first cousins and other consanguineous marriages are relatively rare, such marriages produce more than their share of one or another recessive phenotype. Cousin marriages have a specific additional chance of having offspring homozygous for a rare recessive allele over and above the population expectation of q^2. The exact amount of the additional chance depends on the number of genetic steps which must be successfully taken by the allele in question. Each genetic step reduces the average genotypic resemblance by $\frac{1}{2}$. Identical twins have no genetic steps between them; full sibs have only one step and therefore are half alike, One parent and one offspring are half alike. The ratio of cousin marriages to all marriages among parents of a certain recessive phenotype is higher for the rarer alleles. Use of the cousin marriage ratio formula of Dahlberg has led to the hypothesis of two genetically different but recessive albinos which are mimic phenotypes. The assumption of panmixis allows an estimate of the size of the isolate to be made from the observed frequency of certain consanguineous marriages. Dominant phenotypes and common recessive phenotypes are not increased among the offspring of consanguineous matings.

SUGGESTED READING

Chung, C. S., O. W. Robinson, and N. E. Morton. A note on deaf mutism. Ann. Hum. Genet. **23**: 357–366 (1959).

Dahlberg, G., *Mathematical Methods for Population Genetics*, New York, Interscience, 1948, 182 pp. A classic treatise and reference.

Deraemaeker, R., Recessive congenital deafness in a North Belgian Province. Acta Genet. (Basel) **10**: 295–304 (1960).

Haldane, J. B. S., and S. D. Jayakar. An enumeration of some human relationships. J. Genet. **58**: 81–107 (1962).

Ishikuni, N., H. Nemoto, J. V. Neel, A. L. Drew, T. Yanase, and Y. S. Matsumoto, Hosojima. Amer. J. Hum. Genet. **12**: 67–75 (1960). An interesting history of a small island with a high coefficient of inbreeding and deafness in 6 percent of a population of 175.

Li, C. C., *Human Genetics: Principles and Methods*, New York, Blakiston Division, McGraw-Hill, 1961. Basic aspects of contingency calculation and risks in cousin marriage are emphasized in Chapters 6 and 10.

Schull, William J., Empirical risks in consanguineous marriages: sex-ratio, malformation, and viability. Amer. J. Hum. Genet. **10**: 294–349 (1958). Observations on a large scale by trained personnel in Hiroshima, Nagasaki and Kure.

PROBLEMS

9–1 (a) Count your aunts and uncles, first cousins, and relatives in more distant categories.

(b) What is the average size of family in your known kindred?

9–2 (a) What chance of being an albino would the first child of a man and his albino niece have on account of that consanguinity?

(b) What would the corresponding chance be if the albino were married to a nonrelative?

(c) How would you combine the above two chances into a single expression for the offspring of albino nieces and their normal uncles?

9–3 Two first cousins whose relatives do not show recessive phenylketonuria marry. Express the gene frequency of the PKU gene as q, and state the chance of both cousins being heterozygous for this gene

(a) Because of their ancestors in common.

(b) In spite of their cousin relationship.

9–4 (a) If the first four children are normal although their parents are first cousins by descent from a recessive alkaptonuric grandfather, what chance remains that the parents are both heterozygous for the alkaptonuric gene (consult Figure 3-4)?

(b) What is the corresponding chance if the first eight are normal?

9–5 Figure 9-3 showed 14 muscular dystrophics and 39 nondystrophics in seven sibships. Would it be wiser to compare this with ascertainment tables (Table 7-7) or with simple Mendelian expectation?

9–6 (a) Classify the consanguineous marriages (double lines) of Figure 9-3 as first cousin, $1\frac{1}{2}$ cousin or equivalent, second cousin, etc., by the shortest possible paths.

(b) Which categories of marriages have given rise to the muscular dystrophics in this kindred?

(c) Are male and female dystrophics significantly unequal in this sample?

part two

Regular Chromosomal Behavior

For the understanding of Chapters 10 through 14 it is assumed that the reader understands simple monohybrid inheritance of genes in a very broad sense. This means that he has the viewpoint of population genetics as opposed to preplanned experiments and that he has the necessary statistical tools from simple algebra to deal with small human sibships and that he knows how to use Chi-square with larger sums of data. The Mendelian ratios of 3 : 1, 2 : 1 and 1 : 1 are very frequently encountered, but other fractional expectations occur regularly in collections within a human population group. Consanguineous marriages have the effect of seeming to concentrate the occurrence of recessive phenotypes of one or more rare autosomal alleles.

In Part Two some necessary changes and applications of rules are explained. The inheritance of a gene difference not in an autosome but sex-linked is described. The free assortment of two gene pairs in separate chromosome pairs and the lesser assortment of typically linked loci within the same chromosome pair are contrasted. The interaction effects of genes and the cumulative effects of genes on the phenotype are introduced. Otherwise the environmental background for the development of the phenotype is here still considered as constant.

chapter **10**

Dihybrid Assortment in Chromosome Pairs

The previously described features of monohybrid segregation will continue to operate in almost all aspects of genetics. Yet human beings often differ in many genetic respects, and two or more differences lead immediately to the question of independent assortment or of linkage (less than free assortment). New principles concerning dihybrid and multi-hybrid assortment and individuality will be described in the next several chapters and added to the already studied principles of gametic separation of alleles and of phenotypic segregation. In this particular chapter examples from human genetics will be presented in the light of the principle of independent assortment (Mendel's second law).

Independent assortment of alleles from different gene pairs coincides with the behavior of chromosomes at meiosis. The orientation assumed on the meiotic metaphase plate by the maternal and paternal centromeres of one pair of chromosomes is not necessarily the same as the orientation taken by another pair. In fact, maternal and paternal halves of each tetrad are randomly turned toward the poles of the division figure. The essential facts are presented in Figure 10-1. There the two different chromosomes which were received from one gamete have been left white while the homo-logue of that rod and the homologue of the V-shaped chromosome received in the other gamete have been shown in solid black. Thus the diploid individual has been represented to have an unlike pair of rod chromosomes and an unlike pair of V-chromosomes, and the person may be described as dihybrid. If these two pairs of chromosomes line up on the metaphase plate of the first meiotic division arbitrarily in the manner shown, the white rod and the white V would pass to one daughter gametocyte (and eventually gamete) while the black rod and the black V would pass to the other secondary gametocyte. This disposition before anaphase I would give rise to two cells shown as the first and fourth kinds of gametes; but equally often the paternal members of the two pairs of chromosomes might

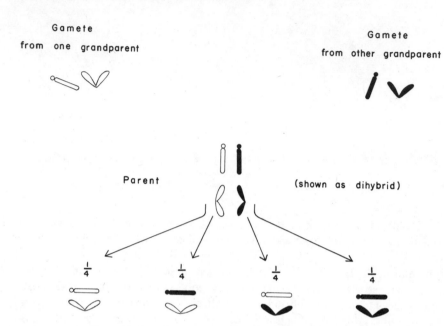

FIGURE 10-1 Independent assortment of maternal and paternal chromosomes in a dihybrid individual. Black and white have been used artificially to show the parental source of chromosomes.

arrive on the metaphase I spindle oriented toward opposite poles, and the resulting two daughter cells would be those shown as the second and third kinds of gametes in Figure 10-1. If the rod pair were heterozygous for the *R-r* alleles and the other pair were carrying *S* and *s*, the expected gametes would show independent assortment of the *R* and *S* loci by having the four kinds of gametes, *RS*, *Rs*, *rS* and *rs*, represented equally often. This is a model for all dihybrid independent assortment.

LOCI WITH DISCRETE EFFECTS

A sibship indicating independent assortment is shown in Figure 10-2 reported by McKusick. The segregating phenotypes include a height pair, normal height versus a recessive type of dwarfism in which the bodily proportions remain normal (Figure 10-3). The second pair is an eye difference, normal lens position versus a displaced lens called ectopia lentis (which should be distinguished from a similar lens displacement caused by other genes). The factor pairs may be designated *D-d* for the contrast in

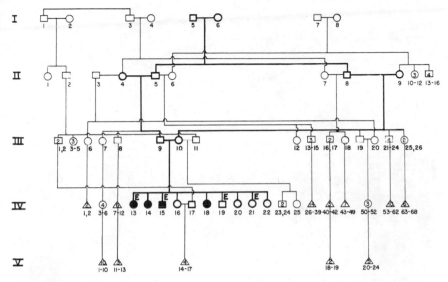

O – Undwarfed female

■ – Dwarfed male

E – Ectopia lentis

FIGURE 10-2 A dihybrid sibship from one of several cousin marriages within the same kindred. Recessive primordial dwarfism and the eye defect ectopia lentis are assorting as each segregates from normal. After McKusick, Amer. J. Hum. Genet. **7**: 190–191 (1955).

height and E-e for the eye lens difference. Among the many normal relatives of this sibship neither dwarfism of this type nor simple ectopia lentis was seen, and so the recessive nature of these two rare phenotypes was indicated. The fact of consanguinity between the parents was another indication of the recessiveness of those offspring which did not resemble them in both height and vision; the parents were first cousins, the children of brothers. These normal appearing first cousins had nine children: three normal, two dwarf, two ectopic and two both dwarf and ectopic. Because no combination is missing, it is clear that some assortment is going on between the two loci.

The question of whether assortment is completely independent would require many more sibships segregating for the same D-d pair and E-e pair; but the existence of 22 pairs of autosomal chromosomes (page 17) in human cells favors the likelihood that these two loci lie in different chromosome pairs, different in shape or in length or both. Only a 1/22 chance exists that the loci are far apart in the same pair. (See the next

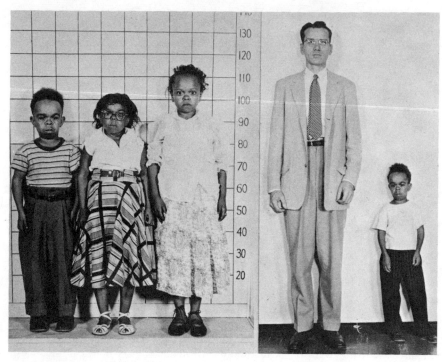

FIGURE 10-3 Left: Adult primary dwarfs in front of a decimeter scale. They are represented at IV 15, 13 and 18 in the pedigree, Figure 10-2. Right: A man of normal height and the 30 year old dwarf shown at IV 15. From McKusick, Amer. J. Hum. Genet. 7: 190–191 (1955).

chapter on dihybrid linkage.) A classic model for dihybrid sibships is to be found in the experiments of Gregor Mendel in which the simultaneous segregation of two pairs of factors and free assortment between pairs gave numerous different F_2 generations in the now familiar 9 : 3 : 3 : 1 ratio of phenotypes. In McKusick's example the most likely expectation would approach the ratio of nine normal Dominants, three dwarfs otherwise normal, three ectopic otherwise normal and one both dwarf and ectopic.

A more general model from human genetics is presented in Table 10-1, for segregation and assortment involving genes having no dominance within pairs. Wherever the four kinds of gametes are formed equally often, the 16 combinations of zygotes will be expected equally often. Study of this diagram will reveal many interesting features, among them the fact that $\frac{1}{4}$ of the table (upper left) is homozygous M, that $\frac{1}{2}$ (diagonally) is heterozygous MN, and correspondingly but independently, that four small boxes are homozygous for A while eight are heterozygous AB, etc. It may be especially noted that double homozygotes are the most difficult to form, only 1/16 each of AM phenotype, BM, AN and BN homozygotes. Monohybrids are formed with frequency 2/16 as for ABM, AMN, and other types. Dihybrids, always ABMN ($i^A i^B L^M L^N$), are the most numerous of the F_2, but even so they comprise only $\frac{1}{4}$ of the generation.

The same information may be obtained algebraically by persons who prefer another method than the checkerboard. If the monohybrid segregation ratio for A versus B is $1:2:1$ and if the segregation for the M-N pair is $1:2:1$ and further if the one segregation does not influence the other (independent assortment), then one may simply subdivide the one by the other distribution using the method of algebraic combination as follows:

$$1\,A + 2\,AB + 1\,B \qquad \text{out of 4}$$
$$\times\; 1\,M + 2\,MN + 1\,N \qquad \text{out of 4}$$

$$1 \text{ of AM, } 2 \text{ of ABM, } 1 \text{ of BM}$$
$$2 \text{ of AMN, } 4 \text{ of ABMN, } 2 \text{ of BMN}$$
$$1 \text{ of AN, } 2 \text{ of ABN, } 1 \text{ of BN} \qquad \text{out of 16}$$

Furthermore, the algebraic method, or else the checkerboard, may be used to predict the joint expectation of a locus segregating $3:1$ and a locus segregating $1:2:1$ independently. The ratio would be $3:6:3:1:2:1$ if properly matched to the subdivided Dominant $(3:6:3)$ and to the subdivided recessive $(1:2:1)$ and to the incompletely dominant middle term of each. If the student properly masters these methods, either or both may be extended to trihybrid and tetrahybrid situations, such as may be encountered in respect to many combinations of blood type differences.

LOCI WITH CUMULATIVE EFFECTS

A very different model of dihybrid and multihybrid inheritance emerges from a consideration of a continuously varying racial difference, skin color. The dihybrid hypothesis presented by Davenport in 1913 is widely known, and it explained his observations in Bermuda and Jamaica very well, but a multihybrid hypothesis based on the same principles is now preferred as the result of much larger studies on skin colors among Negroes in the United States.

TABLE 10-1   Expected proportions of offspring from parents each of blood phenotypes AB MN. (Simplified notation is used instead of showing which pairs are alleles by the locus symbols, $i^A i^B\ L^M L^N$

		Via sperm from father			
		AM	*BM*	*AN*	*BN*
Via	*AM*	AA MM	AB MM	AA MN	AB MN
eggs	*BM*	AB MM	BB MM	AB MN	BB MN
from	*AN*	AA MN	AB MN	AA NN	AB NN
mother	*BN*	AB MN	BB MN	AB NN	BB NN

Summary of phenotypes — 1 AM : 2 ABM : 1 BM : 2 AMN : 4 ABMN : 2 BMN : 1 AN : 2 ABN : 1 BN, as in an F_2 distribution. All MN heterozygotes are in the shaded quarters.

Charles Davenport began his study by getting a quantitative measure of the blackness of the skin by means of a Bradley color top, a compound disk device with variable amounts of white, yellow, red and black. By trial and readjustment color proportions may be found which blend together when spun like a top, such that the blend matches the skin of a subject. The subject may then be given a percentage score for color. The more recent studies of R. R. Gates did not use this refinement of measurement of the degree of black pigmentation. Dr. Davenport designated five grades of pigmentation in terms of the percent of the color wheel which was occupied by the exposed black, such that the known mulattos (offspring of one white parent and one black Negro parent) were predominantly embraced by his designation of the middle range of color. Almost all of the individuals whose color and whose parents' colors were measured in Jamaica and in Bermuda are consistent with a simple dihybrid hypothesis, which is a very instructive genetic model.

The assumptions of two factor pairs without dominance and with equal and additive effects upon pigmentation explain most of the Davenport data. If we suppose that small letter alleles *a* and *b* produce no black pigmentation above that naturally occurring in nonalbino "white persons," whereas each *A* allele and each *B* allele produces additional pigment equally, then white individuals will be assigned the genotype *aabb* and a fully negroid-skinned person would be designated *AABB*. Their mulatto offspring would be *AaBb*. If these two genotypically similar mulattoes (there are other types) had children, the expectations among the latter would be exemplified by the 16 kinds of zygotes from a dihybrid F_2 type of generation as shown in Figure 10-4. Only 1 in 16 would be expected to have the white-skinned genotype *aabb*, and only 1 in 16 would be apt to have the fully black-skinned genotype *AABB*. The others would be expected to be intermediate at the mulatto grade, or a grade lighter or a grade darker. For instance, persons with the genotypes *aabB* and *Aabb* would have more pigment than the typical white person but less than the typical mulatto; and the *AABb* and the *aABB* persons would have more pigment than the mulatto but not as much as the fully pigmented Negro. These two lighter and darker kinds of monohybrids on the Davenport hypothesis of two factors would occur 4/16 of the time each from dihybrid parents. The most likely offspring from two mulatto parents would be the mulatto grade of pigmentation, but such mulattoes, which may be called F_2 as to these gene pairs, would be of three different genotypes, mostly dihybrid exactly like their mulatto-skinned parents but including also 1/16 of *aaBB* and 1/16 of *AAbb* homozygotes. The full range and frequencies are shown in the Figure 10-4. Note that only the dihybrid mulattoes can give a range of offspring from white to black-skinned. Other genotypes give smaller ranges because of being homozygous at one or both loci. Thus a light or white-skinned parent will not have a fully black-skinned offspring such as has been popularly claimed, and a darker than mulatto parent will not have a white-skinned offspring on this dihybrid hypothesis nor on the more recent multihybrid hypotheses.

A much larger set of observations has been made by Herskovits and has been tested by Stern for goodness of fit with the classic hypothesis of Davenport and with other models. Possible agreement with a four locus model, with a six locus model and with more loci was investigated always under the simplifying assumptions of intermediate expression of each heterozygote and equal contributions to the phenotype by pigment alleles at all the loci. The observed population data gave a shape of curve intermediate between the distributions predicted on the four-pair and the six-pair calculations. At the present time the hypothesis of about five pairs of loci being involved is better than the hypotheses of two pairs or of three pairs. The smaller numbers of genes would not assort to fit present

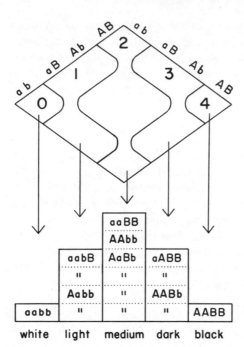

FIGURE 10-4 Simplified explanation of skin color differences, the Davenport dihybrid hypothesis for Negro-white crosses (see text).

observations, even if unequal pigmentation potencies were assigned to them. The supposition that different gene pairs act equally is perhaps an oversimplification, but it is a necessary step in trying to outline the complexity of things as they probably are.

EPISTATIC PHENOTYPES

The presence of a certain gene or of a gene pair is not always evident where one phenotype embraces two or more genotypes. This may be considered further at three historical levels. At the beginning level many genes remain unknown for lack of alleles conspicuous to the observer, and these constitute the hundreds and perhaps thousands of unidentified wild type alleles and of a few wild type *isoalleles* of the species. Isoalleles need not concern us further until we discuss modifiers (page 169). At the monohybrid level of discovery one allele may be recessive to one or more other alleles at that same locus, as we have already noted for the i^o allele, which is recessive both to i^A and to i^B in heterozygotes. Finally, at the dihybrid level and beyond it, the presence of one phenotype may prevent classification for other character pair differences. For instance, complete hairlessness, a genetic trait, naturally prevents direct observation of whether the person is genetically kinky, wavy, or straight haired. Albinism without any iris pigment prevents the classification of persons as blue eyed or brown eyed or of other shades.

The relationship between such characters is an epistatic-hypostatic one. Albinism is *epistatic* to such phenotypes as degree of skin pigmentation, to eye color, to limited white spotting and to several other rare or common pigmentation patterns. Conversely, the difference between each of the latter and normality constitutes a pair of gene differences *hypostatic* to albinism and masked by albinism. It is convenient to note whether the epistatic phenotype is Dominant or recessive within its own pair, and whether there is just one locus with an epistatic effect, or whether two loci have a similar effect on the phenotype. The names for the various possible kinds of simple and duplicate epistases are given in Table 10-2 and in Figure 10-5, and some known examples from human sibships follow.

Boundaries between F_2 phenotypes under epistasis

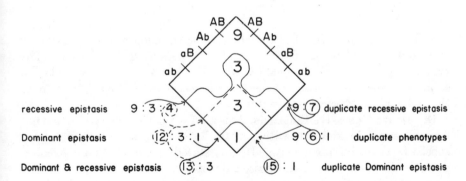

FIGURE 10-5 Modifications of F_2 type ratios when one phenotype interferes with the expression of other phenotypic pairs (see text).

Simple Recessive Epistasis. This is exemplified by the phenotypic expression of albinism, *cc* for the unpigmented body, over the minor pigmentation effects of the *A-a* difference, or of the *B-b* difference, or over both in a trihybrid. Thus, an albino child of Negro parents cannot reveal the light or mulatto or whatever phenotype of the above *A* and *B* loci. Another example comes from the observable presence or absence of the antigens A and B in the saliva. Some persons secrete a water soluble antigen

TABLE 10-2   Modified 1 : 1 : 1 : 1 and 9 : 3 : 3 : 1 dihybrid ratios with epistasis of one or more phenotypes over another pair of phenotypic differences

Testcross genotypes				Testcross phenotypes	Corresponding F$_2$ phenotypes
AaBb	*Aabb*	*aaBb*	*aabb*		
A, Dominant epis.				2 : 1 : 1	12 : 3 : 1
		aa, recessive epis.		1 : 1 : 2	9 : 3 : 4
	bb mimics aa phenotype			1 : 2 : 1	9 : 6 : 1
A, B, duplicate Dominant epis.				3 : 1	15 : 1
	duplicate recessive epistasis			1 : 3	9 : 7
A Dom. and bb rec.		mimics		3 : 1 aaBb	13 : 3 aaB

A in their saliva and are called Secretors; others are nonsecretors of either A or B and are said to be of recessive phenotype and *se se* genotype. The nonsecretors cannot be classified by saliva samples as A, B, AB or O types, so in this aspect of the phenotype there is recessive epistasis of *se se* over the ABO phenotypes in saliva tests.

Duplicate Recessive Epistasis. This kind of phenotypic interaction has been observed in kindreds with genetically deaf persons (i.e., not from rubella fever during pregnancy). It was stated (page 62) that congenital deafness could be due to the possession of a homozygous recessive gene pair, either *dd* (with *EE* understood) or *ee* (with *DD* understood). Evidence for this is, in part, that some deaf parents have only hearing children, and therefore the genotypes of such deaf parents and their hearing offspring would be *ddEE* by *DDee* producing only *DdEe* children. A prediction of the offspring from any two such genotypes as the last will illustrate one of many adaptations of the standard dihybrid checkerboard shown as Table 10-1, or of the algebraic method. In the checkerboard, let NN stand for one kind of homozygous deafness (four boxes in the lower right quarter of the checkerboard) and in addition let a homozygote of the other pair, say BB, stand for the other recessive deafness (four boxes including one already NN and therefore deaf also by the first definition). Thus one would predict seven recessive deaf phenotypes and nine hearing phenotypes among the offspring of two unrelated or related parents each carrying a hidden recessive allele at each of the same two loci for genetic deafness.

Mimic Phenotypes. In the instance of marriage between two persons dihybrid for the same forms of recessive albinism, present data do not distinguish between the foregoing 9 : 7 ratio just illustrated or the typical 9 : 6 : 1 ratio involving mimic intermediate phenotypes. The expectation in regard to one recessive albino phenotype, such as a_1a_1, would be three normals plus one albino; and a similar three normal plus one albino would be expected for the segregation at the second locus, a_2. The dihybrid expectation would be nine still normally pigmented and the remaining seven albino having one recessive pair (3/16) or the other recessive pair (3/16) or both (1/16). It is uncertain at the present time whether the last and rarest genotype would be phenotypically different from the others or would merge with them in a 9 : 7 ratio. For instance, the recessive waltzing in mice (Chapter 5) is proved to be different from a very similar phenotype called Shaker-1 by a similar F_2 test.

Dominant and Recessive Epistasis. If a recessive albinism and a dominant Albinism which came from known separate kindreds were to be found together, the sibship would only very rarely segregate as an F_2 for both of these rare conditions or as a testcross for the recessive albinism. Somewhat more common would be a testcross in regard to the dominant Albinism and an F_2 type of segregation for recessive albinism. The appropriate model for independent assortment of the two loci in the dihybrid parent would predict

1 Dominant Albino + 1 recessive normal from *Aa* by *aa*

also 3 Dominant Normal + 1 recessive albino from *Cc* by *Cc*

---

3 Albinos (Dom.) : 3 normals : 1 albino (Dom. and rec.) : 1 albino (rec.)

A total of 5 albinos : 3 normals

This results from Dominant and recessive epistasis both acting; the dominant *A* blots out the normal pigmentation in some of the C_- segregates, and the recessive albino is epistatic over the recessive *aa* normal. This 5 : 3 ratio is more likely to be encountered from the population standpoint than is a typical testcross 3 : 1 or a typical F_2 of 13 : 3 given in Table 10-2. In each of these three cases one *A* is epistatic over the *C-c* pair phenotypically, and the recessive *cc* phenotype not only mimics *A* but is epistatic over the *A-a* phenotypic segregation.

FREE ASSORTMENT BUT ATYPICAL SEGREGATION

A more often encountered application of dihybrid ratio calculation may be found in the distribution of Dominant and recessive phenotypes among the two sexes. From marriages of blood type O persons and heterozygous type B spouses, offspring of types B and O are expected equally, as in a testcross, and males and females are expected in the proportions 51 : 49 as found in general vital statistics. The combined expectations where one observed segregation is perhaps not ideal will be calculated from

$$.51 \text{ boys } + .49 \text{ girls}$$

$$\text{among }   .5 \text{ type B} + .5 \text{ type O blood}$$

$$.255 \text{ B boys} + .245 \text{ B girls} + .255 \text{ O boys} + .245 \text{ O girls}$$

Thus the algebraic method is adaptable to any degree of fractional expectation.

Independent assortment of loci in dihybrid crosses is to be expected a vast majority of the time when allelic pairs are chosen at random or encountered in actual sibships. The second factor pair in any dihybrid has a random chance of approximately 21/22 of having its chromosomal locus in a pair other than the pair of chromosomes in which the first locus resides. Nevertheless, the accumulation and recording of carefully analyzed examples of assorting dihybrids is important for two purposes. Firstly, it will slowly establish how confident we are of the fact of Mendelian free assortment versus the alternative, to be discussed in the next chapter. Secondly, it will slowly lead to the identification of those factor pairs which

TABLE 10-3   Common and useful marker genes, which assort independently with regard to most other genes, common or rare[a]

ABO series, i^A	Lewis, Le^a
Duffy, Fy	*Lutheran, Lu^a
Gamma-globulin factors, Gm^a, Gm^{ax}	P locus, p^1, p^2
Haptoglobins, Hp^1, Hp^2	Rhesus, Rh_1
Kell locus, K	*Secretor of A, B, H; Se
Kidd, Jk^a	Sutter, Js
Landsteiner, $MNSs$	Taster of PTC, T

[a]From R. R. Race and Ruth Sanger, *Blood Groups in Man*, 4th edition, Oxford, England, Blackwell Scientific Publications, 1962.
*Lu and Se show linkage (see page 157).

are in the same chromosome pair, and which therefore follow the rules of loose or close linkage from hybrids to their immediate offspring.

MARKER GENES

Common gene differences which assort independently from all other readily testable gene loci are called marker genes (Table 10-3). The inference from many such tests is that each series of two or more alleles is on a chromosome pair different from that pair carrying another common locus. Now that there are about five times as many pairs of gene differences known as there are chromosome pairs of the autosomal set, it is a logical necessity that several known loci must be in the longest chromosome pair, several others in the next longest and perhaps even one or two presently known gene loci in each of the shorter chromosome pairs. These numbers doubtlessly will increase, perhaps rapidly in view of many recent discoveries in blood genetics. The need for demonstrated marker genes (common and independent) is great, especially in the shorter chromosomes, because these are occasionally present in extra numbers as trisomics (Chapter 22) or as partially deleted chromosomes (Chapter 23). Out of the 100 or 200 human gene pairs known to science only four or five pairs of autosomal gene loci have so far failed to follow Mendel's law of independent assortment. The exceptions will be treated in the next chapter.

SUMMARY

The simultaneous transmission of two or more segregating gene pairs usually involves free assortment of an allele at one locus with either of the alleles at the other. In this respect the Mendelian independent assortment parallels the behavior of chromosome pairs of different kinds. Two categories of exceptions to the rule of independent assortment are often encountered. One exception concerns the less than free assortment in gamete formation, to be described in the next chapter on linkage. Several other exceptions are collectively due to the developmental and physiological actions of genes after the fusion of gametes. For instance, two genes at different loci may have phenotypically cumulative effects, or duplicate effects, or no effects without each other. Several kinds of epistatic relations in the development of the phenotype modify or condense a typical dihybrid ratio such as 9 : 3 : 3 : 1 to a variety of other proportions depending on the two gene pairs involved. In inheritance between generations independent assortment applies to as many loci as there are different pairs of typical chromosomes; therefore in humans it is 23 pairs in women and 22 autosomal pairs in men. Presently about 15 gene pairs are common enough to serve as marker genes for up to that many pairs of autosomes; many of these marker genes are frequently found segregating in the same sibship, and when thus testable, they assort independently.

SUGGESTED READING

Davenport, C. B., Heredity of skin color in negro-white crosses. Carnegie Institution of Washington, Pub. No. 188, 1913, 106 pp. Philadelphia, Lippincott. Describes a big first step toward the genetic explanation (multihybrid) of skin color differences. Of historical and scientific interest.

Race, R. R., and Ruth Sanger, *Blood Groups in Man*, 4th ed., Philadelphia, F. A. Davis, 1962, 456 pp. Their Chapter XXI has over 74 references to independently assorting loci.

Snyder, Laurence H., and Paul R. David, *The Principles of Heredity*, 5th ed., Boston, Heath, 1957, 507 pp. A standard text which is particularly helpful at this point in regard to modified dihybrid ratios.

PROBLEMS

10-1   What size and shape of checkerboard would you use to demonstrate all possible kinds of offspring from
(a) Two parents who were of blood types ABN and OM?
(b) BMN and ABM?
(c) Both ABMN?
(d) (e) (f) Fill in the margins with the necessary gametes for each of the pairs of parents.

10-2   Compare and contrast the F_2 type generations from dihybrids for two separate gene loci and for two loci whose phenotypic effects are cumulative.

10-3   (a) On the two-locus hypothesis of Davenport could a Negro have a white-skinned offspring?
(b) Could a white person have an offspring with full Negro pigmentation?
(c) Give an expression for the frequency of white-skinned offspring from two mulatto parents on the two-locus model.
(d) Can you estimate what it would be for three loci with cumulative effects?
(e) From two mulatto parents would you expect more segregation of white skin and black skin on the two-locus model or on a five-locus model?

10-4   (a) What genotypes as to the Landsteiner multiple allelic series and the ABO series in a pair of parents would yield a 9 : 3 : 3 : 1 ratio among many children?
(b) Specify the phenotypes for each of these frequencies.

10–5   In man are there more assorting gene loci or more assorting chromosomes?

10–6   Define briefly but adequately:

free assortment	dominance
epistasis	mimic phenotypes
maternal chromosome	marker genes

chapter 11

Linkage in Dihybrids and Multihybrids

Mendel was lucky in his extended study of dihybrids and trihybrids. He successfully synthesized pea strains of all possible combinations among seven segregating factor pairs in a species having just seven pairs of chromosomes without encountering any exception to the principle of independent assortment. Since his day linkage of gene pairs within the same chromosome pair has been demonstrated, studied and used in countless technical ways in many of the better known plants, insects, birds and mammals, even including man.

Linkage is a special genetic concept applicable within one chromosome pair. Gene loci have a definite sequence and spacing, the same along either chromosome of a pair, but the allele occupying any one position may change by recombination in a heterozygote, or by mutation (Chapter 21). In a hybrid of the constitution $\frac{A\ b\ c\ D}{a\ B\ C\ d}$ all of the alleles in the upper chromosome are in *coupling phase*, and all of the genes in the lower chromosome are also in coupling phase. However, we may also say that the dominant genes A and B are in *repulsion phase* in this genotype, or similarly that their recessive alleles a and b are in repulsion linkage. Whatever point of view is taken, genes in coupling phase tend to continue together from a parent to the same offspring in the very next generation, whereas the genes which are in repulsion phase in one parent tend to be transmitted to separate offspring in the next generation. This is the behavior which is to be expected if there is segregation of chromosomes from each other at meiosis. Simple segregation of the two whole chromosomes of the pair would give only two classes of gametes.

Whenever exchanges of equal blocks of genes occur through the process of *crossing over*, two new gene combinations called *crossovers* or *recombinations* are made in equal frequencies. Although the crossover classes will constitute a minority of individuals within dihybrid sibships, the inadvertent massing of crossovers and noncrossovers from coupling- and from repulsion-phase parents would nullify the evidence of any linkage. The population

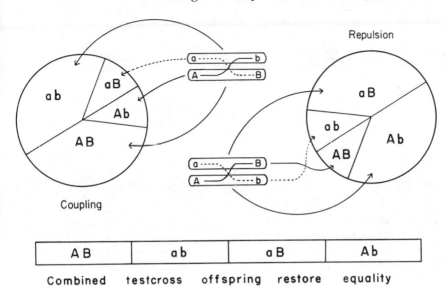

FIGURE 11-1 Linkage at the chromosomal level. Nonrecombination gametes outnumber the crossover gametes in a dihybrid whether initially in coupling linkage or in repulsion linkage. Population totals mask linkage.

data would look like free assortment. Figure 11-1 emphasizes this paradox involving coupling and repulsion.

Linkage is effective between parents and offspring, and in each generation any crossover offspring may need to be renamed as to phase. A coupling-phase parent tends to transmit the specified genes together in coupling to the same offspring. A repulsion phase of genes in the parent is followed by the transmission of the specified alleles preferentially to different offspring. Thus two categories of sibships may be expected, sibships with a higher than random number of *AB* individuals and of the complementary *ab* types, and other sibships with more of *Ab* and of *aB* individuals (Figure 11-2). Should the observer lose track of the family origins of these opposite types of sibships, the combined data would fail to show association of characters any different from that expected according to the prevalence (gene frequency) of each allele in the population. This pitfall is often overlooked.

SYNDROME ASSOCIATIONS NOT DUE TO LINKAGE

Conversely, high correlations of aspects of the phenotype in a random population do not imply linkage. For instance, persons with blue sclerotics instead of white eyeballs very often have brittle bones, and conversely persons with the latter very often have the former, but this association has been traced to the multiple effects of a single Dominant gene at one locus.

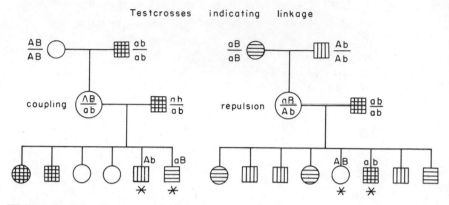

FIGURE 11-2   The opposite and equal biases of sibships from coupling and from repulsion linkage testcrosses.   Only the few persons starred have received crossover chromosomes, which are specified.   All noncrossovers and all other *ab* gametes have not been written.

The offspring of these people tend to segregate into only two kinds, sibs which have the blue sclera, usually have the brittle bones and often also have otosclerotic deafness and other sibs who are normal in respect to the above.   Such segregation is considered to be evidence for the pleiotropic effect of a single gene because of the absence of a corresponding number of sibships showing the opposite or repulsion distribution of characteristics describable separately.

Another association of characteristics due to a single gene locus and not to any linkage is the Laurence-Moon-Bardet-Biedl syndrome.   Individuals homozygous recessive for this rare allele tend to have a constellation of characteristics — polydactyly, hypogenitalism, low intelligence, obesity and failure of maturation during adolescence.   These characteristics tend to appear together or to be absent altogether, which is only a superficial resemblance to a coupling phase of the abnormalities.   However, no clear repulsion phase sibships are known, within the kindred or elsewhere. Kindreds unrelated to the LMBB syndrome, however, show separate modes of inheritance of each of the components which are approximated in the verbal description of the LMBB syndrome.

Neither is a racial association of characteristics to be confused with the idea of genetic linkage.   Fair hair and blue eyes are associated in Scandinavian people, whereas dark hair and brown eyes are found together in many people of the Mediterranean lands, but this is not linkage.   These associations break up freely when crossbreeding has occurred, and independent assortment shows in later generations.   The association of dark hair and of blue eyes among the English is occasioned by the high gene frequency of the blue eye alleles and by the high frequency of dark hair genes; it has no demonstrated basis in linkage. Although a hair color difference has been described as genetically linked to a certain kind of tooth deficiency, this was not on evidence as incomplete as is the above.

EXPRESSION OF LINKAGE: CROSSOVER VALUES

A dihybrid testcross ratio of $1 : 1 : 1 : 1$ represents not only independent assortment but also the upper limit of recombination of loosely linked gene loci. The recombination fractions discoverable in different dihybrids range from slightly below 50 percent to 1 percent or less. If the recombination fraction in a certain dihybrid is the fraction or percent r, the new coupling combinations are divided evenly between the two crossover classes, while the parental coupling combinations are retained in the remaining and larger two classes of offspring. Thus the testcross ratio is expressed as $r/2 + r/2 + (1 - r)/2 + (1 - r)/2$ among the complementary crossovers and the complementary noncrossovers, respectively. For the dihybrids at loci A and B, the r value might be 10 percent; different dihybrids might show 30 percent recombination in the B-C interval along the same chromosome. Other dihybrids for C and D might show close linkage by a mean crossover value of 2 percent. Further data involving the above loci in still different dihybrids allow a linear chromosome map to be constructed. By definition, one *crossover unit* is that length of chromosome which allows 1 percent of crossovers among gametes.

Closer or looser linkage has an effect on F_2 proportions as shown in Figure 11-3. The A and E above the checkerboard are generalized dominant alleles both in coupling or both in repulsion. A particular A locus would always be expected to show the same amount of crossing over with a particular B locus. Thus, for each checkerboard in coupling there would be a reversed (or oppositely labeled) checkerboard of the same proportions. Unless the offspring in coupling F_2 generations are accumulated separately from repulsion sibships, the degree of linkage and perhaps even the fact of linkage might be missed.

The F_2 checkerboards of Figure 11-3 deviate from the Mendelian expectation of $9 : 3 : 3 : 1$ according to whether both parents were in coupling phase for the Dominant alleles, or whether at least one was in repulsion linkage, with A diagonally opposite B. For two parents each in coupling phase of the dominants, the F_2 ratio will be more than 9/16 AB phenotypes, more than 1/16 aabb but less than 3/16 of either Abb or aaB phenotypes. Among F_2 type sibships from parents either or both of whom have repulsion

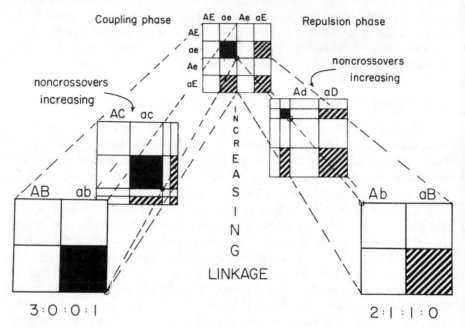

FIGURE 11-3 Effects of various degrees of linkage (from loose to complete) in F$_2$ type data. Front: A and B represent loci closely situated; rear: A and E represent other loci spanning a considerable length of their chromosome pair.

linkage of the dominants, the Abb phenotypes and the aaB phenotypes will each form with more than 3/16 expectation, while the double recessive aabb will be decidedly lower than 1/16 and the double dominant A_B_ phenotypes will be slightly less than the 9/16 free assortment value. The amount of departure depends this time on whether one or both parents are in repulsion phase.

Testcross sibships in humans are usually hard to find when the recessive alleles are uncommon, but when located they give information about the recombination frequency very efficiently. Examples of testcross expectations for offspring may be reviewed in Figure 11-3 by reading vertically in the second column, under the double recessive gamete, *ae*, both into the coupling checkerboards and into the repulsion checkerboards. Two major classes and two minor (crossover) classes of sibs will be found in each. If they were to be added without regard for parental source, they would equalize at $\frac{1}{4}$ for each phenotype and give the impression of free assortment erroneously.

LINKED LOCI IN HUMAN SIBSHIPS

ABO and the Nail-Patella Syndrome. Genetic linkage of the isoagglutinogen locus for *ABO* blood groups and the *Nail-Patella Syndrome* has been demonstrated by Renwick and Lawler. In this Syndrome two widely separated parts of the body, fingernails and kneecap, usually are both abnormally reduced or both normal together under the control of a single gene pair, here called *Pt-pt*. This correlation distinguishes syndromes from linkage of, for example, separate genes for presence or absence of a patella and for normal sized versus diminutive fingernails. Due to the incompleteness of our knowledge we speak of the component parts of a syndrome as the manifold and diverse aspects of a single gene difference; someday later we may describe the phenotype of this syndrome as the several direct and logical outcomes of a particular chemical change in the embryo at a particular time. Until then the term syndrome is very useful. The Syndrome phenotype of small nail and absent patella is dominant to the normal condition, and this means that many of the marriages of persons with this Syndrome are monohybrid testcross types of marriages. Studies of this Syndrome phenotype were further facilitated by a relative abundance of dihybrid testcross types of marriages (blood group O persons with normal kneecaps to spouses with the Syndrome and a heterozygous blood group composition, such as many A persons, most B persons and all AB phenotypes have). Some of the marriages had the hybrid parent in coupling phase, others had the dihybrid in repulsion phase; but from either possible starting genotype only about 7 percent recombination offspring were found in one study and about 12 percent of the small sample in a different series of sibships. These results are mutually consistent. Thus the ABO locus and the nail-patella syndrome locus are in the same chromosome pair, a pair not yet specifiable as to length and shape.

Lutheran and Secretor Types. Linkage of Lutheran and Secretor loci has been detected, although the chromosome pair remains unidentified. There are at least two alleles at the *Lutheran* locus, Lu^a and Lu^b, which denote antigenic differences in the blood; and possibly there is a third and rarer allele Lu^- with no presently known reaction. The dominant *Secretor* allele, *Se*, allows the detection of blood group antigens A and/or B in the saliva; by contrast *se se A* (or *B*) persons do not secrete these substances into the saliva, and neither does the blood type O person. Indications of fairly close linkage between the *Lu* and *Se* loci have long been known but were regarded with caution. Recently, however, Greenwalt has studied the blood and secretor ability of 73 families having four or more children each and has found some 16 percent of recombination between Lutheran and Secretor loci.

Some 15 common genetic differences have received the group name of *marker genes*, because they are investigated repeatedly for linkage with one or another rarer gene. Except for evidence of Lutheran–Secretor linkage the 15 show independent assortment with each other, and their loci are certainly far apart and more likely are on different pairs of chromosomes. These useful reference genes include PTC-tasting ability, Secretor of ABO antigens, Haptoglobin types, Gm serum groups, and ten blood group loci (Table 10-3). In time loci will be found linked to one or to another of the above sites of common genetic heterozygosity.

Duffy Blood Type and Lamellar Cataract. Recently Renwick and Lawler have reported linkage between a harmless blood difference and a particular form of eye defect, zonular or lamellar cataract in the lens. Duffy heterozygotes, $Fy^a Fy^b$, are numerous among the population of Great Britain, and because of the presence of a third allele, Fy^-, heterozygotes may exceed 50 percent of the population. In Negroes there are fewer heterozygotes, and these are chiefly with Fy^-, which does not produce either of the first two kinds of Duffy antigens. The Duffy blood group differences are classifiable in children, and by contrast the vision is not often hampered until adulthood. Since this Cataract gene is dominant, it may be traced back to one or another grandparent, and if the transmitting parent is also heterozygous for Duffy, the Cataract will go preferentially in coupling with one Duffy allele to children. Conversely, children receiving the other Duffy allele would tend to be free of the dominant Cataract gene. For this particular Cataract early classification is possible, but the principle of determining who received late-acting genes by the observation of linked characters will be a very useful principle.

Rhesus and One Kind of Oval RBC. Investigation of recombination between the rhesus antigen locus and an abnormal shape of the red blood cells also showed linkage in early studies and later revealed a heterogeneity of genetic causes for the oval rather than round outline of red blood cells. In passing we may note that ovoid blood cells are normal for the camel. In some human sibships there is now evidence for free assortment of the rare dominant Oval blood cells and the rhesus series of alleles, but in other sibships there is very little assortment. From the latter families it is estimated that there is 3 percent recombination between *El* (for Elliptocytosis) and Rh loci. It may be appropriate to give the designation *Ov*, or any symbol not easily confused with the foregoing, to that Ovalocytosis locus which assorts independently with the Rh locus.

The Rhesus Genes, Rh or DCE. The interpretation of the antigenic differences resulting from the rhesus locus or loci has had an interesting and controversial history since 1940. When two or three allelic differences always showed monohybrid segregation, it was natural to think that they might all be at the same locus, and a single Rh locus is still the correct explanation according to Wiener. The early antisera, obtained originally from rabbits which had been immunized against the red blood cells of the rhesus monkey, were tested against several human antigens which were given the designations C, D, E and very soon c (Table 11-1). This terminology suggested simple allelism not only between *C* and *c* genes but also between *D* and *d* as well as between *E* and *e*. At this time, 1943, R. A. Fisher made several predictions on the assumption of the known rhesus alleles being closely linked combinations among three loci, *C, D* and *E*, an idea which persists as an hypothesis. Fisher predicted the eventually found antisera anti-d and anti-e, although until recently no very useful anti-d was demonstrated. Fisher also predicted some additional properties of an incompletely tested and rare *CDE* genotype (his terminology) and the existence of an eighth kind of chromosome, *CdE*. When the latter was found as another rare rhesus type, it rounded out the totality of eight possible combinations of large and small letter alleles at each of three loci. These signal achievements favor but do not prove the three-locus theory or deny the one Rh locus idea.

TABLE 11-1   Multiplicity of antisera distinguishing the phenotypes from the rhesus allelic series, early and later discoveries (an incomplete list)

anti-C	anti-E	anti-D
anti-c		
anti-C^w	anti-e	anti-D^u
anti-C^u	anti-E^u	
anti-C^x	anti-E^w	

[a]Modified from R. R. Race and Ruth Sanger, *Blood Groups in Man*, Oxford, England, Blackwell Scientific Publications, 1962.

The rhesus locus problem is like that resulting from the use of anti-M, anti-N, anti-S and anti-s sera to distinguish phenotypes at the Landsteiner locus (page 116). Present difficulties involve a lack of understanding of the numerous contrasting aspects of a pleiotropic phenotype, if a single rhesus locus is at work, and a lack of equilibrium among the trihybrid combinations on the other hypothesis. The question of gene action will be deferred until Chapter 15. Separate loci should allow a balance of combination types, as was pointed out in Chapter 8 regarding the Landsteiner MNSs system, where the four commonest aspects of the phenotype may be tested separately. The rhesus allele or chromosome developing the *CD* aspect of the phenotype occurs with much higher frequency than the random expectation, i.e., higher than the product of the C allele and of the D allele frequencies as if each were at its own locus (data from Table 11-2). Yet the CDE terminology has some convenience in coinciding with the named antigens present on the red blood corpuscles; and the two systems of naming are used together on bottles of antisera used to test for more than ten antigens. If this number of antigens traceable to a single locus or chromosomal region in humans seems large, still longer series of multiple alleles are known in cattle, and several different loci in *Drosophila* have recently been shown to be complex. There are now other examples of three and four closely linked loci with several alleles at each of them.

TABLE 11-2   Correspondence of Weiner and Fisher terminologies for rhesus "genes" and the frequency of each allele in England

Weiner	Fisher	Freq., %	Weiner	Fisher	Freq., %
R_1	DCe	40.74	r'	dCe	0.98
R_2	DcE	14.11	r''	dcE	1.19
R_0	Dce	2.57	r	dce	38.86
R_z	DCE	0.24	r^y	dCE	rare
R_{1w}	DC^we	1.29	r_{1w}	dC^we	rare

[a]After R. R. Race and Ruth Sanger, *Blood Groups in Man*, 4th edition, Oxford, England, Blackwell Scientific Publications, 1962.

The inheritance of the single letter phenotypes is simple and monohybrid. The D antigen-antibody reaction is dominant over the lack of reaction. Antigens C and c show monohybrid segregation and can each be identified in the heterozygote by use of the two commonly available sera. Likewise heterozygous Ee reactors can be separated from possessors of antigen E alone.

TRIHYBRID LINKAGE

When three loci show measurable crossing over between any two of them, the question of their linear order arises. Which of the three is in the middle? As a general example we may consider the loci a, b and c. Suppose that we have information from an accumulation of dihybrid sibships that a and b are 30 crossover units apart (defined on page 155) and that b and c are 20 units apart. If the b locus is truly between the others, then the a-c interval would be about 50 units apart and might easily appear to show free recombination in available dihybrids. Contrarily, if the c locus were within the longer interval, then the a-c distance would allow only about 10 percent recombination. A tabulation of sibships segregating both for a and for c would eventually favor either the higher crossover value for the longer possibility or the lower value for an interval included between a and b. One practical difficulty arises from the fact that if both of the abnormal traits are rare, dihybrid sibships are much harder to find. If either one of the intervals should be short instead of intermediate as above, a much larger roster of sibships would be necessary to distinguish between the higher and the lower of the predicted crossover frequencies. Hence again, all new dihybrid human sibships should be considered as possibly reportable. Later discoveries may show that some of them are trihybrid.

The action of trihybrid linkage is more informative as to gene order. One such trihybrid might be as revealing as 30 dihybrids adding up to the same crossover percentages, if the linkage phase can be identified by any kind of information in the pedigree. On the chromosome pair the linear order of three genes is the same; either a is flanked by the other two genes, or b is or c is, provided all are known to be linked to each other. In whichever linear order is correct, there are four possible kinds of trihybrid mothers to be encountered in equal expected frequency. These equally likely trihybrids would have their three different *wild alleles* (+) arranged in full coupling, $+++/* * *$; left locus (arbitrarily) in repulsion, $+* */* ++$; center in repulsion, $*+*/+*+$; or right wild in repulsion to the other two wilds, $* *+/++*$. Any sibship necessarily comes from just one of these four genotypes, so the eight kinds of sons will be explained from the one which is perhaps easiest to remember.

The gametes formed by a hybrid of the arrangement $+++/abc$ may represent eight different combinations. Whenever there is no crossing over between the outside loci, parental types $+++$ and abc would result with equal expectation. Exchange anywhere between the a and b loci would result in approximately equal numbers of the crossover chromosomes containing $a + +$ or $+ bc$. Similarly, crossing over anywhere in the next interval would result in $ab +$ or $+ + c$ chromosomes going to the gametes equally often. If the process of crossing over takes place in both intervals in the same cell, two double crossover chromosome strands become possible. The relative frequencies of these complementary pairs of gametes depend on the chromosomal distances, in crossover units, between the several loci. For three closely linked loci, the double crossover classes may both be absent. At the other extreme, as among pea hybrids, loci far apart in the human X-chromosome (page 185) might assort in as many double crossover individuals as residual noncrossovers among comparable sibships.

METHODS OF DETECTING AUTOSOMAL LINKAGE

If two loci are not too far apart along the length of the same chromosome pair, that fact may be determined even among small collections of data.

However, some situations are more favorable for the detection of linkage than are others. We may consider separately methods involving pedigrees and methods involving merely the accumulation of sibships. In the first we determine the genotypes of the parents; in the second we seek to find whether sib pairs have a mean population distribution which is different from that of sib pairs in regard to unlinked loci.

Only a small fraction of marriages in the population can reveal whether locus A is in the same chromosome pair as is locus B. Therefore it is desirable to identify these parent pairs, if possible. Individuals can be either homozygous, or monohybrid or dihybrid in regard to the loci A and B, and only the dihybrid individual can give evidence of a lack of independence among his or her four classes of gametes. The other four monohybrid and four homozygous genotypes cannot show assortment among their gametes. Furthermore, the necessary $AaBb$ dihybrid, if phenotypically dominant, must mate with one of four kinds of individuals in order to reveal the assortment of its recessive alleles. Thus the few marriages diagnostic of the possibility of linkage are $AaBb$ preferably with $aabb$ (a testcross), with $aaBb$ or with $Aabb$ (partly testcross and partly an F_1 cross) and lastly with another dihybrid to produce an F_2 type of sibship. Any other marriages of a dihybrid will reveal nothing as to the major noncrossover and minor crossover classes of its gametes.

Linkage in Known Testcrosses. In testcrosses of dihybrids the relation of phenotypically crossover offspring to crossover gametes received is a direct one requiring little interpretation. Data from families of this general testcross kind will be presented in Chapter 12, where they are more easily recognized because of a special testcross situation, one involving sex-linkage. Wherever crossover offspring and noncrossover offspring can be correctly identified, all crossovers regardless of phenotype may be added together whether from coupling dihybrids or from repulsion parents, and the fact of linkage can be most readily established and the percentage of recombination easily measured. Of less value are the partial testcrosses, such as dihybrid by $aabB$ or by $Aabb$, but these will not be considered in detail in this text.

Linkage in Known F_2-Type Families. The third type of marriage which is revealing as to linkage is that of two dihybrid parents. The phenotypic outcomes differ depending on whether both parents have the recessive alleles in coupling phase, ab/AB, or whether at least one has the recessives in repulsion linkage. The offspring from either of the contrasted situations will have opposite deviations from that $9:3:3:1$ distribution which would be typical for the phenotypes from unlinked dihybrid loci (independent assortment). The coupling sibships will show more than

56 percent AB phenotypes, more than 6 percent *aabb*, and correspondingly, less than 18.75 percent each of phenotypes aaB and of Abb (see Figure 11-3). In close coupling linkage of the recessive alleles the F_2 type distribution approaches three double Dominants to one double recessive. Without any crossovers in a given body of data it could be surmised erroneously that the phenotypic aspects of *A* and of *B* were pleiotropic effects of a single gene and that the phenotype including both *a* and *b* was the opposite pleiotropic difference occasioned by the recessive allele in homozygous individuals. This enigma has already been encountered in connection with the possibility of multiple allelism in regard to the rhesus antigen differences. Obviously, any F_2 distributions which depart significantly from the ratio $9:3:3:1$ double recessive either in the direction of $3:0:0:1$ or in the direction of 2 double Dominants : $1:1:0$ double recessives are evidences of genetic linkage.

Linkage in Sib Pairs, Parents Unseen. Evidence for linkage may be sought in population data by comparing only sib pairs. The method of Penrose involves the population expectations for the chance that any two persons are alike and Dominant, alike and recessive or one of each in regard to the first factor pair, and this will be influenced by the gene frequencies for that pair. Similar expectations are needed for any two persons from the same population in regard to the second gene pair, which may of course have a different gene frequency from the first gene pair. These expectations, the fractions u, v, and w of Table 11-3, representing the distribution of sib pairs merely according to the A-a criterion, are cross multiplied by other fractions, x, y and z representing the distribution of sibs according to the B-b difference or resemblance, to give random expectations for unlinked loci suitable for any one population. With complete linkage (no crossing over) only five kinds of sib pairs would be recorded, those in the corners because they are alike in both respects and those in the center box because they are different in both respects. Ordinary linkage and some

TABLE 11-3 Sib-pair combinations, which show systematic deviations from random population distribution with close or loose linkage[a]

PHENOTYPE A	PHENOTYPE B				
	Both dom. B	B and bb	Both rec. bb		
both dom. A	$ux + \Delta$	$uy - 2\Delta$	$uz + \Delta$	$=$	u
A and aa	$vx - 2\Delta$	$vy + 4\Delta$	$vz - 2\Delta$	$=$	v
both rec. aa	$wx + \Delta$	$wy - 2\Delta$	$wz + \Delta$	$=$	w
$(x + y + z = 1)$	x	y	z	$(u + v + w = 1)$	

[a]From L. S. Penrose, Ann. Eugen., **6**: 133–138 (1935).

crossing over would produce some sib pairs who are alike in only one respect but different in the other character. Within a population moderate linkage in coupling phase will tend to increase the number of sib pairs along one diagonal. Repulsion linkage will similarly increase the number of sib pairs above the population expectations along the other diagonal. In the table notice the systematic increases and decreases, shown by the delta symbol, against the population expectations. The details of the test are given in Penrose (1935).

SUMMARY

Linkage is effective at each step in a line of descent and also between sibs, but it averages out to random association in population data. Genes in the same chromosome (coupling phase) tend to go together to one offspring, whereas genes in opposite chromosomes of a pair (repulsion phase) tend to go to two different offspring. Thus sibs are more often alike in two respects or more often different in those same two respects if the two phenotypes are controlled by pairs of genes in the same chromosome pair. The tendency is altered by crossing over, which reciprocally exchanges long parts of homologous chromosomes before gametes are fully formed.

Linkage may be detected in accumulations of coupling testcrosses and of repulsion testcrosses or of the F_2 type sibships from coupling or from repulsion parents. It may also be detected by Penrose's sib-pair method in comparison with resemblance between random pairs of persons in the population. Autosomal linkage has been detected in four different dihybrid comparisons. When overlapping regions of a chromosome are measured as above or simultaneously in trihybrids, linkage maps for the human autosomes will become possible. By linkage an easily classified gene can be a marker for predicting the presence or absence of a later-acting linked gene having a dangerous effect and calling for medical or surgical treatment.

SUGGESTED READING

Mather, Kenneth, *The Measurement of Linkage in Heredity*, 2nd ed., London, Methuen, 1951, 149 pp. Contains two whole chapters on linkage in human genetics.

Neel, J. V., and W. J. Schull, *Human Heredity*, Chicago, University of Chicago Press, 1954, 361 pp. Describes methods of detecting and estimating linkage in man.

Penrose, L. S., The detection of autosomal linkage in data which consist of pairs of brothers and sisters of unspecified parentage. Ann. Eugen. (Ann. Hum. Genet.) **6**: 133–138 (1935). In journal now known as the Annals of Human Genetics.

Penrose, L. S., *Outline of Human Genetics*, New York, Wiley, 1959, 146 pp. One large chapter contrasts association with both autosomal- and sex-linkage.

PROBLEMS

11–1   (a) If in a panmictic population there are 45 percent of blood group O and 33 percent of nontasters, what association of phenotypes would you expect?
    (b) Give the percent for each.
    (c) What does this show about linkage?

11–2   (a) What would make for a high association of fair hair and blue eyes in people?
    (b) Association of dark hair and blue eyes?
    (c) Association of dark hair and brown eyes?

11–3   (a) If a sibship included five children with Nail-Patella syndrome and blood type O and five normal blood type A children, what does this indicate about the blood type A and the Nail-Patella syndrome?
    (b) If two more children were born in this sibship one having the Syndrome and blood type A, the other having normality and type O, what would the sibship then demonstrate?

11–4   Define:

        coupling   recombination
        repulsion   crossing over
        linkage   crossover gamete
        linkage phases   crossover offspring

11–5   (a) In Figure 11-2 what percent of crossover offspring is represented?
    (b) Does it differ significantly from free assortment?
    (c) Within what range of values would you have 95 percent confidence that the true (parametric) crossover value lies?

11–6   (a) Where and how would one classify the Secretor phenotype?
    (b) How would it assort with the ABO locus?
    (c) With the Lutheran blood group phenotype?

11–7   A woman has several children of two Duffy types and later develops the dominant lamellar Cataract in both of her eyes.
    (a) What chance of developing Cataract does each child have as he grows up?
    (b) What information about the husband and the grandparents on both sides would you like to have in order to revise your estimate?
    (c) Set up a problem for yourself in which you predict chances other than 50 percent for each and every child on the assumption that there is 40 percent recombination between the two loci.

11–8   (a) Are oval blood cells linked with the rhesus negative blood group?
    (b) Are either of these linked with anything?
    (c) Precisely what is linked?

11–9   (a) From a parent hybrid at three linked loci what category of gametes is most common?
    (b) What kinds of gametes are the rarest?
    (c) How rare can that be?

11–10   What are two opposing hypotheses as to the structure of the place on the chromosome determining the rhesus antigenic differences?

chapter 12

Inheritance in the X-Y Pair of Chromosomes

A beginning to the study of genetics might well start with this chapter. Historically, in fact, specific rules for the inheritance of abnormalities now known to be due to recessive genes in the X-chromosome were elaborated without the comprehension of their extended applicability. Red-green color blindness was known to the ancient Greeks, and the bleeder's disease now called hemophilia was of great concern to the Hebrews by the second century A.D.

Pragmatic rules were developed for these characteristics. Circumcision was not required in those sibships where two other sons had previously died from unquenched bleeding, and the practice was further omitted for those sons of the sisters of victims of hemophilia. These were correct but limited ideas. Much later but still before the relation of genes to chromosomes was known, two further rules were specified to be applied vertically through three generations. Nasse's rule for hemophilia was formulated in 1820 and, as translated by Stern, states "Women whose fathers were bleeders transmit the trait to their children, even if married to normal men. In these women themselves and, in general, in no female person, is the trait ever expressed." Much later, in 1876, the Swiss ophthalmologist Horner pointed out that the common form of color blindness was following the same pattern of inheritance as did hemophilia, from man through normal daughters to some grandsons. Darwin in 1875 described men without sweat glands and having virtually no teeth, a syndrome inherited through females. Horner's law and Nasse's law, as they were often called during the nineteenth century, remain today as accurate but limited rules. Now we can extend them to any relatively rare recessive gene carried in the X-chromosome.

CYTOGENETICS OF THE SEX CHROMOSOMES

The special features of sex-linkage follow directly from the omission of one of the chromosomes of the X-pair and, in man, from the substitution of a visibly different chromosome called the Y. The X-pair and the Y are jointly called *heterosomes* to distinguish them from the usual category of chromosomes (autosomes) whose partners appear alike in length and shape in both sexes. In women there are 22 pairs of autosomes and an XX pair, and in men there are the same number of autosomic pairs plus one X and a very short Y-chromosome (see Figure 2-2). The Y synapses endwise at meiosis with a chromosome of medium length, the X-chromosome, and then separates from it into sperm so that males are the heterogametic sex among humans in that all men regardless of ancestry always form two kinds of sperm.

The heterosomes are received and transmitted differently by the two sexes. The Y-chromosomes of humans are found regularly and almost exclusively in men because the Y-chromosome determines the initiation of male development. Hence the Y is always paternally received, and in going to children it regularly goes to sons. By contrast the X-chromosomes are found in both sexes, but twice as many of them are in women. Thus only one third of those X-chromosomes in the population are in men. Mothers receive two X-chromosomes one from each parent and transmit one to each offspring just as happens typically with any pair of autosomes. However, a father has received his X-chromosome from his mother, and he will transmit that X to his daughters. These facts have given rise to the somewhat misleading term "criss-cross inheritance," which applies better to males than to females. It should rather be remembered that the man's Y chromosome, paternally received, is handed on regularly to his sons, and that his X, maternally received, regularly goes to his daughters. Thus the human species may be said to be in a permanent testcross for the presence or absence of the Y, a homogametic woman and a heterogametic man producing a 1 : 1 ratio of sons and daughters.

A different testcross situation exists in respect to genes in the X-chromosome. Since there is only a single X in the male, the phenotypic complication of dominance and recessiveness in that one X-chromosome does not arise and he is called *hemizygous* for genes in his X-chromosome. Consequently, the brothers in a family are in effect the offspring of a testcross for any heterozygous loci in the X-chromosomes of the mother. Thus sons tend to show a 1 : 1 ratio for a single gene pair, or to be all alike and dominant, or else all alike and recessive while their sisters might be dominant in all three kinds of families. Brothers would also reveal dihybrid and trihybrid testcross ratios which might show the crossover frequencies for the lengths of the X-chromosome marked in a dihybrid or trihybrid mother. These widespread testcrosses occur because the Y-chromosome seems to be empty of the kinds of loci which might carry an allele dominant over some X locus. The common and regularly occurring events in the heterosomic pair are brought together in Figure 12-1, which shows heterogameity for

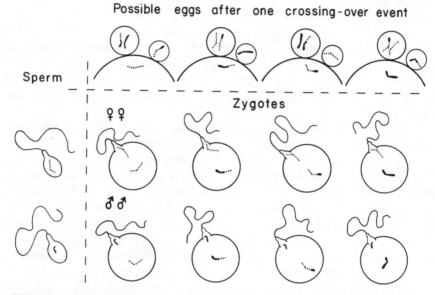

FIGURE 12-1 Representative behavior of the X and Y-chromosomes. Left: male transmits either an X-chromosome (long) to all his daughters (middle row) or a Y-chromosome (short) to all his sons (bottom row). Top: one event of crossing over (very common in the long X pair) produces four kinds of chromosomes which may go to either sex of offspring. The two small polar bodies degenerate.

the male, hemizygous X sons, simple segregation of maternal and paternal X-chromosomes during polar body formation and products of single crossing over between X-chromosomes.

COMMON DIFFERENCES ON THE X

A new, interesting and useful genetic difference in blood antigens among both men and women has recently been traced to allelic differences at an X-chromosome locus. Many persons have an allele called simply Xg^a, and a large minority lack it and have its allele Xg, sometimes called Xg negative. The difference between the phenotypes Xg(a) and Xg is that the red cells of the former react positively and cells of the latter react not at all with an antibody which laboratories presently have in very scant supply. Retrospectively, the geneticist would say that there were *isoalleles* of a wild type category at this locus, until they were shown to be different from each other by reaction with the new test antibody. When family studies were made, two Xg-negative parents were found to breed true for that phenotype among all their children, but no other pairs consistently did so, thus the recessiveness of Xg to Xg(a) was indicated. A comparison of the two *reciprocal testcross matings* was interesting and departed conspicuously from the results of testcrosses for autosomal inheritance described previously. The couples of Xg(a) mothers and Xg fathers had sons and daughters of both kinds; but from the reciprocal mating, Xg mothers and Xg(a) fathers, only recessive sons, Xg, and dominant daughters, Xg(a), resulted. From the fourth type of marriages, where both parents were dominant, daughters were of the dominant phenotype and the sons included a minority of Xg recessives ($\frac{1}{2}$ of the sons where the mother was heterozygous, none where she was Xg^a/Xg^a). A summary of these four kinds of marriages appears as Table 12-1, in which the reciprocal testcrosses are not equivalent. This is a representative pattern of the distribution of recessives in the simple monohybrid segregation of X-linked loci. In brief, the recessives are not equally divided between males and females in all categories. Neither do reciprocal testcross matings give similar results.

TABLE 12-1 **Segregation typical for an X-linked character, the Xg(a) antigenic reaction of red blood cells. Reciprocal testcrosses contrast sharply, second and third lines.**

			DAUGHTERS		SONS	
Marriages			$Xg^aXg^?$	$XgXg$	Xg^a	Xg
♀ $Xg^aXg^?$	by	♂ Xg^a	71	0	60	24
$Xg^aXg^?$	by	♂ Xg	25(het.)	10	18	6
♀ $XgXg$	by	♂ Xg^a	8(het.)	0	0	7
$XgXg$	by	♂ Xg	0	6	0	2

Color blindness occurs in many varieties from complete blindness for all colors, to blindness for red to blindness for green to difficulty with red or the most common category, difficulty with green. Some 8 percent of X-chromosomes in the North American white population carry a recessive allele which differentiates one or another of the last four types from the normal color vision. Those affecting perception at the red end of the spectrum are the more severe *protanopia* and the less severe *protanomaly* alleles; those affecting chiefly in the green region of the spectrum are *deuteranopia* and the milder (and more common) *deuteranomaly* alleles of normal. The question of whether there is one locus, *cb*, for any one of these five alleles, or whether there are two closely linked protan and deutan loci each with a series of three alleles may now be raised.

The pattern for monohybrid inheritance of any one of these rare recessive sex-linked differences follows the plan just presented for the recessive Xg-negative condition and repeated in Figure 12-2. Four phenotypic kinds of marriages are shown here instead of the former three kinds (1)

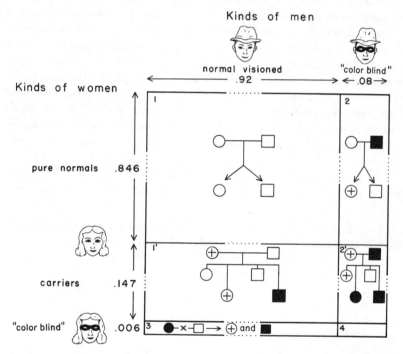

FIGURE 12-2 The inheritance of the red-green varieties of color blindness in a representative population (see text).

recessive by recessive (2) testcrosses and (3) Dominant by Dominant as presented for autosomal recessive inheritance in Figure 6-4 of the chapter on gene frequency analysis. The four types are obtained by considering the testcrosses separately. The testcross of a female of recessive sex-linked phenotype and a Dominant (single X-chromosome) male produces all Dominant daughters (who are heterozygous) and all recessive sons (who are called hemizygous rather than homozygous). This testcross is shown in box 3 of Figure 12-2. The reciprocal of this testcross is shown in boxes 2 and 2′, where the two kinds of dominant females are married to males showing a recessive sex-linked character. This kind of a testcross produces exclusively Dominant offspring where the woman is homozygous for normal (color vision), but the same kind of testcross produces recessives to the extent of about half of their sons and daughters wherever the mother is heterozygous for an X-linked recessive gene (boxes 2 and 2′ in the figure). Males show one or another of these phenotypes, but no males have yet been reported with combinations of color blindness. In a representative population 5 percent of males are deuteranomalous; 1 percent are deuteranopic; 1 percent are protanopic and 1 percent are protanomalous. These figures allow the prediction of frequencies of heterozygous women and of recessive homozygotes in a population which has had an adequate chance (several generations) to come to Hardy-Weinberg equilibrium (Table 12-2).

TABLE 12-2 **The observed population frequencies for X-linked recessive phenotypes among males and among females and the monohybrid equilibrium expectations**

Phenotype	Observed, q, among males	Expected, q^2	Observed among females
Xg negative	.36	.130	.107
g-6-P-d deficiency (U.S. Negro)	.15	.0225	.02
color blindness (France)	.09	.0081	.0050
deuteranomaly and deuteranopia	.06	.0036	.0036
protanomaly and protanopia (U.S.)	.02	.0004	.0004
hemophilias	.00002	4×10^{-10}	lower

If all of the four recessive red-green genes form a single series of multiple alleles, then the observation of a total of .08 such males would lead to the prediction that the locus would be homozygous nonnormal in females with frequency $(.08)^2$, or 0.64 percent, because that is the frequency with which an X-chromosome from a hemizygous male would meet a similar recessive X-chromosome from a female. Observations of color-blind women do not match this estimate; only about 0.4 percent are color blind. Furthermore, some women who test as normal in color vision have two kinds of color-blind sons, deuteranomalous or else protanopic, as if each of the mother's X-chromosomes carried one recessive allele. This may be called *complementation*, or formation of the Dominant type when two similar recessives are brought together in the same genotype. Complementation indicates that each chromosome of this pair is carrying the normal allele of the recessive in the other, and so the woman with normal color vision who has two kinds of colorblind sons is actually dihybrid. Conversely she is not monohybrid for two different abnormal alleles of the same series as was at first expected. One such woman reported by Vanderdonk and Verriest had three kinds of sons, protanomalous, deuteranopic and normal in vision.

We may therefore consider two loci, the R locus concerned with vision at the red end of the spectrum and a separate G locus concerned more with green perception. Deuteranomalous women who have a similar son and also a deuteranopic son give clear evidence for allelism of these latter two genes at a locus conveniently called the *deutan* locus. Its deuteranopia allele, g, is recessive to the anomaly gene, g^M, and both are recessive to the wild type allele, G, of the deutan locus. Similarly, at the *protan* or red vision locus, the normal allele, R, is dominant over either of the other two, and the mild protanomaly, r^M, is dominant over the more severe protanopia, r, in female heterozygotes. These clues from family studies may now be tested on a population-wide basis.

On the second hypothesis the frequency of recessive color blind women would be predicted separately for protan women and for deutan women. In a population with 1 percent protanopic males, meaning also that 1 percent of the X-chromosomes of eggs contain the protanopia allele, 0.01 percent of females should be protanopic homozygotes. Similarly, random union of either this r or the milder kind of protan recessive, r^M, would occur among 0.04 percent of women, those resulting from the gene pool in which 2 percent of the sperm are not normal in genes affecting this part of the visual spectrum and unite with 2 percent of eggs of similar content. Because of the dominance between these two lower members of the allelic series, some 0.03 percent of women should show protanomaly and some 0.01 percent should show protanopia. Similar reasoning with regard to the deutan locus, at which 6 percent of males have one or another recessive allele, leads to the prediction that 0.36 percent of women will be green color blind, either as deuteranomalous homozygotes, as deuteranomaly/deuteranopia heterozygotes or rarely (0.01 percent) as homozygous deuteranopics. Studies made by Waaler among schoolgirls in Oslo, Norway, agree more closely with the two-locus hypothesis. The frequency of the several genotypes of girls with combinations of two of the rare color vision alleles is presented in Figure 12-3. The combinations marked 1 . . . 8 would have shown some kind of color blindness on the single locus hypothesis. Studies of the linkage relationships of the two kinds of color difficulty each with a third locus, glucose-6-phosphate dehydrogenase

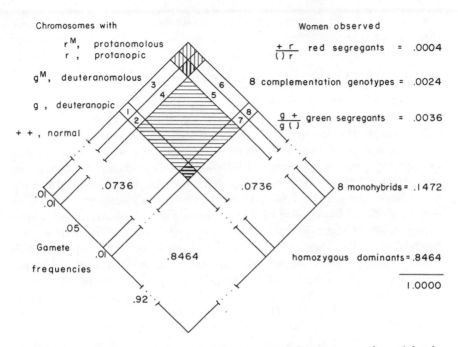

FIGURE 12-3 The more common phenotypes and genotypes of partial color blindness. Note dominance of certain alleles at each locus and complementation (areas 1 through 8) of chromosomes bearing recessives at nonallelic loci.

deficiency, indicate separate loci for the protan and the deutan mutants.

The presence or lack of a certain enzyme is a genetically X-linked character which differentiates the third most common X-linked recessive group of people from the normal. About 7 percent of males in some Negro populations and about 1.5 percent of white males are deficient for the enzyme glucose-6-phosphate dehydrogenase or g-6-P-d. Still higher frequencies are found among Asian Indians and Iraqi Jews. For lack of this enzyme, persons are sensitive to the eating of the broad bean and have hemolytic anemia, a reaction called Favism, which for centuries has been identified with that ancient item of food. During World War II it turned out that such persons are also sensitive to the modern drug primaquine and to high concentrations of naphthalene in clothing. Classification for genetic purposes can be made by testing the enzyme activity. Some environmental conditioning via immune reactions results from small doses of bean or drug. The *g6Pd* locus is important in human genetics because it is common enough to use in linkage studies aimed at mapping the gene content of the

X-chromosome. The same gene is also sex-linked in two other mammals, sheep and goats.

RARE RECESSIVE PHENOTYPES

Fortunately, the recessive gene for *hemophilia A* is not common in man even though it is found in other mammals. The severe hemophilia mentioned earlier (page 3) was the first to be recorded in medical history. It results in a form of "bleeder's disease" in which the sequence of steps in the clotting reaction is interrupted by the lack of *AHF*, the *antihemophilic factor* (factor VIII), which ordinarily promotes the formation of thrombin in the blood plasma. Lack of AHF in the blood can cause severe illness or even fatal loss of blood from such small events as nosebleed, minor cuts or the shedding of the milk teeth. Any boys with such a constitution are severely limited in their scope of play and work, and the impact of this handicap easily spreads to parents and sibs. The fact that classical hemophilia appeared in some ten of the male descendents of Queen Victoria of England has contributed perhaps profoundly to important events of modern European history. This recessive hemophilia gene passed through one or more generations of the female line from Queen Victoria, and it is of particular note that it passed to two of her granddaughters who became queens. One of them, the last Tsarina of Russia, passed it on to her only son, whose plight provided the occasion for the insinuation of the charlatan Rasputin not only into the trust of the Tsarina but also into the political circle of the Russian court. Doubtlessly, it added to the weakness of the Romanoff dynasty. In Spain the last queen, Victoria-Eugenie, transmitted the hemophilia gene to her oldest and her youngest of four sons, and both of them died young thus leaving the present Juan as pretender to the throne of Spain until he recently renounced it.

The possibility of women showing hemophilia was debated for many years before any cases were found. Explanations then current were (1) that females might have physiological blocks to the expression (see sex-limited expression, Chapter 16), or oppositely (2) that two doses of hemophilia genes might be so severe as to be lethal during early pregnancy, or correctly (3) that they had seemed to be absent merely because of their extreme rarity. Meanwhile the correct answer was approached via some diligent animal experimentation performed by Brinkhous and Graham starting with hemophilic male dogs. Hemophilic pups had been appearing in several breeds of dogs; but the information was usually covered up, and so potentially valuable experimentation was delayed. After one of the hemophilic dogs was raised in the laboratory of a medical school and bred, his daughters in turn produced additional hemophilic male pups. Several of these produced hemophilic daughters when the dogs were backcrossed to their mothers. Testcross ratios typical of X-linkage were obtained, and this demonstrated the possibility of hemophilia showing in a female mammal. Concomitant studies of the clotting mechanism showed that the cause was a deficiency of the same AHF factor in these dogs as in hemophilic men. Raising these handicapped dogs to maturity was a difficult technical feat which required among other things massive blood transfusions at any hour of the day or night. The final demonstration of the recessive determination of hemophilia was the breeding of hemophilic female to hemophilic male dogs and getting litters containing only hemophilic pups.

Eventually human hemophilic women were located and described. They generally came from a hemophilic father and a carrier mother, and marriages of this kind are rare indeed because of the early death of so many of the hemophilic boys. One of Queen Victoria's sons, Leopold, survived and had a normal son and a daughter who later gave him a hemophilic grandson, but generally boys with hemophilia A do not become fathers.

A milder type of hemophilia is known as *hemophilia B*, Christmas disease, factor IX deficiency or *PTC deficiency* with the initials standing this time for plasma thromboplastic component. The chemical effects of this gene, which is also X-linked and recessive to the normal allele, are initiated in an earlier part of the clotting mechanism than the biochemical block caused by classical hemophilia. The same bleeding disease occurs within a breed of dogs and it also is X-linked. In man, hemophilia B is found at less than 1/5 of the frequency of classical hemophilia; and because these mild bleeders live longer than the "royal bleeders," inheritance through the X-chromosome of their daughters has been demonstrated.

Another rare and recessive gene on the X-chromosome leads to the development in males of the *Duchenne* type of *muscle dystrophy*. Boys may appear normal during their preschool years, except for aldolase activity, but then their leg muscles swell and later become weak and waste away. The name *pseudohypertrophic muscular dystrophy* stems from the initial swelling. Afflicted boys die in their teens usually leaving no offspring. Afflicted cases are thus related through the female line (Figure 12-4). Because several years of outward normality precede the onset of the typical symptoms of this kind of muscle dystrophy, present research may discover some way of preventing the breakdown of muscle under the usual control of the gene. Such study could be greatly facilitated by the discovery of some other and common X-linked differences which may be classified well in advance of the onset of Duchenne muscle dystrophy symptoms and

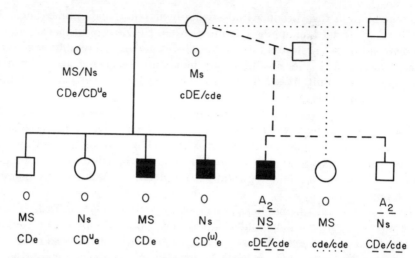

FIGURE 12-4 The sex-linked recessive Duchenne muscular dystrophy in some sons (black squares) of a carrier woman. Several paternity exclusions were made on the basis of blood types. Those alleles contributed to each child by the biological father are shown, but most of those from the mother have not been written. Alleles not expected from the husband are underlined. Compare with pedigree of another muscular dystrophy in Figure 9–3. After R. R. Race and Ruth Sanger, *Blood Groups in Man*, 4th edition, Oxford, England, Blackwell Scientific Publications, 1962.

which are closely linked with this locus. Other muscle dystrophies are known, one of them also X-linked (peroneal atrophy) and another of them due to an autosomal Dominant gene. Mice, sheep, cattle and chickens also have muscle dystrophy.

The human X-chromosome is large enough to contain many additional genes, and a total of more than 50 have been described. A thickened skin condition called *ichthyosis vulgaris* is of interest partly because it must be genetically different from two other scaly skins, one autosomal and another once cited as a striking example of a Y-borne allele dominant to normal skin (the "porcupine men," page 185). Another skin abnormality involves the absence of sweat glands, and such men therefore lack the ability to endure high temperatures or hard work. Men with this *anhidrotic ectodermal dysplasia* are advisedly lazy and even in summer paradoxically may be found wearing long underwear, but this they keep wet to supply the evaporation effect which persons with the normal allele obtain from functioning sweat glands. Although anhidrotic ectodermal dysplasia is mainly recessive to normal, it is possible to distinguish the heterozygous women from their homozygous normal sisters. One form of *hydrocephaly* is also an X-linked recessive in man, but somewhat similar abnormalities are not sex-linked in the mouse. The human eye defects of *night blindness* and one form of recessive *retinitis pigmentosa* are both sex-linked, but the existence of a dominant form of the latter is doubted by Morton. Two of four separate kinds of *diabetes insipidus* are apparently sex-linked and are incompletely recessive in females; hence these carriers can be identified phenotypically, and other normal sisters can be assured of not having sons of this type.

Some X-linked conditions originally described as recessive may continue to be listed as such even though it is now possible to distinguish heterozygous women from their homozygous normal sisters or daughters. Such *incompletely recessive* phenotypes include one form of retinitis pigmentosa, two forms of deafness which develop after the child has begun to speak and which are clearly different from the old term "deaf-mute," one form of toothlessness accompanied by absence of eyebrows and eyelashes, and a form of dwarfism called gargoylism. The last is doubtless of ancient origin, as evidenced by the widespread architectural use of such faces both in the interior of churches and around the cornices of buildings.

SEX-LINKED RECESSIVE LETHALS

A final category of X-linked recessive alleles is perhaps the largest group of all, *sex-linked recessive lethals*. Because they are recognized by their absence, if they are noticed at all, they are apt to remain undifferentiated one from another. However, we know from studies of X-linked lethals in the insect *Drosophila* that recessive lethals may be demonstrated at more loci than recessive visible alleles can be shown in the same chromosome. Conversely, there must be a large number of very important normal genes in the living population at these "lethal loci" and a smaller number of less vital normal genes at the loci of "visibles" in a surviving phenotype. Some geneticists speak of the graduations on a scale of lethality which goes far into the normal range. The original and most pragmatic use of the term *genetic lethal* is for a genotype not represented among classifiable offspring where there was a clear chance for such genotypes to be formed by parents. From the viewpoint of population genetics, however, a genotype which consistently does not produce children is lethal, such as hemizygous males with Duchenne muscle dystrophy.

In general, any gene which shortens life has lethality as part of its syndrome of pleiotropic effects. However, the late-acting genes are often known by more specific names referring to the aspect of the body affected, clotting mechanism, kidney function, hydrocephaly, or atrophy of one set of muscles of the body. From the research standpoint, a lethal genotype is one which has disappeared from among the living beings observable at or shortly before birth. Among birds lethals would cause a certain fraction of eggs not to hatch even though they were fertile. Among insects used in radiation damage tests there can be egg lethals and larval lethals and pupal lethals, none of which give rise to the group of adults which are usually observed and sorted.

If the time of classification for sex were moved from birth to age 20 in sibships which have segregated for Duchenne muscle dystrophy, a 2 : 1 ratio of sisters to brothers would be approximated. Likewise, after the death of AHF hemophilics, the sex ratio observable among the survivors is 2 females : 1 male. Similarly, in other instances of X-linked recessives which kill off the hemizygous males early, both of the parents would have to be phenotypically normal at the locus of the lethal, and only the female sex can carry the recessive lethal hidden by the dominance of the normal allele. When the female is heterozygous, the genotypes expected among fertilized eggs would be 1 : 1 : 1 : 1 leading to homozygous normal daughters, carrier daughters, normal sons and lethal male embryos or fetuses. (See Figure 12-2, marriages 1'.) This will be modified into 1 : 1 : 1 : 0 sooner or later by the single recessive lethal acting in the hemizygous male. A typical recessive lethal would remove the recessive male phenotype before birth; classical hemophilia would remove it sometime between birth and the early twenties; X-linked Duchenne muscle dystrophy would remove the same fraction of the sibship during the teen years. Note that the 2 : 1 sex ratio indicating an X-linked recessive lethal is a modified testcross ratio and should not be confused with the 2 : 1 remainder of an F_2 ratio where the phenotypes are abnormal Dominant and normal recessive, respectively. (Contrast with homozygous yellow mice, page 67.) Only the testcross for sex is possible and not an F_1 by F_1 mating because the female sex is always homogametic and the heteromorphic X-Y chromosomes of the male initiate a 1 : 1 segregation as to sex determiners.

MAPPING THE X-CHROMOSOME

Although a mother has only two X-chromosomes, a dihybrid mother may have more than two kinds of sons in respect to X-chromosome phenotypes. The ease with which these additional combinations appear depends on the particular genetic characters involved; thus, free assortment is observed between hemophilia B and deuteranopia, whereas the latter and hemophilia A cross over infrequently in any one generation. The former pair demonstrates loose linkage within homologous chromosomes, whereas deuteranopia and hemophilia A show closer linkage. Moderately close linkage is simpler to explain first.

Adam found no recombination among the 37 boys in 10 sibships studied because the males were capable of segregating for color blindness and for deficiency of the enzyme glucose-6-phosphate dehydrogenase. Most of these came in sibships of repulsion type, whose mothers were phenotypically normal *cb* + / + *g6Pd*, and these sibships (each with from two to five brothers) included only two kinds of males, 17 color blind and 15 enzyme deficient. From these repulsion sibships the theoretically possible double wild type was lacking and so was the double recessive. A consistently opposite picture was exhibited by the coupling sibship; four boys were both color blind and enzyme deficient, and one was neither of these two phenotypes, so again there was no recombination individual. This did not indicate that exchange was impossible, but it did indicate that any crossover value able to remain unsampled in 37 tries must be a rather low fraction.

A crossover value of 5 percent between the same two loci was indicated in another study by Porter, Schulze and McKusick, and the two studies are not inconsistent. This second study had 30 scorable sons from six deutan and enzyme dihybrids plus eight more sibs from two protan and enzyme dihybrid mothers. An example of one of their pedigrees is given in Figure 12-5. The first son received from his normal mother the two

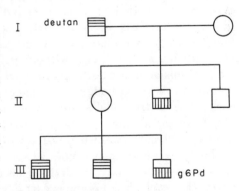

FIGURE 12-5 One of six sibships dihybrid for deutan color blindness and enzyme deficiency. The first son is a crossover, having in his single X-chromosome two recessives which were in separate chromosomes of his mother and in separate grandparents. After Porter, Schulze and McKusick, Nature, **193**: 506 (1962).

recessives which showed separately in his maternal grandfather and maternal uncle. He was thus a recombination product of crossing over within the X-chromosome pair of his mother. The other two sons had noncrossover chromosomes which produced the same phenotypes already shown by their grandfather, I-1, who was deutan with the enzyme normal, or by their uncle, II-2, who was normal-visioned enzyme-deficient. Without the information from these relatives of the mother and without the knowledge of close linkage from the study by Adam it would not be possible to designate which phenotypes were the noncrossover types. By having enough information per sibship and by the use of an IBM 7090 computer the authors found the most likely crossover value to be in the range .18 to .009 for the deutan to $g6Pd$ interval and most likely at .05 frequency. The smaller number of protan $g6Pd$ heterozygotes gave possible crossover values in a similar but wider range.

An even occurrence of the coupling and repulsion families is the rule in linkage. The great rarity of the chromosome containing both rather rare recessives is compensated in the forming of dihybrid mothers by the wide prevalence of chromosomes normal at the two loci. This is figured very simply. If in a population at equilibrium the frequency of color-blind males is 8 percent due to recessive c and the frequency of males with df, the recessive enzyme deficiency, is 2 percent, then $.08 \times .02$, or .0016 of the X-chromosomes would have both recessives (by previous crossing over and/or mutation). By subtraction this would leave .0784 chromosomes with $c +$ and only .0184 with $+ df$ and a .9016 proportion of $+ +$ chromosomes. Dihybrid women will be formed as the product biologically and mathematically of the complementary chromosomes meeting. Dihybrids form from the repulsion chromosomes meeting, $.0784 \times .0184$, or .00144256, and another .00144256 fraction, $.0016 \times .9016$, in which coupling types combine at fertilization. This low expectation of dihybrids (only 2/7 of 1 percent for both kinds together) indicates the difficulty of measuring linkage, particularly when one remembers that only a fraction of human families have two or more sons and are thereby suitable for linkage analysis of X-chromosomal distances without pedigree information.

Close linkage between the protan and the deutan loci for color blindness appears to exist. Although it was once thought that the genes were interchangeable as true alleles, the accumulating evidence is against allelism of red- and green-blind. While it is true that they may show approximately the same linkage values when tested with distant loci, they do not produce a clearly recessive phenotype when present in the same hybrid. A protanopic-deuteranomalous hybrid has almost normal color vision, which means that each chromosome is carrying the normal allele of the recessive contained in the other member of the pair, thus the genotype *pro d$^+$/p$^+$ deut*. From such a mother a sibship has been reported by Vanderdonk and Verriest containing a normal XX daughter and three kinds of sons. One son had protanomaly, two sons had deuteranopia and two others had normal color vision. It may be reasoned that the two normals were crossovers and that the first three sons revealed the noncrossover chromosomes; but it is also possible, conversely, that the two normals were noncrossovers and that the three were crossovers. Such tentative and alternate conclusions must often be made in human genetics. Additional segregating sibships should not be much harder to find than previously described sibships involving one color-blind allele and *g6Pd*. With the increased rarity of certain dihybrids, the value to science and human welfare of reporting each such sibship becomes correspondingly greater.

Gene loci can be mapped along a chromosome when there are sufficient three way comparisons among three loci. The most numerous comparisons would come from the three kinds of dihybrid sibships each one revealing a certain percentage of crossovers detected in its interval. For instance, the woman dihybrid for *g6Pd* and *Xg* has approximately 25 percent recombination individuals among her sons. Similar data from *Xg* and color-blind dihybrids show a larger frequency of recombination. Since the interval between color-blind and *g6Pd* loci allows only about 5 percent crossovers, the enzyme locus must lie between the other two loci showing the largest of the three crossover values. Ideally, the sum of the two shorter distances should equal the crossover value for the outside marker loci, but in a direct dihybrid test the larger distance usually falls short of the expectation obtained by summation because undetected double crossovers restore the noncrossover coupling phase.

Double crossovers may be detected in a sufficiently large collection of sibships composed of trihybrids for the same three loci; and, better yet, the gene order may be determined more readily. The generally applicable plan for trihybrid linkage is set forth beginning on page 160. As a second example we may consider a woman trihybrid at three rather closely linked loci on the X-chromosome pair. Suppose that she were trihybrid for the severe hemophilia A, for deuteranomaly and for deficiency of the enzyme g-6-P-d. Such a phenotypically normal woman, symbolized + + +, might have as her particular genotype *ahf + +/ + deut g6Pd*. This would mean that the recessive hemophilia allele was coupled with the normal alleles of the other two loci in the same X-chromosome and that normal anti-hemophilic factor production was in coupling with the two recessives in the other X-chromosome. Previous studies of dihybrid sibships have already shown that more noncrossover than exchange offspring result from the degree of linkage characteristic of this part of the chromosome pair. The same dihybrid studies have demonstrated that the crossover distance between the *ahf* locus and the deutan color-blind locus is about 12 units, but that a smaller distance of about 5 units lies between the deutan and the *g6Pd* loci. Consequently, we may predict that our trihybrid will have a very small chance (.12 × .05, or up to 0.6 percent) of producing a double crossover son of either of the two complementary kinds. Practically, this reduces the kinds of sons of this trihybrid from eight to only six kinds. She would have just under a 5 percent chance of having sons of the two kinds resulting from exchanges in the shorter region, sons who would have either the *ahf* + *g6Pd* chromosome or the opposite crossover chromosome. With almost a 12 percent chance (after subtracting the small expectation for double crossovers) she would expect sons with all three recessives and sons with all three normal genes. These considerations would leave an expectation of something over 83 percent noncrossover sons, + *deut g6Pd* and *ahf* + + boys. Each of the four different numerical expectations would be divided into halves to get the eight complementary classes individually. The complementary classes by exchange categories would be two noncrossovers, two kinds of single crossovers for one region, both kinds of singles for the other region and complementary double crossovers.

The above gradation among the four paired classes of offspring is truly representative of the results of linkage studies in many other animals and plants; the double crossover classes together are smaller than either of the component single crossover classes. Furthermore, the pair of complementary single crossover classes does not exceed the pair of classes which is noncrossover with respect to that same region. However, the many noncrossovers may make up only a plurality and not a majority of a large total of properly collected trihybrid sibships. For instance, if the chromosomal distances were 40 and 30 units, double crossovers might be as high as 12 percent. After proper subtraction of the frequency of doubles from the totals of each of the regions of possible exchange, only some 42 percent of noncrossovers would remain. As the length of the regions is increased with the choice of more distant loci, the frequency of double crossovers is also increased and the expectation of noncrossovers is reduced to 12.5 percent of each.

The currently indicated map of the human X-chromosome which has been used for the foregoing calculations may be drawn as follows:

	←deutan→			
ahf	protan	*g6Pd*		*Xg*
12	5		25	

The deuteranopia and the protanopia loci are indicated tentatively here, for Kalmus has suggested another possibility, that they straddle the *g6Pd* locus. Omitted from the above linear order are hemophilia B, Duchenne muscle dystrophy and myopic night blindness. These three sex-linked genes show 50 percent recombination with each other and with the loci already mapped. Therefore it cannot for the present be stated which lies beyond *ahf* or which lies beyond the *Xg* locus. Many other sex-linked genes (see McKusick, 1962) have yet to be located in relation to the known map positions of the above genes.

Against this background an actual kindred of *trihybrid linkage* as reported by Graham may be presented. This sibship located in North Carolina contained five sons who were each different from the others in respect to the assortment of protanopic color vision, the Xg antigen and the mild hemophilia B. This is apparently the first linked trihybrid human sibship to be reported, but it may be hoped that others will come to light as the new genetic difference, possession or nonpossession of the Xg(a) antigen, can be included in current studies. The first and the last son of the pedigree (Figure 12-6) are exactly opposite in the three genetic characters and therefore represent complementary classes. Each of the other sons is not paired with an opposite complementary class, so it is certain that the five sons represent the four typical categories of trihybrid linkage studies: noncrossovers, double crossovers, single crossovers in a first region and single crossovers in the second region. Present knowledge about the X-linked genes of humans or about the mother's parents and relatives does not permit conclusive statements about linear gene order nor about the three alleles which must have been in coupling phase on one chromosome of the mother. However, the family is highly illustrative, if we make one assumption about the gene map and another assumption about the coupling-repulsion aspect of linkage. In the figure it is assumed that the locus for the alleles *Xg* or *Xgᵃ* is flanked by the loci at which the other two pairs of alleles are present. This is as good an assumption as any, because double crossover sons are not rare under any assumption in loose linkage.

Once that gene order is assumed (or determined) the mother must have been one of four equally likely genotypes, designated in the figure as "options." Option 1 is in the form of the previous general explanation (page 161) in that all recessives are in coupling on one chromosome (because Xg is recessive to Xg(a) by present serological tests). Therefore all dominant alleles of this trihybrid, representable as + + +, are in the opposite chromosome of the sex pair. The second son in this sibship would then be a noncrossover individual carrying all three recessive alleles in the X-chromosome which he received. The middle son would be a crossover in respect only to the second region, because he still has the *cb* and *Xg* genes which were in coupling phase in his mother, and yet he now has the + allele of PTC hemophilia, which had been in repulsion linkage to the other two. Exchange between these first two loci would and did result in complementary crossover types, which we may call crossovers for the first region.

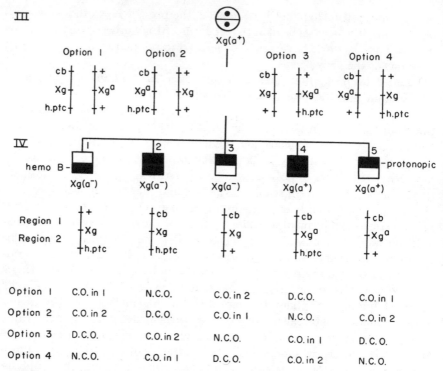

FIGURE 12-6 Double and single crossovers from a trihybrid female. The genotype of the normal Xg(a⁺) mother remained unknown but was more likely that of option 1 or 2. The chromosomes of her five sons must include one or more noncrossovers and at least one double on any option. After Graham, Tarleton, Race and Sanger, Nature, 195: 834 (1962).

The first and fifth sons represent opposite recombinations following the process of crossing over somewhere between the *cb* and *Xg* loci in the separate developing oocytes of the female. Finally, one kind of double crossover individual is represented by the fourth-born son who was protanopic in vision, had the mild hemophilia and was Xg positive. Notice that the double crossover chromosomes in the offspring agree with the genotype of the mother except that the alleles in the middle locus have exchanged places. Noncrossovers and double crossovers typically differ at whatever is the in-between locus.

The occurrence of sibships with double crossover individuals is more likely where the two chromosomal distances involved are long. Such is known to be the case among these three loci, hemophilia B, Xgᵃ and either of the two (closely linked) red-green color-blind loci. Many large studies have shown 50 percent recombination, and the usual interpretation for this finding would be independent assortment in the Mendelian sense, if each of these loci were not also showing typical monohybrid sex-linkage. Therefore the X-chromosome of humans must be a long chromosome; as measured in genetic terms it could be 100 or even more than 150 crossover units in length according to C. E. Ford. With the cytological knowledge that many human chromosomes are longer than the X-pair (Figure 2-2), one may extrapolate that crossing over may be high within a majority of the human chromosomes. Consequently, many pairs of loci may fail to show the reduced assortment characteristic of linkage. This pedigree more readily included one or two double crossovers because the linkage was loose. Conversely, if certain loci are so close to each other that crossovers are very rare, then the dihybrid or trihybrid nature of the family may be very hard to demonstrate within a sibship. Perhaps the rhesus alleles (Chapter 11) occur at several very closely linked loci.

POSSIBLE Y-LINKAGE

Stories of eager pioneering and of scholarly review and prediction are associated with the question of Y-linked genes. An open invitation to discover Y-borne genes lies in the fact that a conspicuous type of pedigree would be produced. Inheritance from an affected man would go to all of his sons but to none of his daughters nor to the daughters' children of either sex. Such *holandric inheritance* has been approximated, usually in small kindreds, by about 17 differently described conditions (and some kindreds were reported under more than one category). However, contrary kindreds in large number and from widely separated countries have been recorded in which the inheritance of these same (or mimic) conditions is in the usual autosomal pattern to both sexes and through both sexes to grandchildren. For instance, many pedigrees show an autosomal dominant transmission of blue sclera with brittle bones, of hyperextensibility of the thumbs (Figure 26-3), of one or another form of cataract, of slight webbing between the second and third toes, of black hairs on the ears and of *ichthyosis histrix*. The last was present, in very severe form, in the "porcupine man" Edward Lambert, born about 1717, in one of his sons and in two of his grandsons according to a careful review of the documentation by Penrose and Stern; yet earlier reports claimed that there were 11 affected male descendents and no affected women among eight in one generation. Needless to add, the more striking version of this Lambert pedigree was widely quoted!

A review by Stern (1957) of the previously published reports of all examples of supposed Y-linkage concluded that the simpler explanation of a gene in one of the many autosomes is preferable to the special interpretation suggested in the individual author's reports. Information was often lacking about the numbers of daughters and about the offspring of unaffected daughters in many of the original reports, which must therefore be considered as inadequate. Although oddity-appeal may not yet have turned up a clear case of a Y-linked gene, Stern points out that some may yet be found, possibly on aberrant Y-chromosomes changed at one end by the translocation (Chapter 23) of part of some autosome onto the Y-chromosome. After Stern's suggestion was made, intensive studies in human cytogenetics have revealed Y-chromosomes of unusually long or short dimensions. Either of these changes might have brought several or many genes to the holandric pathway of inheritance, but so far no mutant alleles have been found among the new or old residents of the Y-chromosome, except for the gene or genes directing the embryo to the development of maleness.

SUMMARY

The visibly unequal X- and Y-chromosomes in men pair at meiosis but have few or no demonstrated loci in common. While the Y determines maleness alone, the X genes also act in single dose in hemizygous men even if these alleles may be recessive in their mothers or daughters. The gene frequency for X-linked alleles in a population is the same as is the phenotypic frequency among the hemizygous males, but homozygotes among females are the square of that frequency, as usual. Population equilibrium for X alleles, however, takes several generations to achieve. The severe type of hemophilia is sublethal as well as rare, and so hemophilic women are very unlikely but not impossible. The same type of AHF hemophilia has been found in dogs of two breeds and has demonstrated typical recessive inheritance in X-chromosomes.

Reciprocal testcross families are of two kinds in regard to sex-linked inheritance unlike their equivalence for the segregation of autosomal genes. Because of the single X in men sons show segregation for X-linked genes more often than do daughters of a heterozygous woman. Where there are several boys of a rare recessive phenotype in a kindred of true X-linkage, these males are related mostly through one or more females in the direct line from a carrier ancestor unlike autosomal pathways to be reviewed in Chapter 16. The cousin marriage of normal parents does not increase the frequency of recessive X-linked offspring in either sex.

More genes in the X-chromosome are known by name than in any other larger or smaller chromosome of the set, and their dihybrid linkage and crossing over have already placed four of them in linear order. Hemophilia A and B are too far apart on the X-chromosome to show linkage directly with each other, but the protan and deutan color-blind loci (with three alleles each) are close together. Coupling and repulsion linkage in dihybrid women are expected equally often; similarly, there are four equally frequent kinds of normal trihybrid women each with different kinds of crossover sons to be expected. The principles of most of the previous chapters are applicable to the XY males and the XX females with adjustment for the chromosomal change in number and content.

SUGGESTED READING

McKusick, Victor A., On the X chromosome of man. Quart. Rev. Biol. **37** (No. 2): 69–175 (1962, June). An explanation in detail, an appendix of more than 58 sex-linked genes and a bibliography.

Sarkar, S. S., A. R. Banerjee, P. Bhattacharjee, and Curt Stern. A contribution to the genetics of hypertrichosis of the ear rims. Amer. J. Hum. Genet. **13**: 214–223 (1961). They find that six pedigrees which allegedly show inheritance in the Y-chromosome do not fit the patroclinous pattern. Only one small kindred fits but does not prove the hypothesis of holandric inheritance.

Snyder, Laurence H., and Paul R. David, *The Principles of Heredity* 5th ed., Boston, Heath, 1957, 507 pp. Contains a color chart for the detection of color-blind vision. Sex-linked inheritance is clearly distinguished from sex-influenced and sex-limited modes of expression in separate chapters.

Sturtevant, A. H. and G. W. Beadle, *An Introduction to Genetics*, Philadelphia, Saunders, 1939, 392 pp. For those who prefer to begin with the special case of linkage and who like a concise text.

Stern, Curt, The problem of complete Y-linkage in man. Amer. J. Hum. Genet. **9**: 147–166 (1957). Reviews the weight of the evidence and the reasonableness of more common alternative explanations.

PROBLEMS

12–1　How do autosomes differ from heterosomes? What is a hemizygote?

12–2　Define:

isoalleles	complementation
reciprocal mating	X-linkage
protanopia	Y-linkage
deuteranomaly	holandric inheritance

12–3   (a) Do sex-linked recessive hemophilic dogs breed true?
(b) What are the expected distributions of X-linked recessives from reciprocal testcrosses?

12–4   What are some differences between Hemophilias A and B at the physiological level and at the chromosomal level?

12–5   How do the proportions of muscular dystrophic offspring compare in Figures 8-3 and 12-4 and how do they differ importantly?

12–6   If a single recessive allele in the X-chromosome were a recessive lethal, and if a woman bearing it had no other testable heterozygosity in her two X-chromosomes, how could the presence of a lethal possibly be suspected?

12–7   What is the difference between X-linkage and autosomal linkage?

12–8   How can both hemophilia A and Duchenne muscular dystrophy be sex linked and yet not show ordinary dihybrid linkage?

12–9   What kind of offspring from a trihybrid for protanopia, deuteranomaly and Xg antigen would indicate the gene order of these three? Answer by giving genotypes of parents (and of grandparents or of sufficient offspring).

12–10   The present Queen Elizabeth of England married a remote cousin both having Queen Victoria as a common ancestor and both having normal fathers. Did this consanguinity increase the chance of their having hemophilic children? Explain how.

12–11   Is the number of kinds of mutant gene loci in the human X-chromosome overrepresented, proportional to size or underrepresented?

12–12   About .999 males have the XY chromosome pair. What evidence points to the action of the presence of the Y or the absence of the second X in causing maleness?

chapter 13

Individuality and Family Resemblance

The principles of dihybrid inheritance, if extended, can and do explain a great amount of genetic variability. As the number of heterozygous gene pairs increases, the number of kinds of offspring goes up more rapidly than the number of loci segregating. In a multihybrid situation it is no surprise that individuality emerges from continued subdivision of classes by additional segregating gene pairs. Seen in this light it may appear that it is unusual to have any family resemblances within a generation or down through several generations. Furthermore, the close similarity of identical twins takes on appropriate significance only against the vast possibilities for segregation within the sibship. These contrasting tendencies toward genetic individuality and toward the retention of family resemblance, will be discussed in this chapter.

VARIETY FROM MULTIHYBRIDS

Testcrosses. The number of genetically different kinds of offspring from parents only one of whom is hybrid increases by successive powers of two as the number of heterozygous loci increases. Thus the monohybrid has two classes of offspring, 2^1, corresponding to his or her two kinds of gametes. The dihybrid individual may expect any of four kinds of offspring, 2^2. A trihybrid person can have any or all of eight kinds of children, or 2^3; and a tetrahybrid may expect his children to represent any of 16, or 2^4, possible kinds. Thus the number of possibilities, 2^n, established by pairwise segregation and by assortment increases at a rapid rate, by doubling, with each increase of genetic complexity. This number of classes from any one level of multihybrid remains essentially the same whether all loci assort independently and each combination is expected with frequency equal to any other class, or whether there are two or more linked loci (Chapter 12). Linkage reduces the frequencies of some pairs of classes, the complementary crossovers, but the total of common and of remotely possible classes remains as stated. The number of classes of testcross offspring corresponds directly to the number of kinds of gametes formed by the one hybrid parent of the testcross.

F_2 **Type Assortments.** When both parents are hybrid for the same alleles, the number of possible kinds of children is greater than in testcrosses and therefore increases more rapidly. Monohybrids have three genetically different kinds of children among an F_2 type of generation. Dihybrids have nine kinds, and trihybrid parents have 27. Thus the increase in genetic variety of children increases by the appropriate power of three when the two parents are heterozygous for the same alleles at one or more loci. The progression is 3^1, 3^2, 3^3, 3^4 ... 3^n where n is the number of mutually hybrid loci. The above gives the full genotypic variety rather than the total of phenotypic classes, which might be reduced in kind by the action of Dominance. Even if linkage is acting, the total number of classes to be considered is as given, although the relative proportions of the classes may be modified by less than free recombination at the time of gamete formation.

Crossbred Hybrid Assortments. Because humans are often in the crossbreeding rather than in the F_1 by F_1 category, a wider kind of variability needs to be considered. Parents both of whom are monohybrid at the same locus, such as Landsteiner MS, etc., might have three or even four different alleles instead of duplicating the same two alleles. Four alleles is the maximum possible for one pair of parents at one locus, and that will be the basis of the computations in this paragraph. If alleles A^1 and A^2 segregate into two kinds of eggs and if alleles A^3 and A^4 segregate into two kinds of sperm, then offspring with any of four kinds of genotypes may be formed. This corresponds to the size of the ordinary monohybrid checkerboard of Chapter 4. Using this extreme possibility of four alleles per locus in the parental pair we compute the maximum variety, or checkerboard sizes, to be 4^1 for all of the single locus alleles, 4^2 or 16 for the two locus maximum assortment, 4^3 or 64 for the trihybrid checkerboard size and 4^4 or 256 for the zygote number in a tetrahybrid F_2 generation. The above sizes are necessary in order to represent each possible kind of zygote just once.

The relation to each other of the above three power sequences for testcrosses and for minimum and for maximum genotypes in F_2 segregations is given in Table 13-1. The table shows how rapid is the increase in genetic variety among offspring as the level of heterozygosity in the parents is increased. It may be added that if two parents were heterozygous at 20 loci and with the same alleles at each locus, they could have offspring in any of more than 1,000,000,000 different kinds. This is less than one hybrid locus per chromosome pair and far less than the number of human gene loci already identified. If the parents were heterozygous in the same way just once in each of the 22 pairs of autosomes, the varieties of genotypes possible among their children would be more than 31,000,000,000 or 3^{22} more exactly. This figure is some ten times greater than the number of persons in the world population today! Hence the genetic individuality of human beings should be no surprise.

TABLE 13-1   Rapidity of increase of genotypes with increase of hybridity of parent(s)

Hybrid loci, n	Testcross offspring, 2^n	Typical F_2, 3^n	Checkerboard of 4 alleles /locus, 4^n
1	2	3	4
2	4	9	16
3	8	27	64
4	16	81	256
10	1024	59,049	1,048,576

Blood Type Combinations. By means of blood samples alone individuals could be classified into many different groups. Snyder has pointed out that with the kinds of antisera available in the year 1950 and testing for the then known alleles at 11 loci 8,294,400 different kinds of men could be recognized. Some of the possible combinations are so rare that they would probably not appear even once among 10,000,000 persons. At the other extreme the most common combination of blood types at the 11 loci among the English population would be found no more often than 1/300 of the time. At the present date more blood-differentiating loci are known and more alleles are recognized at some of the 11 loci which Snyder's calculation included; hence the types would be more numerous and the commonest combination (the *mode*) would be less frequent than formerly. The range of presently recognizable blood phenotypes approaches and may someday reach the tremendous range of fingerprint variation.

FAMILY RESEMBLANCE

If on reasonably simple assumptions more varieties of persons are possible than there are people in the world population, resemblances within a sibship or vertically within a family line call for explanations. One answer is in regard to the assumptions of the preceding section; not all parents are heterozygous at many loci. Other answers involve luck.

Similarities Among Sibs. Genetic segregation may be impossible within many sibships. Whenever one of the two parents is homozygous for a dominant gene there will be but one phenotype for that aspect of facial feature, let us say, among his or her offspring. Homozygosity at one locus or another was present in an important fraction of the millions of genotypes computed above, so it is appropriate to consider the effect of parental homozygosity on the next generation. One homozygous locus with conspicuous dominant effect or several homozygous loci with slight effects will lead to uniformity of offspring along one pattern in one sibship and along some different pattern within another sibship. Recessive uniformity will exist in other families. Two parents homozygous for the same recessive gene pair will not be found as often as the above situation of a single parent being dominant, yet in an appreciable minority of marriages recessive gene pairs will be inbred. Obviously, all the children of two recessive parents will show the recessive phenotype. Combinations of identity of certain recessive gene pairs in parents and of homozygous dominants of other pairs in the mother and of still other homozygous loci in the father explain a considerable amount of the similarities among siblings. Thus no phenotypic segregation is possible for many of the genetic factors in a sibship.

Additional resemblances among sibs will be found for statistical reasons. Runs of luck may also produce similarity among all the children in many of the smaller sibships and among most of the children in other and in larger sibships. In the smaller sibships all of the children may be alike in spite of the possibility of genetic segregation. This is particularly so for the two-child sibships, where chance resemblance either as two dominant sibs or as two recessive sibs can occur in 62 percent of families, $(3/4)^2 + (1/4)^2$ and in as many as 25 percent of two-child families having a dihybrid testcross expectation, $4 (1/4)^2$. Other monohybrid and dihybrid expectations rank between these two probabilities and are shown in Table 13-2.

TABLE 13-2   Chance of phenotypic identity of all Sibs in smaller sibships subject to segregation

Segregation ratios	SIBSHIP SIZE			
	2	3	4	5
3 : 1	.625	.438	.321	.239
1 : 1	.500	.250	.125	.062
9 : 3 : 3 : 1	.391	.194	.103	.056
1 : 2 : 1	.375	.157	.071	.031
3 : 3 : 1 : 1	.312	.109	.040	.015
1 : 1 : 1 : 1	.250	.062	.015	.004

In sibships of three, the chances of three-way identity are lower than those shown in the smaller sibships for each of the genetic expectations, but the lowest given in the table is still above 6 percent chance of identity. At lower but still appreciable frequencies chance can produce four-way identities among sibs in potentially segregating families, from 32 percent of sibships in which the dominant is expected 3/4 of the time down to 1.5 percent of sibships of four segregating as dihybrid testcrosses (column 4).

Once a rare phenotype appears in a family the chances that the same parents will have one or more other children of that rare kind is increased above the general population level. Furthermore, the rarer the trait in the population the greater the proportional increase among full sibs. These statements apply not only to recessive phenotypes but also to uncommon dominants and to phenotypes dependent on several pairs of genes. When the exact ratio of increase is plotted against the trait incidence in the population, two natural groupings emerge (Figure 13-1). Conditions due to a single gene lie close to one slope whether the rare gene is dominant or recessive. A separate group of abnormalities most of which seem to have a multifactorial mode of inheritance plot out along a different slope. Such large scale comparisons of the incidence of different diseases may henceforth help to clarify the mode of inheritance or point to out-of-line conditions which are mixtures from the standpoint of genetic causation.

Vertical Similarity in Ancestors and Descendents. Examples of a characteristic running down through a line of descent have always been intriguing. The Hapsburg lip, which is a protruding lower lip and lower jaw, is an example of a genetic character which seems to have been determined by a single dominant gene in a succession of Austrian royalty through a period of three centuries. Other rare dominant alleles doubtlessly achieve runs of luck down through many generations. The chance that any particular gene will pass from one individual to a certain one of his or her offspring is $\frac{1}{2}$; therefore the chance that the named gene will pass to a specified great grandchild is $(1/2)^3$. Conversely, the chance that a person has received any one gene from an illustrious ancestor who was heterozygous for it n generations back would be $(1/2)^n$.

This computation serves also for the mean expectation of genes received from an ancestor. A child receives $\frac{1}{2}$ of his genes from one parent; he in turn passes on only $\frac{1}{2}$ of them to a child of his. Hence a grandchild has on the average $\frac{1}{4}$ of the actual genes possessed by the grandparent, and the great grandchild has around $\frac{1}{8}$ of the genes from his great grandfather excluding, of course, the sex-linked genes which do not always run the half chance of loss but which pass regularly with the X-chromosome from father to daughter. An old popular expression which is consistent with this effect

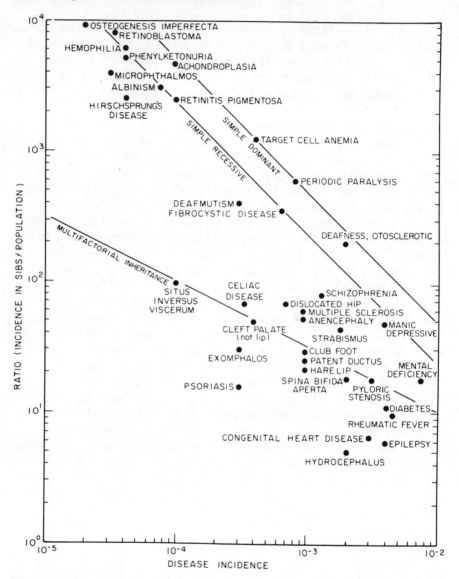

FIGURE 13-1 Incidence in sibs compared with the incidence in the population for the rarer genetic diseases having any of three modes of inheritance. From H. B. Newcombe, *Congenital Malformations*, New York, International Medical Congress, 1964, p. 347.

of the continued halving of one line of inheritance by meiosis says, "It is six generations from success to poverty."

FIGURE 13-2 Family resemblance through five generations. From *Life* Magazine © 1956 Time Inc. All Rights Reserved.

However, the individuality of an illustrious ancestor depended, in all probability, upon some particular constellation of genes. The chances that the desirable alleles at two, three, four or ten loci would pass together to just one generation is a much smaller figure, and the chance that even a small constellation of genes would independently pass together through several generations is highly unlikely. For rare alleles at loci able to assort independently the dihybrid, trihybrid, tetrahybrid and decahybrid transmissions would be $(1/4)^g$, $(1/8)^g$, $(1/16)^g$ and $(1/1024)^g$, respectively, where g is the number of successive generations to which the rare combination is transmitted without its being broken up by assortment. In spite of such low average chances one may find lines of descent showing remarkable family resemblance (Figure 13.2).

There are countertendencies which sometimes but not often modify the above principles of calculation. An infrequent but effective one of these is genetic linkage of loci. Linkage does lessen the chance of assortment in each generation; and if our interest is in the maintenance of a coupling arrangement for several generations, the chances fall off less rapidly than in the foregoing calculations for independently assorting loci. Yet a considerable amount of assortment goes on in just a few generations, and that is why at the population level of comparison genes linked in chromosomes are randomly associated in people. As the extreme of linkage is approached, two loci seem to be one (see Figure 11-3). Even so, the size of the constellation of desirable alleles from the ancestral genius would be only one less and the remaining assortment of alleles would break up almost as easily in the first generation or soon thereafter.

The second and greater counterinfluence to the rapid breakup of a rare human genotype is assortative mating, including cousin marriages. At the upper extreme, where both partners carry the same two rare alleles at independent loci, survival of an AB combination into an individual of the next generation would advance to 9/16 from the outbreeding expectation of only 1/4. Even so, the expectation of handing on AB for merely two generations of assortative mating would decrease to a minority expectation, $(9/16)^2$. Assortative mating is doubtlessly effective in many parts of the world, where people travel in their own social circles and choose marriage partners with many similarities to themselves. Nevertheless, it is well to remember that opposite characteristics are sometimes attractive, as in examples of negative assortative mating. The story is told that a very eminent intellectual wit was accosted by an attractive and ambitious young woman who said, "With my beauty and your brains what a wonderful child we could have!" He replied, in all fairness, "And suppose it should have *my* beauty and *your* brains?"

Correlation Among Relatives. Near relatives tend to show greater similarity with a subject than do more distant relatives. This is especially true for quantitative characters, but it applies also to segregating phenotypes. In regard to height Francis Galton long ago showed that tall parents tended to have children not quite as tall as themselves, and that short parents had children with heights intermediate between that of the parents and the population mean, and he referred to this as regression toward the mean. Today the term regression is used in describing the change of one dependent variable in relation to change arbitrarily in another. The customary use of regression might well be illustrated by the rate of change of weight at increased levels of food intake, or, for negative correlation, with increasing muscular activity. By contrast Galton's regressions were actually *coefficients of correlation.* A general plan for correlation is presented in Figure 13-3 showing a range from complete positive correlation to zero correlation. If there are no differences caused by the environment, cor-

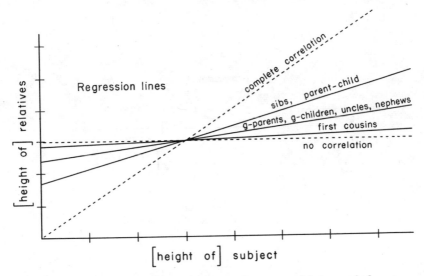

FIGURE 13-3 Scheme of correlations to be expected between index cases and those relatives at distances of one, two or three genetic steps removed and involving characteristics with a strong hereditary component.

relation of +1.0 would be found between monozygotic twins, and this is represented by the steepest line; and correlation around 0.0, shown as a line with no slope, would be expected among unrelated persons compared for a character which is known to vary in the population. Sib correlations or parent-child correlations are higher than uncle-nephew correlations or grandparent-grandchild correlations. Correlations between first-cousins would be less steep than the above, and among more distant relatives they would be still lower and perhaps zero.

TWINS IN A MULTIHYBRID FAMILY

In the midst of so much human diversity one kind of twin pair stands out among other twins and sibs. Some twins, triplets and quadruplets, and the Dionne quintuplets are *monozygotic*, MZ, meaning that they have arisen from the union of one egg and one sperm followed by separation of

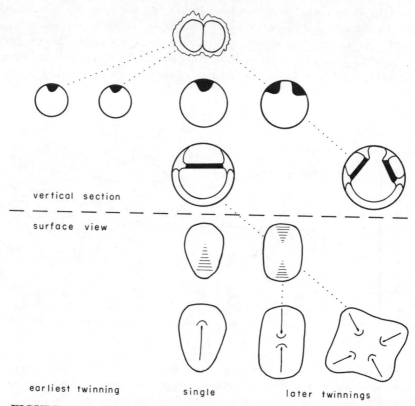

vertical section

surface view

earliest twinning   single   later twinnings

FIGURE 13-4 Times and methods of origin of monozygotic twins and higher multiples. Left, by separation of blastomeres; top right, by formation of separated inner cell masses; lower, by multiple organization of body axes on the embryonic shield.

cells at some later time (Figure 13-4). Therefore their genetic endowments are the same. Frequently the term identical twins is used, but if this implies phenotypic identity it is a misleading term, as will be explained in Part Three on variable expression of the genotype in certain environments. A minority of twin pairs in the United States and a different minor fraction in other populations around the world are MZ twins and genetically identical. Slightly more often twins are *dizygotic*, DZ, from the union of separate eggs and separate sperm. Because they came from four different gametes, DZ twins are no more alike genetically than are two sibs born at different times and are often called fraternal twins. The question of whether members of a dizygotic twin pair choose the same environment during youth and maturity to as great an extent as do monozygotic twins will be discussed later; for the present it is obvious that a D Z boy-girl twin pair would be under more diverse environmental influences than M Z twins would be, because all M Z twins will be either boy-boy pairs or girl-girl pairs. Dizygotic twins will differ in sex approximately in half of the pairs. For similar genetic reasons, the dizygotic twins can differ in other aspects of their genotypes as much as brothers and/or sisters can differ in inheritance. Therefore, fraternal twins are genotypically the same in 50 percent of their genes even though their parents were heterozygous at many loci; but by contrast the monozygotic twins will be genetically identical in spite of variety among the gametes of the mother and of the father.

Diagnosis of the kind of twin pair may be made by reciprocal skin grafts or by a battery of serological and other genetic tests. Monozygotic twins are so much alike in their body chemistry that they may readily accept skin grafts from each other. If identity is proven by skin grafts, a damaged kidney in one M Z twin may sometimes be successfully replaced by a healthy kidney from the other (Figure 13-5). The tissues of dizygotic twins reject implants from each other because the cells are genetically different, chiefly in having different histocompatibility genes. If serological methods are used to decide on zygosity, the blood samples of twins are tested with many different sera for agglutination of corpuscles or the lack of it. The finding of one genotypic difference, shows conclusively (barring mutation, Chapters 21 and 24) that the twins are dizygous. A few easily found identities do not establish the monozygosity of twins, but more and more identities of genotype tend increasingly toward that conviction.

TABLE 13-3 Monozygotic twin diagnosis by reduction of chance identity between two zygotes[a]

Father	Mother	Twins		Sister		Brother
X Y	X X	$\frac{1}{2}$	X X	X X		X Y
A_2 O	O O	$\frac{1}{2}$	A_2 O	O O	alike	O O
Ms NS	MS	$\frac{1}{2}$	MS Ms	MS NS	alike	MS NS
$P_1 P_2$	$P_1 P_2$		$P_2 P_2$ $\frac{1}{4}$	P_1	alike	P_1
C^wDe cde	CDe cde		CDe cde $\frac{1}{4}$	C^wDe cde		CDe cde
K k	K k		K K $\frac{1}{4}$	K k		K k
Le(a − b+)	Le(a + b−)		(a − b+)	all sibs alike		
Fy^b	$Fy^a Fy^b$	$\frac{1}{2}$	Fy^b	first three alike		$Fy^a Fy^b$
$Jk^a Jk^b$	Jk^b	$\frac{1}{2}$	Jk^b	first three alike		$Jk^a Jk^b$
		.001 =	$(\frac{1}{2})^5$ times	$(\frac{1}{4})^3$ =	this identity at random	

[a]After Ruth Sanger and R.R. Race, Amer. J. Hum. Genet., 3: 340 (1951).

FIGURE 13-5 Twin with three kidneys (on the left), one surgically implanted from his monozygotic twin brother (right). Identity of genes and of the tissue proteins in monozygous twins allows successful grafting between such persons and not between other twins or sibs. Courtesy of Wide World Photos.

An unusually conclusive diagnosis of monozygotic twinning was reported by Race and Sanger in 1951 (Table 13-3). Among four children born to a couple there were twin girls, and the blood of all of these sibs and their parents was later tested with most of the more common antisera. It may be noted in the table that the father was heterozygous at six of the gene loci and that the mother was heterozygous at four loci, including some which were the same as those of the father. The parents represented testcross situations in regard to differences in AO, MNS, Duffy (Fy) and Kidd (Jk) loci. They were like a simple F_1 by F_1 mating in regard to K and P loci and to a crossing of two hybrid individuals with a total of three alleles of the Rh series. They were like a P_1 cross in respect to Lewis antigens, and they were both alike and homozygous at the Lutheran locus. In brief, they could have a wide variety of children. Although all of their children would be alike in their Lutheran and Lewis phenotypes, they could and did show one difference among them in each of the remaining seven blood phenotypes and in sex. In spite of the opportunity for genetic diversity these twin girls were identical in all eight ways.

These facts are evaluated for diagnosis of zygosity in the following way. Monozygotic twins are expected to be alike in as many blood types as are tested, and monozygotic twins are expected among some 30 percent of all twins in the English population to which the parents belong. It would be higher or lower in other populations. For contrast the probability that the twins are truly dizygotic but by chance alike in this number of genetic traits may now be computed. The population expectation for dizygosity among all twins born is the remaining 70 percent, and most of such twins will show their dizygous origin by the segregation of one or more genetic differences. We wish to compute that this will not happen in the battery of tests which were applied and which could reveal segregating phenotypes. For the probability of likeness in sex and in the four other characters in which testcross ratios were to be expected in this family, one must multiply the initial probability by $(1/2)^5$; and for the three F_2 segregations in which both twins were KK and P_2P_2 and heterozygous with a paternal *cde* and a maternal *CDe*, one must multiply by $(1/4)^3$. The combined chance that these twins in this family will be this similar even though they are from two fertilized eggs is therefore $.7 \times .5^5 \times .25^3$, or a $.00034$ chance. The ratio of this chance of resemblance from dizygotic beginnings to the chance of monozygous twins being born, $.30$, is about $1/1000$ so that the monozygosity of the twins reported by Race and Sanger is $999/1000$ assured.

As described above, evidence for monozygosity is always negative. Positive evidence of the separate zygosity of each of the Bellingen quadruplets is given by merely three loci while four other phenotypes were alike in parents and quadruplets. Two of the quadruplets were blood type O, but one was Ns while the other was MNS and in addition one of these two was female and homozygous in the rhesus region whereas the other was heterozygous rhesus and male. Although the other two quadruplets were by chance both A_1, they differed in sex, and they also were MNS and Ns.

SUMMARY

Individuality within the limits of the human species should be no surprise. Any hybridity of parents allows genetic variety among their separately conceived children. As the number of heterozygous gene pairs increases from dihybrid and trihybrid to n pairs of heterozygous loci, the number of different kinds of children possible increases by the nth power. With dominance or a testcross situation it is 2^n kinds; in other sibships the possibilities are 3^n or 4^n depending on the number of alleles at the locus and/or on the detectibility of the heterozygote.

In spite of the variety possible, many examples of family resemblance exist both among sibs and contemporaneous cousins and vertically up or down the family tree. Some of the similarity stems from homozygosity, some comes from assortative mating in respect to certain obvious and desirable characteristics, and some resemblance is a matter of genetic luck in segregation and assortment.

Twins resemble each other either for the above reasons or in spite of the above. Dizygotic twins may be similar in several respects as a run of luck, but the luck is usually no greater than that between two separately born sibs; and if enough comparisons are made, twins which just happen to look alike can be diagnosed as fraternal twins. If resemblance can be shown to correspond to smaller and smaller chance resemblance among separate zygotes, the continued and unexceptional identity (genetically speaking) of twins steadily increases the conviction that twins similar in many genetic respects came very likely from but one fertilized egg.

SUGGESTED READING

Maynard-Smith, S., L. S. Penrose, and C. A. B. Smith, *Mathematical Tables for Research Workers in Human Genetics*, London, Churchill, 1961, 74 pp. Many tables of considerable interest and great use. There are concise explanations of each group of tables.

PROBLEMS

13–1   If a man is $i^{A_1} i^{A_2} L^{MS} L^{Ns}$ and his wife is $i^{B} i L^{Ms} L^{Ns}$, how many kinds of children could they have as to these two loci?

13-2 (a) How many of the above would be homozygous?
(b) How many dihybrid?

13-3 In what fraction of sibships of three coming from parents both heterozygous for blood group B would you expect
(a) All dominant offspring?
(b) All recessive offspring?
(Check your answers by the total of both given in Table 13-2.)

13-4 What fraction of sibships of three persons from MN parents would consist
(a) Of three M persons?
(b) Of three N persons?
(c) Of three MN persons?
(d) Does the sum check with Table 13-2?

13-5 In families of parents both of whom are heterozygous for Free earlobes show what fraction of sibships of two will be alike both as to sex and earlobe.

13-6 (a) What is the random chance that girl quintuplets of blood type O from type A mother and an O father would be from five separate eggs?
(b) From one egg?
(c) What is the ratio of the two chances?

13-7 What is the chance that the younger sister and brother of the MZ twins of Table 13-3 would be alike (omitting the Lewis character) as much as they are?

13-8 The Bellingen quadruplets segregated for sex, for A_1 and O, for Rhesus homozygous and heterozygous and for Ns versus MNS. Assuming that all of these segregations resulted from a 1 : 1 expectation, what was the random chance that they might have resembled each other completely in these four respects? Name the phenotypic combinations contributing to this total.

chapter 14

Traits Not Segregating:
Quantitative Characters

Graduated traits of domestic animals are more common than are segregating traits controlled by a single gene pair. Among the latter fur colors, spotting, length of tail, and hair form are indeed interesting to the geneticist but hardly seem vital to the success of the animal except as these relate to camouflage in natural surroundings. The single gene differences seem more often to be associated with some disease or abnormality rather than with positive attributes like the production of milk, eggs, meat or amount of wool per shearing. Similarly, among humans single gene loci make the difference between normality and dozens of different pathological conditions of great interest to the medical man and to anyone who has that genetic disease himself or sees it among his near relatives or neighbors. However, being on the short side or long side of average height does not seem to have a single gene explanation. Neither do skin color differences rest on as few as two pairs of genes but rather upon many more. Nor do we find that intelligence in the general population shows segregation into bright and dull classes but rather shows continuous variation.

The characteristics which do not segregate into phenotypically separate classes may show their continuous gradation mainly for genetic reasons alone or for additional environmental reasons. The methods used to estimate the relative contributions of heredity and of environment to phenotypic differences are beyond the scope of this introduction to human genetics, but some fundamentals of quantitative inheritance are pertinent.

TRANSITION TO MULTIHYBRID VARIATION

Although a gap between segregating characters and quantitative characters once existed in the early history of genetics, the scientific gap was soon closed. If we consider the earlier hypothesis of Davenport about skin color differences of Negroes and whites in Jamaica and if we should work out the consequences of three factor pairs or of four factor pairs acting equally and cumulatively, we should be getting well along toward quantitative inheritance. If we graph the distributions resulting from the segregation of larger and larger numbers of gene pairs as to whether they are plus genes or minus genes in regard to a quantitative trait, that would be equivalent to graphing the distributions of tosses of larger and larger numbers of coins and tabulating for the number of heads. In Figure 3-1 we have stated the expected distributions for tosses of two coins, four coins, eight coins, and 16; and this can be a model also for the assortment of a monohybrid without dominance, a dihybrid with equal additive effect, a similar tetrahybrid or even an octohybrid. The distributions figured are computed on the binomial expansion $(h + t)^n$ where the expectation of one allele and of the other allele for reaching a gamete are equal (therefore $h = \frac{1}{2}$ and $t = \frac{1}{2}$), and where n represents the number of genes transmitted or of coins tossed. It will be noted that the peak of the very small "curve" decreases as the number of tosses increases, representing fewer chances of obtaining precisely the mean outcome. Furthermore, the spread of the curve increases on that scale of numbers of deviants as more classes of outcomes are possible, and this may be thought of as a consequence of the decreasing height of the peak. For samples as small as these, the binomial model is the best for computing expectations, and that is why this Figure 3-1 was placed in an early chapter.

APPROXIMATING THE NORMAL CURVE

In coin tossing, or in sex-ratio studies, anything is possible. Consider tossing a coin 20 times. It is possible to get 20 heads and no tails, although this is very unlikely. It is also as remotely possible to get 20 tails; and it is 20 times easier, but still very unlikely to get 19 tails and 1 head. The most likely single outcome is 10 of each, but two other outcomes are almost as common. For instance, getting 9 : 11 either way is much more likely than the mean outcome. Furthermore, the sum of 8 : 12 and 12 : 8 is also more probable than the equal 10 : 10 result. Although a 10 : 10 sample is considered to be the "perfect" sample, it is far from the complete picture. Exact expectations for any possible sample may be figured most accurately by use of the binomial expansion, but the approximation by the normal curve may conveniently be used for larger numbers. Here 20 is not a large number (50 or 100 would be much better at approaching the normal curve distribution); yet a comparison of the two methods of estimation — normal curve versus binomial expansion — will be made at this size sample.

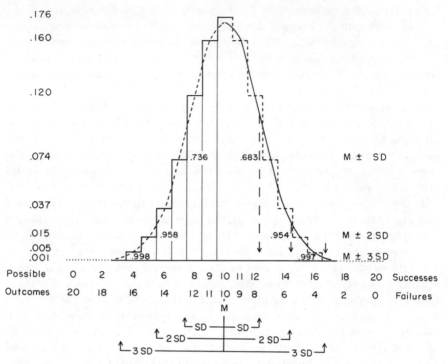

FIGURE 14-1 Comparison of a binomial frequency polygon and the normal distribution curve. Decimal fractions show areas of polygon (left) or of curve (right) embraced between 1, 2 or 3 standard deviations above and below the mean.

In Figure 14-1 all possible outcomes of tossing 20 coins from $0:20$ to $20:0$ are indicated on the bottom paired scales. Above them are drawn columns in proportion to the probability of any single outcome. Although the column heights for such remote outcomes as $2:18$ do not show on this scale, probabilities reach levels such as .001 for the outcome $3:17$, to the peak at .176 for the $10:10$ samples and down again. Of course, the sum of all of these columns is 1.0, meaning the whole of the distribution. We shall speak of this whole distribution as the *area* under the step curve, or simply as the area under the frequency polygon. Equal areas will thus signify equal probabilities. The chief point to be made from the comparison of the two curves is that the area under the frequency polygon drawn for large-sized samples is distributed approximately as is the area under various segments of the normal distribution curve.

All curves of the *normal distribution* family of curves have the same distribution of area although they may have different means and they may spread by different amounts along the scale being used. The customary measure of the spread of a curve, normal or otherwise, is the *standard deviation.* It is often estimated by the formula

$$\text{SD}_{\text{sample}} = \sqrt{\frac{\Sigma d^2}{n - 1}}$$

where d is the magnitude of each deviation from the sample mean; where Σ, sigma, stands for a summation (of all the d^2 terms) and where n is the number of items or variates in the sample. Normal curves have a specified total of their whole area lying within one standard deviation above and below the mean, namely, .6826 parts of the whole. Within two standard deviations lies .9544 parts of the whole. Within $2\frac{1}{2}$ SD lies .9974 of the area under the curve (see Figure 14-1 right half). Generalizing we may say that any fraction or multiple of the standard deviation of two normal distribution curves includes the same proportion of the total area of the two normal curves. It turns out that at the distance of one standard deviation above and below the mean, M ± SD, lie the two *points of inflection* of every normal distribution. Between these two points of steepest slope the curve is concave downward; beyond the points of inflection the normal distribution curve is convex into both tails. Because the areas above and below the mean increase in a precise manner as measured by the standard deviation, any normal curve can be completely specified by stating its mean and its standard deviation. Tables giving the areas in terms of the standard deviation are available in the Handbook of Physics and Chemistry.

The computation of the sample standard deviation by machine calculation employs a different equation in which the actual measures of the individual items, each called a *variate*, x, are used instead of the individually computed deviations, d, which are often awkward fractions. Thus for machine calculation, where $\bar{x}$ is the sample mean

$$\text{SD}_{\text{sample}} = \sqrt{\frac{\Sigma x^2 - n\bar{x}^2}{n - 1}}$$

The standard deviation may be called a primary value in contrast with the standard error, SE, which is derived jointly from it and from the size of the sample actually measured. The standard error is used for forecasting, among other purposes. Such forecasts are in terms of a range within which one may expect, with a specifiable degree of confidence, to find that the true parameter lies and within which other samples will tend to be normally distributed. Thus the SE around a single computed mean or other measured statistic is used to describe a hypothetical normal distribution curve, just as a real distribution of measured variates is described by its sample mean and its SD.

INFERENCES BASED ON THE NORMAL CURVE

The general purpose of measurement in science is usually to go beyond the existing data in the search for more comprehensive yet reliable generalities. In other words, from the sample statistics one seeks to express overall *parameters.* Among the many diverse experiments of Mendel one may calculate the mean of all dominant phenotypes in F_2 generations as 75.06 percent, a *statistic,* and then the scientist may extrapolate that the parameter operating in such experiments is the overall probability of 75 percent dominants. How far away from actual statistics may the true parameter be? Estimation of true parameters or the estimation of additional experimental outcomes makes use of a repetition of the idea of the spread of a normal distribution around a central measurement. However, at this level of abstraction the spread of the imaginary curve is defined by the *standard error*, SE, of that particular sample measure. The standard error of a value becomes smaller as the sample on which it is computed becomes larger; and the standard error is larger if the material within the sample is more variable. Different formulas relate various standard errors to the sample statistics. A measured mean has the following value for its standard error

$$SE_{mean} = \frac{SD}{\sqrt{n}}$$

This equation and the mean specify a normal distribution curve within which other similarly obtained sample means are expected to fall. Similarly, but without taking and measuring other samples the first sample mean and its standard error may be used to express, at any desired confidence level, the range within which the true mean of the whole population (largely unmeasured) lies. At the 95 percent *confidence level* one would specify that the parameter in operation lies in the range between 2 SE below the sample mean and 2 SE above the sample mean. One would then not infer wrongly by chance more than 5 percent of the time. At the 99 percent confidence level one would say that the parameter lies in the interval, mean $\pm 2\frac{1}{2}$ SE, and he would be wrong only 1 percent of the time by chance. Other confidence levels are sometimes used.

Just as a sample mean is not absolute except for that one sample, so is a sample standard deviation not to be generalized without computing its standard error. When that has been done predictions about the parameter, or expectations about additional samples may be made. The standard error associated with the standard deviation is

$$SE_{SD} = \frac{SD}{\sqrt{2n}}$$

When this has been computed, one takes the existing measured standard deviation as the mean of a new but normal distribution curve having its spread determined by the computed standard error. Further reasoning as to the possible parameters and as to possible additional samples is the same as in the previous paragraph. However, this time the projected curve represents the frequency distribution of all other possible standard deviations around the one measured standard deviation taken, for prediction purposes, as the mean of the hypothetical curve. Similarly, the coefficient of variation, another statistic, is subject to sample variation when additional samples may be taken or when a general prediction about the coefficient of variation is attempted, and its standard error is computed by a still different formula and then used in the manner of the previous paragraph.

Although the above exposition arose from an illustration of coin tosses, it is of general application to data measuring weight, height, volume, temperature, I.Q. or to other continuously varying characters. A common and special kind of continuous variable is the ratio or the percentage of one kind within a sample, such as 51 percent boys, or 77 percent dominants or 30 percent crossovers. There is some sampling error in any size of sample, and generalization in respect to either parameters or comparison of two samples requires the consideration of the standard error of ratios. For intermediate proportions (away from zero and from one) the standard error of a proportion is

$$SE_p = \sqrt{\frac{pq}{n}}$$

where p is the decimal fraction in one class; q is the fraction remaining in the other class, and n is the number of individual items in the sample. The standard error of a proportion is smaller, percentagewise, within larger samples, and it is smaller for smaller proportions. Both of these effects are illustrated in Figure 14-2 where predictions from observations in samples of 100 and of 1000 are compared. These proportions are already too near zero for the exact application of the above formula, but the general effect is informative.

From Table 14-1 any of the sample outcomes for coin tosses may be used to illustrate the application of the use of the standard error of a proportion. Independent tosses of coins were made and the resulting proportions were subtotaled either by tens, or by twenties, or by hundreds or combined at random into thousands. Line 3 of the table is conspicuous for the round numbers and for the identical or complementary proportions therein and will be used for illustration. The standard error of .40 among 10 tosses is .155 by the formula $\sqrt{pq/n}$. By similar calculation the standard error of .40 in a sample of 20 tosses is .11 above and below the result. Among

Parameters possible within 95% confidence intervals

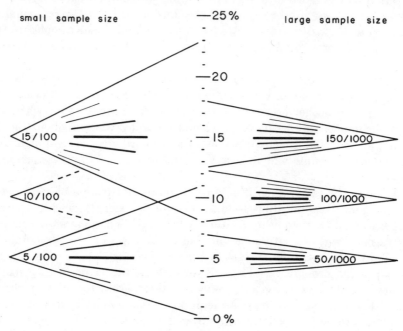

FIGURE 14-2   The estimation of small parameters within a chosen confidence interval, from smaller and larger samples.

TABLE 14-1   Percentage of heads in successive groups of tosses of a penny[a]

| | PERCENTAGE OF HEADS | | | |
Group No.	10 tosses	20 tosses	100 tosses	1000 tosses
1	40	40	47	49.6
2	40	50	47	46.5
3	40	40	60	50.4
4	60	45	47	48.8
5	50	60	53	52.0
6	30	35	57	52.1
7	60	35	53	49.9
8	30	50	52	50.0
9	80	50	44	46.4
10	40	65	36	50.9
Average	47	47	49.6	49.66

[a]From H. Levene, in *Principles of Genetics* by Sinnott, Dunn and Dobzhansky. Copyright 1958. McGraw-Hill Book Company. Used by permission.

100 tosses the standard error of a 60 : 40 proportion is .049, and among 1000 tosses the standard error is .0158 above and also below this proportion or, with a very small change, for a 50 : 50 division. As these standard errors decrease, the range within which 68 percent of other samples tend to fall also decreases correspondingly. A comparison may be made with the small numbers of other samples which are given in the four columns. The samples falling within one standard error of sample group 3 of Table 14-1 are, from left to right, 6/9, 7/9, 1/9 and 5/9. Although these few samples are themselves the results of random variation, only one of them departs conspicuously from the probabilities usually marked off by one standard deviation of a normal distribution curve. Among only ten sample proportions it is hardly possible to demonstrate that the mean ± 2 SD embraces approximately the 95 percent confidence interval, but the existing data are illustrative. Again noting how many of the samples in the successive columns fall within 2 SE of the computation based on sample groups 3 we find 8/9, 8/9, 3/9 and 7/9 of the sample proportions. Again the low number included is in the third column, where we have figured around the .60 sample as a mean for prediction of the population. Even the parameter for coin tossing, as we understand it, is outside of the prediction based on .60 of 100 tosses, although a 60 : 40 proportion among 20 tosses would not miss the known .5 parameter by as much as 2 standard errors.

STANDARD ERRORS OF DIFFERENCES

An approximate rule may be stated for the estimation of the significance of an observed difference between two sample means. The formula may be used if the two independent populations have approximately equal *variances*, namely $\Sigma [(X - \bar{x})^2]/n - 1$, which have been computed on the way to obtaining each standard deviation. The standard error of the difference of two uncorrelated means, $\bar{x}_1$ and $\bar{x}_2$, or of their sum, is

$$\text{SE}_{\bar{x}_1 - \bar{x}_2} = \sqrt{(\text{SE}_{\bar{x}_1})^2 + (\text{SE}_{\bar{x}_2})^2}$$

If the difference is small in relation to its standard error, it is a nonsignificant difference. If the difference is large in comparison with its own standard error, it is becoming significant. Whenever it is twice as great as its standard error, it is significant at the 95 percent level, and if it is $2\frac{1}{2}$ times its own standard error, it is a difference significant at the 99 percent level. Tables showing the areas of the normal distribution curve in terms of the standard deviation may be consulted to obtain other levels of significance.

MULTIPLE FACTOR DETERMINATION IN MAN

If one phenotypic character such as adult height or intelligence or finger print pattern is determined by many genes no one of which produces an overriding difference, certain correlations based on average chromosome and *polygenic* assortment are to be expected. Monozygotic twins should show near perfect correlation for the polygenic trait. Sibs should show .5 correlation. One parent should show only .5 correlation with his offspring. However, offspring and the average of the two parents, called the midparent measure, would show a higher correlation, according to Penrose, of .71 under one set of conditions having additive effects of genes. For more distant relatives the correlation coefficient would be lower, and for husband and wife in the absence of assortative choice of partner the correlation might be zero for some continuously varying characteristic.

Fingerprint Patterns. The arches, loops and whorls of the fingers show greater similarity between a person's left and right hand than do any two corresponding hands of different persons except one's monozygotic twin. The uniqueness of fingerprints is widely used in the recording of new births in hospitals and in criminal investigations. This array of unique patterns can nevertheless be arranged on a single quantitative scale by the method of *ridge counting*, between specific points on the whorl or loop pattern but not on any finger with a simple arch (Figure 14-3). On whorl patterns the

Examples of the three basic types of finger-print pattern

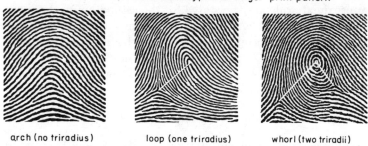

arch (no triradius)   loop (one triradius)   whorl (two triradii)

FIGURE 14-3 Examples of the three basic types of fingerprint pattern. Left: arch (no triradius) score 0; center: loop (one triradius) 13 in this example; right: whorl (two triradii) score 17 plus 8 here. From Sarah B. Holt, Brit. Med. Bull., **17** No. 3: (1961).

number of ridges between each of two triradii and the center of the whorl are counted and added. On loop patterns the total ridges crossed along a single line from the one triradius to the top center of the loop are counted and added; and a zero score is given for any simple arch pattern. The total ridge count from the ten fingers runs from zero up nearly to 300 in a population survey (Figure 14-4). These patterns are established during the first half of pregnancy. Husbands and wives do not show assortative

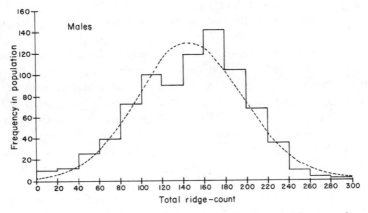

FIGURE 14-4 Total ridge-count distribution (with grouping interval 20) for 825 British males, and the calculated normal curve having the same mean and standard deviation. From Sarah B. Holt, Ann. Hum. Genet., (1955).

mating in respect to this characteristic. Sarah Holt has made extensive studies of various familial correlations of the total ridge count and has found good agreement with expectations based on multiple gene determination. The parent-parent correlations were not significantly different from zero, actually .05 with ±.07 as its standard error. At the other extreme monozygotic twin pairs showed a correlation coefficient of .95 ± .01 among 80 pairs measured by Dr. Holt. This value, which is significantly below 1.00, is an example of the fact that MZ twins are not really identical, and the expression "identical twins" is often a misleading term as applied to phenotypes. For dizygotic twins, for sibs and for one parent and child the correlation coefficients were .48, .49 or .50, and the midparent-child correlation was .66 ± .03 in general agreement with the fact that all of the children's genes come from the parents but with some variety. Thus the finger ridge count is a good example of quantitative inheritance in man. It is established early enough to be free of many of the environmental differences which may affect weight, height, intelligence quotient or length of life.

SUMMARY

When the effects of several gene pairs add along the same scale of effect, segregating classes merge and a continuous curve of quantitative effect appears. Similarly, the direct observation and measurement of many traits often reveals a continuous curve which may be due simply to normal variation resulting from the environment or a combination of that with genetic variation.

Each curve of the normal distribution family is characterized by having a mean and a standard deviation such that a certain portion of the whole area under the curve, 0.6826 of it, lies between plus and minus 1 SD from the mean. A normal variate, X, lies inside or outside these limits with the probability figure just stated. Means and standard deviations themselves are measured usually from samples and are subject to sampling errors, which are distributed and described in terms of their own parameters (estimated). Thus every sample statistic has a sample standard error, larger where the sample contained few variates and smaller from larger samples out of the same uniform population. Confidence levels about estimated parameters and about repetitions of sampling not yet performed are based on the use of computed standard errors as estimated from the observed and measured standard deviation of variates in the actual sample. Standard errors of differences (or sums) of samples tend to vary in a normal distribution curve.

Many characteristics tend to vary quantitatively among people. One fine example of this is the total ridge count from the ten fingerprints, which are established early in fetal life and are well protected from environmental modification during pregnancy and subsequent life.

SUGGESTED READING

Brit. Med. Bull. **17** (No. 3): 241–261 (Sept., 1961). Contains four excellent review articles on human multifactorial inheritance by J. A. Fraser Roberts, Sarah B. Holt, C. O. Carter and A. C. Stevenson.

Falconer, D. S., *Introduction to Quantitative Genetics*, New York, Ronald Press, 1960, 365 pp. For advanced use here and in chapters on mutation and selection in Part Four of this textbook.

Fuller, J. L., and W. R. Thompson, *Behavior Genetics*, New York, Wiley, 1960, 396 pp. An extensive treatment of behavior in man and in experimental mammals often involving traits having polygenic determination.

Mather, K., *Biometrical Genetics*, New York, Dover Publications, 1949, 158 pp. The principles of continuous variation as contrasted with phenotypic segregation due to specifiable and recognizable gene loci.

PROBLEMS

14–1 By algebraic or checkerboard methods figure the phenotypic classes of an F_2-type generation of a trihybrid aAbBcC in which each capital letter adds 1 inch of height and in which aabbcc has the phenotype of 64 inches.

14–2 (a) If the mean height and SE of a sample of men is 69 ± 1.5 inches, within what range of heights would you expect with 95 percent confidence that the mean of other random samples from the same population would fall?
(b) With 99 percent confidence?

14–3 Which of the following sample proportions may be considered with 95 percent confidence to be not significantly different from 3 : 1 segregation?
(a) $.76 \pm .01$ (d) $.81 \pm .04$ (g) $.80 \pm .03$ (j) $.24 \pm .005$
(b) $.73 \pm .01$ (e) $.85 \pm .05$ (h) $.19 \pm .04$ (k) $.22 \pm .015$
(c) $.70 \pm .02$ (f) $.73 \pm .005$ (i) $.20 \pm .025$ (l) $.15 \pm .06$

14–4 Samples of blood types from different racial groups are being compared for M blood types. Which of the following pairs show differences which may be considered significant at the 95 percent level?
(a) $.60 \pm .04$ and $.50 \pm .03$
(b) $.58 \pm .02$ and $.50 \pm .03$
(c) $.58 \pm .01$ and $.55 \pm .01$
(d) $.70 \pm .10$ and $.50 \pm .10$

14–5 Compute the standard errors for the proportions of heads in the coin tosses reported on line 6 of Table 14-1.

14–6 Compute the standard errors of the ratios of heads in column 2 (20 tosses) in the same Table 14-1. (Note: far less than 10 calculations will be needed).

14–7 Is there any evidence for assortative mating if the correlation coefficient between parents in regard to finger ridge count is $.12 \pm .07$?

14–8 If the correlation coefficient of ridge counts on the left and right hand is $.93 \pm .01$ and that between MZ twins is $.95 \pm .01$, is there any significant difference?

14–9 Holt found that the mean ridge count in a sample of 400 men was 145 from a sample with the SD = 51 ridges and in a sample of 200 women was 127 where SD was 52.5 ridges. Is this a significant difference?

part three

Biological Interactions

In the next several chapters we shall consider the problem of enlarging our understanding of the gap which remains between the zygotes resulting directly from the union of gametes and the adult or child with a classifiable phenotype. Whereas the previous examples have been chosen because they are clear textbook examples, the phenotypes which will follow are thrust upon us by the biological misfortune of our friends, our families or ourselves. The genetic answers to these imposed problems are harder to find than those already defined, but they doubtlessly include the continued application of the processes of genic segregation and of chromosomal assortment already described. Even the magnitude of the part played by heredity and the part played by environment cannot be well estimated because of the numerous and perhaps continuous interactions between genes and their near and distant surroundings.

217

chapter 15

Biochemical Pathways from the Genes

Knowledge of the chemistry of the human body comes partly from direct studies on man, partly by the study of microorganisms and partly through very recent studies on cell cultures from humans. No one organism has been observed so intensely and so comprehensively by man as man himself, although one or another microorganism, insect or plant may be the species chosen for a particular type of investigation. Demonstration of the importance of chromosomal DNA resulted from the study of bacteria, in which the amazing phenomenon of genetic transformation was discovered. Recognition that *ribonucleic acid*, RNA, had a key role in heredity came in part from the study of tobacco mosaic virus. The finer details of mutant proteins from the human blood stream were unveiled when it was found that several kinds of hemoglobin each differed from normal hemoglobin by the substitution of one amino acid for another in a sequence of almost 300 prescribed positions of amino acids. This primary (linear) structure of proteins is determined by the structure of the DNA acting with several sizes of RNA along the nuclear-cytoplasmic pathway.

FROM NUCLEAR DNA TO CYTOPLASMIC PROTEIN

The amount of DNA per nucleus shows a remarkable constancy within the body even though widely separated species have different amounts. Regardless of the source tissue the DNA from somatic cells has the same ratio per nucleus, and by contrast the mature egg or sperm has only half as much — a natural consequence of the meiotic segregation of chromosomes and reduction of their number. (See Chapter 2.) Although the DNA per nucleus in birds is different from that in mammals and still different from that of insects, the amount is constant per somatic cell nucleus and is half that much per egg or sperm nucleus before fertilization. The DNA is found only in the nucleus and only along the chromosomes.

219

The double-stranded DNA of the chromosomes directs the activity of several sizes of RNA stepwise in the assembly of strands of protein. From an optically very short part of one chromosome — a length of DNA corresponding to a functional gene or *cistron* — the information of its nucleotide sequence is copied in complementary form by a chemically long strand of *messenger ribonucleic acid*, designated m-RNA. In some presently unexplained manner only one strand of the DNA is translated by the single-stranded m-RNA before the messenger leaves the nucleus. Although the nucleotide sequence of DNA is apparently continuous, it is interpreted at this step or at the next step as a sequence of triplets forming the *genetic code*. (See Figure 15-1.) Each triplet will specify a certain amino acid, and the sequence of triplets will specify the sequence of amino acids within a protein. Thus if the DNA strand being read contained simply the

DNA	TTC TTT CAA CTC TAA AAG CGC ATA TCA AAA CAG GGG

$\downarrow$ step 1

m-RNA	AAG AAA GUU GAG AUU UUC GCG UAU AGU UUU GUC CCC

$\downarrow$ step 2

protein	glu	lys	cys	gly	tyr	leu	gly	leu	met	phe	arg	pro

FIGURE 15-1 Steps in the formation of a sequence of amino acids in a polypeptide (primary protein). After Ochoa, Experientia, **20**: 57 (1964).

sequence of thymine and cytosine as follows, TTC TTT, the messenger RNA would form the complementary sequence of adenine and guanine as AAG AAA. However, the converse is not true, for the RNA would translate the sequence TAA of the chromosome as AUU, because RNA regularly contains the nucleotide uridylic acid (including the base uracil) instead of the nucleotide deoxythymidylic acid (with the base thymine). These terms may be reviewed in Chapter 2. Because the DNA code is commaless (without empty spaces), it is necessary that the reading of the nuclear DNA shall begin at a certain point, otherwise the meaning of the message would be changed at the next step. This reading from the correct start and proceeding in the proper direction is somehow accomplished in the living cell and in appropriate test-tube mixtures.

The discovery of the triplet genetic code stems from the work of Crick, of Nirenberg and of Ochoa as an answer to the problem of designating

20 amino acids by a nucleotide code consisting of only four characters. While a two-letter code could specify only 16 different meanings, a triplet code could express 64 differences. Some of the 20 amino acids seem to have only one code name; others have two or more synonyms. The several triplets able to code for the same amino acid seem to have the same two nucleotides consistently and to show variety only in the remaining one nucleotide. This kind of a code (with synonyms) is called a *degenerate code* in that several code words may call for the same amino acid. Although phenylalanine is coded by the RNA sequence UUU, the amino acid lysine is coded by AAA or also by one or more other triplets. Other examples of degeneracy will be found in the two amino acids which are shown twice in Figure 15-1, glycine and leucine.

The sequence of the triplet code words determines the sequence of amino acids in the initially formed polypeptide chain or primary protein. When the m-RNA reaches the cytoplasm with its message fresh from the nucleus it makes contact with one or more *ribosomes*. These are conspicuous spheroids of another kind of RNA long known to be centers of protein synthesis. Recent studies on hemoglobin synthesis by Rich and colleagues show that a ribosome moves along a length of m-RNA often followed by four or more other ribosomes. From each of these ribosomes a length of protein steadily grows as the ribosome moves along reading the sequence of nucleotide triplets in the messenger RNA. By the time each ribosome leaves the end of the m-RNA there has been completed a chain of some 150 amino acids suitable for incorporation into a hemoglobin molecule. This polypeptide chain has been assembled because the ribosome is visited by many kinds of *transfer RNA*, t-RNA, all of small molecular weight and therefore called soluble RNA but each carrying one molecule of a particular amino acid. The varieties of soluble RNA must have specific structure at two places, one for union with a certain one of the 20 kinds of amino acids (AA) and one for a triplet complementary to the m-RNA code for that amino acid. In the vicinity of the large ribosomes t-RNA-AA compounds get into place along the slender m-RNA in an order which depends on the triplet sequence. While the t-RNA molecules are on the m-RNA, each attached amino acid joins by new peptide linkages laterally with the two neighboring amino acids and then the amino acid is released from the t-RNA which had helped to align it. Thus a length of polypeptide grows in the cytoplasm far removed (two or more RNA steps away) from the DNA code of the nuclear blueprint. In the cytoplasm each t-RNA molecule can repeatedly bring its kind of amino acid to the ribosome for assembly purposes, and the same m-RNA can be used by several ribosomes to make several molecules of one kind of primary protein in the same cell.

The polypeptide product may serve as building material or as an enzyme. In either event the initial linear structure of such a *primary protein* may be changed by secondary folding of the polypeptide chain (Table 15-1) and by new cross-linking with other chains until a native protein with a

TABLE 15-1   The principle of sequence analysis[a]

a. The sequences of amino acids within peptide residues from various digests of the same hypothetical polypeptide chain.

1. D D A
2. B F B C
3. A E B
4. B A C D
5. C D D D
6. G G
7. B C G
8. G H I J

b. Order of peptides deduced from overlapping amino acid sequences.

```
4.  B A C D
5.      C D D D
1.          D D A
3.              A E B
2.                  B F B C
7.                      B C G
6.                          G G
8.                              G H I J
```

c. Sequence of amino acids.

B A C D D D A E B F B C G G H I J

d. Presumptive structure of polypeptide chain if "C" is cysteine permitting a disulfide cross linkage.

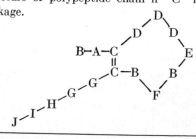

[a]After William Hayes, *The Genetics of Bacteria and Their Viruses*, New York, Wiley, 1964.

particular three dimensional shape has been formed, such as that characteristic of myoglobin in muscle or of hemoglobin in blood. This means that
the historic hypothesis of one gene-one enzyme indicated by Garrod and
formulated by Beadle and Tatum just before beginning their brilliant
work on *Neurospora* is now stated in the form one gene-one polypeptide.

HUMAN HEMOGLOBIN TYPES

The hemoglobin molecule is a four-parted structure called a tetramer
and is formed under the blueprint of at least two long cistrons. Each Hb
tetramer is composed of two dimers, and each dimer consists of two of the
same kind of primary hemoglobin chain, alpha or beta or gamma or delta
plus two of the iron compounds known as heme groups. Most adults have
the standard molecule called hemoglobin A, which consists of a dimer of
two alpha chains made according to the code of the alpha gene plus a dimer
of two beta chains controlled by an unlinked beta locus. Note, however,
in Figure 15-2 that the beta locus is in turn closely linked with another

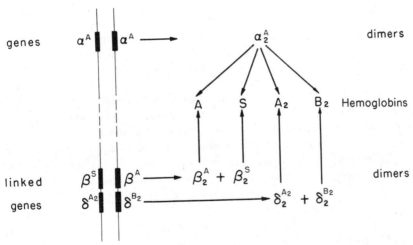

FIGURE 15-2   Four hemoglobins in a dihybrid adult. Each gene forms one
kind of product. Identical polypeptides combine as dimers. The alpha
dimers unite with beta dimers to form the various hemoglobins shown.
Compare with next figure. After C. Baglioni, in J. H. Taylor, ed., *Molecular
Genetics*, New York, Academic Press, 1963.

locus, the delta hemoglobin locus. The presence of one partially dominant
gene at a locus is sufficient for the formation of one kind of polypeptide

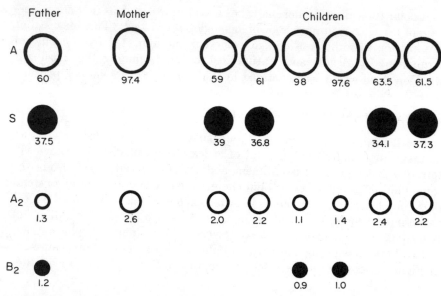

FIGURE 15-3 Hemoglobins separated by electromigration moving upward. Figures show percent of that kind in that person. The genotype of the father is that of Figure 15-2. From R. Ceppellini, in *Ciba Foundation Symposium on the Biochemistry of Human Genetics*, London, J. & A. Churchill, 1959.

chain, and when several such chains have been produced they can unite by twos. A dimer of alpha chains from a person with normal hemoglobin A (and from some other phenotypes also) is symbolized by $\alpha_2{}^A$. The other dimer from a normal adult is $\beta_2{}^A$. Other hemoglobins result from the union of other dimers. For instance, in normal persons there is about 2.5 percent of a hemoglobin variant named Hb A_2, produced by the union of the usual alpha dimer and the normal although rare delta dimer, $\delta_2{}^{A_2}$.

A third hemoglobin is characteristic of the fetal period of development and contains an alpha dimer and a gamma dimer, $\alpha_2{}^A\gamma_2{}^F$. The gamma dimer is made up of two chains which are the same length as the beta chain and which have many similarities to the amino acid sequence of beta, but nevertheless they are made by the blueprint of the gamma locus. Thus types of hemoglobins may be formed simply by the union of different kinds of polypeptide chains, alpha with gamma or with beta or with delta. These variants as well as other hemoglobins due to smaller changes to be described next have different electric charges and can be separated as an electropherogram by their characteristically different mobilities (Figure 15-3).

Amino Acid Substitutions. Analysis of other and rarer hemoglobins also showing gross differences for the whole molecule nevertheless may reveal identity in all amino acids of one chain and in all but one amino acid of the other polypeptide chain. Such differences may be detected after the hemoglobin is partially digested such as by trypsin, followed by separation of peptide residues in two directions at right angles to each other; one separation can be by migration in an electrical field and the other (or both) in a chemical solvent migration. Most peptides move repeatedly to the same relative positions under this treatment, hence this is called *fingerprinting* a protein. If proteins from different sources show a disagreement in the relative positions of two peptides, those two are subjected to further analysis for their amino acid content and sequence. By such analysis Vernon Ingram has found that the only chemical difference between Hb A of normal adults and the Hb S of *sickle cell trait* heterozygotes is the substitution of a single amino acid.

The physiological effects of some of these substitutions may be very profound, of others very slight. For instance, in the beta chain at position 6 substitution by the amino acid valine results in sickle cell trait in heterozygous persons and in *sickle cell anemia* in homozygotes. The whole red blood cell changes shape and becomes pointed or multiangular where there is reduced oxygen tension in the blood stream all because the many hemoglobin molecules have a change from glutamic acid to valine in position 6 (Table 15-2). Deformation is sufficient to cause red blood cells to rupture, and the homozygote to sicken and die of anemia. Additional studies have shown that another kind of genetic defect, hemoglobin C, comes from a different substitution at the same place in the hemoglobin and results in a milder but definite anemia known as *hemoglobin C disease*. It shows allelism with hemoglobin S in the C/S heterozygote by always segregating to different progeny of such a monohybrid. Whether other combinations of mutants in the same hemoglobin chain will complement or not or whether they will cross over or merely segregate (Chapter 11) is not readily known, because most of the mutant hemoglobins are too rare individually to be found together in one or more persons.

With so many mutants already known (between 14 and 30) it might be supposed that the number discovered would steadily increase until many or most of the 141 amino acid positions in the alpha chain and the 146 positions in the beta chain would be represented by one or more mutants. However, some of these substitutions might produce lethal phenotypic effects so that the mutant individual might die early and remain undiagnosed. At the other extreme some substitutions might have such slight effects under most normal conditions that they would only rarely be

TABLE 15-2   Some known amino acid substitutions in abnormal human hemoglobins[a]

Hemoglobin	ALPHA CHAIN								
	1	2	16	30	57	58	68	116	141
A	Val	Leu	...Lys$^+$	...Glu$^-$	...Gly	His$^+$	...Asp^{NH_2}	....Glu$^-$	....Arg$^+$
I			.Asp$^-$						
G (Honolulu)				.Glu^{NH_2}					
N (Norfolk)					.Asp$^-$				
M (Boston)						.Tyr			
G (Philadelphia)							.Lys$^+$		
O (Indonesia)								.Lys$^+$	

Hemoglobin	BETA CHAIN								
	1	2	3	6	7	26	63	67	121	146
A	Val	His$^+$	Leu	...Glu$^-$	Glu$^-$	...Glu$^-$	...His$^+$	...Val	....Glu$^-$	....His$^+$
S				.Val						
C				.Lys$^+$						
G (San Jose)					.Gly					
E						.Lys$^+$				
M (Saskatoon)							.Tyr			
M (Milwaukee)								.Glu$^-$		
D (Punjab-D$_\gamma$)									.Glu^{NH_2}	
O (Arabia)									.Lys$^+$	

[a]After Vernon M. Ingram, Amer. J. Med. **34:** 675 (1963).

discovered as isoalleles of normal hemoglobin A. An *isoallele* is one which usually produces a phenotype like the standard type and is detected only in a special diagnostic situation, either opposite an uncommon mutant allele or in an unusual environment. Although a great range of amino acid substitutions is imaginable and although their biochemical effects cannot be predicted in advance of their discovery, amino acid substitutions are not the only source of variant hemoglobins.

Options in Tetramer Formation. Four kinds of completed hemoglobin are possible in a double heterozygote for hemoglobin S and for the alpha chain substitution called Hopkins 2. The normal beta chains combine in the cytoplasm with either Hopkins 2 or the normal alpha to make hemoglobins A and Ho 2, respectively, while the abnormal beta combines with either of the two alphas to produce hemoglobin S and a new hemoglobin called hemoglobin X. The production of several dimers and the subsequent union of an alpha dimer and a beta dimer to produce a hemoglobin merely extend the scheme already presented in Figure 15-2. The random union of primary gene products will be a model for the description of isozymes later.

THE CONTROL OF GENIC ACTIVITY

The presence of two genetically determined and chemically defined hemoglobins in normal fetal and normal adult life poses a clearly defined problem of development. What turns off the activity of the genes specifying the amino acid sequence for the gamma chain of fetal hemoglobin? Conversely, what turns on the genes for the structure of the beta chain formed soon after birth? The answer is contained in ideas from the investigation of the genetics of repressor mutants in maize, in bacteria and in other organisms. In *Drosophila* certain genes are known chiefly or entirely as suppressors of the phenotypic effect of other genes.

Because all genes seem to be present in all somatic cells at all times from birth onward, it is simplest to think of the customary state of the average gene as being turned off or otherwise inactive except when replicating itself. From studies in bacteria the idea of the normal *repression* of genes and the occasional but timely *derepression* has emerged. According to the ingenious model of Jacob and Monod, genes are classified as structural genes, operator genes and regulator genes, with certain spatial and physiological relations between them in bacterial cells. (Study Figure 15-4 at this point.) The *structural gene* contains the code for a certain polypeptide, such as the alpha, beta or gamma chain of hemoglobin or the somewhat similar myoglobin. One or more closely linked structural genes, SG_1, SG_2, are also closely linked to an *operator gene*, O, which either permits or does not permit the adjacent structural genes to form or release their messenger

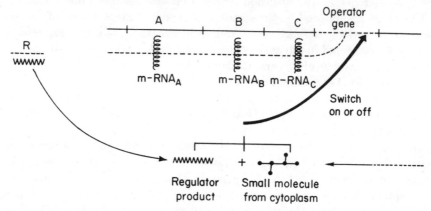

FIGURE 15-4 Schematic representation of the regulation complex. *R*, regulator gene. *A, B, C*, are linked structural genes determining the enzymes of the synthetic pathway, and m-RNA$_A$ is the messenger RNA synthesized by the gene *A*, etc. Production of m-RNA and its arrival in the cytoplasm is either permitted or inhibited by the operator gene, which is turned on or off by the reaction between the regulator product and the small molecule from the cytoplasm. From David M. Bonner and Stanley E. Mills, *Heredity* 2nd edition. © 1964, by permission of Prentice-Hall, Inc., Englewood Cliffs, N. J.

RNA. Whether the operator gene is turned on or off depends on reactions between it and substances in the nucleoplasm. Such substances might be enhancers of the operator, but in the Jacob-Monod model the operator gene is usually combined with a repressor formed by a certain kind of *regulator gene*, *R*, in any one of the chromosomes of the nucleus. If this regulator substance is interfered with by some chemical from the cytoplasm, it may fail to reach and bind the operator gene; hence the operator becomes derepressed, and the adjacent structural genes begin to function.

The mechanisms of living cells seem to be geared so that functioning occurs when there is a certain amount of substrate for the cell to use, or when there is a lower than normal amount of product from the particular structural gene or gene sequence. This implies that some cellular reactions are self-limiting by a feedback path from product to the repressor of the operator gene. The Jacob-Monod model fits situations in bacteria where as many as 11 structural genes are closely linked in the same strand of DNA. When these are turned on simultaneously by a single operator gene all 11 kinds of messenger RNA strands can be formed. The model for turning a structural gene on or off may be expanded to include the production of regulator substances from two structural genes each having its own linked operator gene thus, O_1R_1 and O_2R_2. If the product of one affects the operator of the other, either directly or through binding with intermediate regulators, a balanced system is formed, one which is flexible yet homeostatic.

In human genetics many mutants are known to alter the structure of a product (amino acid sequence) and many others alter the amount of a protein product. The former we may again call structural gene mutants and the latter we had best call *control gene* mutants because of the greater difficulty of investigating close subunits of the functional gene in humans than in bacteria. Parker and Bearn list more than 70 structural gene mutants of man including the 14 of Table 15-2, several thalassemia mutants, g-6-P-d deficiency of the red blood cells and many different plasma proteins such as gamma globulins, alpha and beta isoantibodies, several haptoglobins and many transferrins (Figure 15-5).

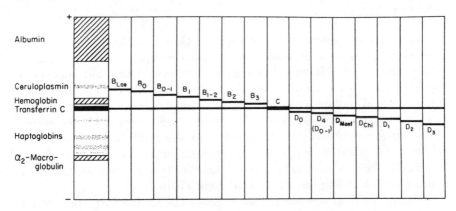

FIGURE 15-5 Inherited variants of human transferrins separated by electrophoresis of human plasma and including other plasma proteins as reference points for the extent of migration. From A. G. Bearn, in *Congenital Malformations*, New York, International Medical Congress, 1964.

SYSTEMIC BIOCHEMICAL BLOCKS

The earliest discoveries in human genetics were on a scale much larger than the above intracellular changes although cellular in origin. The slowly blackening urine of some few persons having *alkaptonuria* was shown by Garrod in 1902 to be a recessively inherited condition involving the failure of homogentisic acid to be normally metabolized within the body. Other

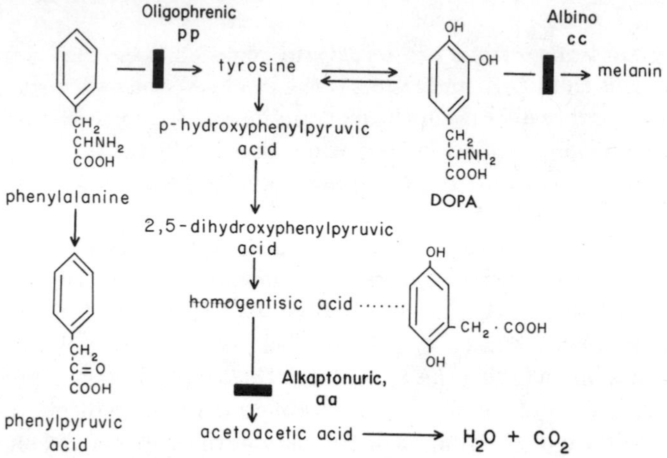

Oligophrenic
pp

Albino
cc

phenylalanine
CH₂
CHNH₂
COOH

→ tyrosine ⇌

→ melanin

DOPA
CH₂
CHNH₂
COOH
OH
OH

p-hydroxyphenylpyruvic
acid

2,5-dihydroxyphenylpyruvic
acid

homogentisic acid ⋯⋯
OH
CH₂·COOH
OH

phenylpyruvic
acid
CH₂
C=O
COOH

Alkaptonuric,
aa

acetoacetic acid ⟶ H₂O + CO₂

FIGURE 15-6 Blockage of related biochemical reactions at specific steps in genotypes recessive for one or another of three independently inherited genetic defects (see text).

inborn errors of metabolism described by Garrod include albinism, also due to a recessive, and the more recently discovered phenylketonuric idiocy. These three genetic defects are biochemically related by what appears on paper to be relatively few chemical steps (Figure 15-6). Phenylalanine, an amino acid having a phenol ring, is normally present in the diet and has several optional fates in the body. Some of it is converted in the normal body into phenylpyruvic acid, harmless to the body in small amounts. Much of it is changed by enzymes into tyrosine which in turn may proceed one way to forming acetoacetic acid or another way to be deposited as the black pigment melanin in the skin and elsewhere.

In albino individuals the recessive genes fail in the formation of one enzyme producing melanin, and so all parts of the body are without this black pigment even in small amounts. No direct chemical harm seems to come from this blockage, but the lack of pigment in the back of the iris causes discomfort in albino people, who therefore avoid long exposure to bright daylight. In the alkaptonuric individuals no enzyme is present and so acetoacetic acid is not made rapidly from homogentisic acid; this latter accumulates in some tissues of the body and reaches the urine in an eventually conspicuous amount.

In phenylketonuric children the pathway to tyrosine is effectively blocked for lack of an enzyme, a little melanin is formed by an alternate pathway and the usual minor reaction path to phenylpyruvic acid becomes very active. Excess amounts of phenylpyruvic acid escape into the urine but not before slowly contributing to permanent damage of the brain (*oligo-*

phrenia). Detection of phenylketonuria by a ferric chloride diaper test and the modification of the disease by an early change to special diet low in phenylalanine has been described on page 59.

Note that in these three biochemical blocks the conspicuous effect may be a missing substance (melanin) or a substance incompletely used (homogentisic acid) or a shunt pathway brought to greater activity (phenylpyruvic acid excess). These are general models for other genetically changed systems. More than 20 enzymatic defects of genetic origin in man were listed by Lenz in 1961 (1963 translation).

ISOZYMES FROM PRIMARY GENE PRODUCTS

Some enzymes are mixtures of molecules having different electric charges although the same molecular weight. Among hundreds of enzymes known to have various isozymes, *lactic dehydrogenase*, LDH, occupies an important physiological niche in cellular metabolism by supplying the quick energy of cells through the fermentation step of cellular respiration. Extensive studies on mice by Markert and coworkers have shown that five forms of the enzyme exist in the different tissues in different proportions depending on the tissue and the time of development. There is a preponderance of LDH-1, the fastest moving and relatively most acidic isozyme, in cells of the kidney. Heart muscle of the adult mouse has large amounts of this isozyme and also of LDH-2 and LDH-3 but only traces of the two slower migrants. By contrast the fetal heart muscle of the same mouse strains has mainly LDH-5 and LDH-4 functioning as enzymes before birth, and afterward this cardiac tissue progressively changes over to production of the adult pattern. (See Figure 15-7.) Meanwhile the skeletal muscle continues to make mostly LDH-5 throughout fetal and postnatal life. Other patterns are shown by lactic dehydrogenase extracted from other tissue. We may assume that these adjustments are advantageous. Even pathological human heart tissue and plasma show a permanent change of the isozyme mixture.

The variety of isozymes comes from the formation of tetramers from just two polypeptide chains of equal weight. In the normal mouse the A chain of lactic dehydrogenase seems to be made first, and the union of four such polypeptides makes the slow moving LDH-5 isozyme. When a little of the B chain is manufactured in cells a 1 : 3 union of it with A chains in tetramers makes the slightly faster moving LDH-4 isozyme. Smaller amounts of still faster LDH-3 also appear as if by random union of the primary polypeptide chains. In test-tube mixtures of equal quantities of the A and B chains, all five isozymes are formed in quantities indicating

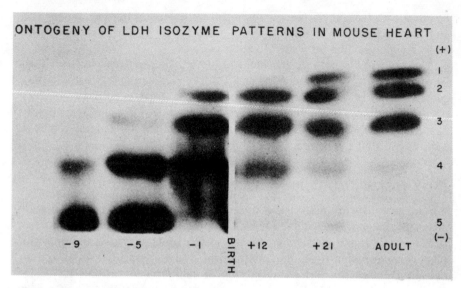

ONTOGENY OF LDH ISOZYME PATTERNS IN MOUSE HEART

FIGURE 15-7 Forms of the intracellular enzyme lactic dehydrogenase in one kind of tissue during prenatal and postnatal development (see text). From C. L. Markert, Develop. Biol., 5: 373 (1962).

random union into tetramers; for instance, LDH-3 molecules are the most numerous, and the extremes give the least and equally weak densities in the electrophoretic separation. A similar pattern is found from the normal lung tissues of the adult mouse. It is plausible to suppose that the genes producing A and B chains are turned on at different times, that they may produce amounts of the two chains in various ratios, and that feedback from the cellular environment maintains a continuous regulation of the enzyme production. Tissues with the more abundant supply of oxygen seem to have more of the LDH-1, whereas tissues subject to some temporary lack of oxygen have more of the LDH-5 isozyme.

Comparison of different species of vertebrates and the chance finding of mutants in cattle and in man allow the above ideas of random union and physiological effect to be further tested. The incubated chick egg having plenty of oxygen forms the B chain first and produces the tetramer LDH-1 first, unlike the enclosed mammal fetus. The chance finding of one human carrying a mutant allele for the B chain structure was the starting point for a demonstration by Boyer and Fainer that the 15 isozymes could be formed by combination in vitro, including five subkinds in the former LDH-1 region.

SUMMARY

The main steps in the pathway from gene to protein are now known. The nucleotide sequence of the DNA in the chromosomes gives specificity to the sequence of cytosine, guanine, thymine and uracil of the messenger RNA which then moves to the cytoplasm and initiates the production of one or more chains of polypeptides. Soluble RNA transfers amino acids to the ribosomes and positions them to form polypeptide chains in the order specified on the messenger. The code for the 20 amino acids is a code of nucleotide triplets which is nonoverlapping and which is degenerate rather than one-for-one. Messenger RNA is not released from all genes of the chromosome at one time. Normally, the activity of a gene for a structural polypeptide sequence is turned off because an adjacent operator gene is repressed by some soluble suppressor substance. Only when the suppressor molecule is absent or chemically bound elsewhere will the operator gene become derepressed and the structural genes of the cistron become active.

Polypeptide chains have their primary sequence determined by the structural genes, and the time of appearance and the amount of the chain depend on the effect of external and internal reactions upon the regulator genes. Primary polypeptides fold on themselves in certain ways as secondary proteins and combine with other primary or secondary proteins as functional molecules, such as a molecule of lactic dehydrogenase or of hemoglobin (both tetramers) or of myoglobin. Thus the product of gene action is an enzyme or a polypeptide. By a variety of unions there may be a variety of isozymes of lactic dehydrogenase, or varieties of hemoglobin such as Hb F, Hb A, Hb A_2 and rarer forms. Other rare hemoglobins such as Hb S and Hb C of certain anemias result from mutations in the cistron of the structural gene. Many human mutations fall into the latter kind, structural mutants within a cistron. Many others are mutations of regulator genes in various locations in the nucleus.

Enzymes which are in short supply or which are missing cause biochemical blocks in metabolic pathways. Intermediary products normally used by the enzymes which are deficient are dammed up in excess or spill over into abnormal pathways, and products beyond the location of the biochemical defect may be in short supply or absent as if dried up. Albinos, PKU children and alkaptonurics show blockage at different places in an interconnected reaction system.

The changing patterns of enzymatic activity as cells mature and as cells specialize may be the cause of embryonic differentiation; they at least assist in that differentiation.

SUGGESTED READING

Brit. Med. Bull. **17**: 213-240 (1961). Five separate review articles by H. Harris, A. Holzel, H. Lehmann et al., D. A. P. Evans, and C. A. Clarke on aspects of human biochemical genetics are helpful at this point. Other articles in this same September issue review general aspects of quantitative genetics and cytogenetics.

Jukes, T. H., The genetic code. Amer. Sci. **51**: 227–245 (1963). Replete with many tables and references to this fascinating new subject.

Markert, C. L., and F. Moller, Multiple forms of enzymes. Proc. Nat. Acad. Sci. **45**: 753–763 (1959). Describes patterns of isozymes in different species, tissues and stages of development and of pathology.

Parker, W. C., and A. G. Bearn, Amer. J. Hum. Genet. **15**: 159–181 (1963). A theory of control gene mutants in regard to haptoglobin production is evaluated both from the viewpoint of pedigree analysis and from population data.

Parker, W. C., and A. G. Bearn, Application of genetic regulatory mechanisms to human genetics. Amer. J. Med. **34**: 680–691 (1963). Both structural mutants and control mutants are categorized and discussed. This May issue of the journal has also been the source of other illustrations and references for this chapter.

Rich, A., Polyribosomes. Sci. Amer. **209**: No. 6 44–53 (1963). An account of chemical and electron microscope studies on the relation of ribosomes to messenger RNA and protein synthesis.

PROBLEMS

15–1 Diagram the composition of hemoglobin tetramers A, A_2, S.

15–2 (a) What would be the genetic constitution of the parents of a child showing sickle cell anemia?

(b) What proportion of his normal sibs would be able to hand on the gene for sickle cell hemoglobin?

15–3 (a) What offspring would you expect from two persons having the combination type of C/S hemoglobin?

(b) If C and S were not allelic, what kinds of offspring would be expected and in what proportions?

15–4 What kinds of hemoglobin can form from two kinds of alpha chains and two kinds of beta chains?

15–5 What kinds of isozymes may form at random from the union of two kinds of lactic dehydrogenase monomers?

15–6   If the linkage shown for the beta and delta cistrons in Figure 15-2 is defined as coupling linkage, was the father of the sibs shown in Figure 15-3 also in coupling phase or in repulsion phase?

15–7   Define briefly:

isoalleles	t-RNA	cistron
isozymes	regulator gene	degenerate code
primary protein	operator gene	triplet of RNA
fingerprinting	structural gene	ribosome
m-RNA	derepression	biochemical block

chapter 16

Sex Influences upon Phenotypic Differences

Genes are not always sure-fire in their most obvious effects; some, in fact, are called "leaky" genes. To the teacher and to the geneticist this is perhaps an unsatisfactory state of affairs, but some very important aspects of the human phenotype are influenced by genes which in our present state of knowledge we must call "irregular genes." By that term we mean that the phenotypic expression of some gene pairs is irregular, although the transmission of alleles from generation to generation and even from cell to cell remains regularly tied to the inheritance of the chromosomal material.

In this brief chapter some definite reasons for the irregular expression of certain genic differences will be described before some less well understood genes of widespread occurrence are described in the following chapter. Before going further into the question of the various phenotypic modifications caused by the sex of the developing zygote, let us review and emphasize by way of contrast the definition of sex-linkage, as discussed in Chapter 12. Sex-linkage concerns differences at gene loci on the X-Y pair, mostly on the X-chromosome and only rarely on the Y-chromosome. As a result of the Y-chromosome going only to males, a character (perhaps hairy ears) may appear only in males. Or as a result of typical males having only one X-chromosome, a recessive character may appear more often in males than in females. However, the excess is a particular ratio; the ratio of recessive hemizygous males to recessive homozygous females is the ratio of q to q^2 wherever the single gene difference is transmitted in the X-chromosome. The finding of any other relationship in any panmictic population would contradict the assumption of there being X-linked inheritance at work. In this chapter we shall see two kinds of inheritance which are usually autosomal in transmission, wherein there is also a different expected ratio of affected males to affected females, or in which one sex does not reveal the genotypic difference at all.

SEX-INFLUENCED DOMINANCE

Baldness of a certain type is much more prevalent among men than it is among women or eunuchs. This much was known as a generalization from observation even in ancient times, and now we may add the additional observation that ovariectomized women sometimes become bald after that surgery, particularly if any of the patient's near relatives (brothers, father, or uncles on her mother's side) has had baldness. Already it should be apparent to the reader that this kind of baldness, starting from the crown of the head and spreading outward and forward during the decade from about ages 30 to 40 years and defined as *pattern baldness*, shows an interplay of genetics and of endocrinology. It is perhaps fortunate for explanatory purposes that we have an illustration in which both heredity and environment are clearly at work and are interacting with each other.

The contrast between pattern baldness and a normal covering of hair may currently be explained by assuming a single pair of autosomal genes with two separate definitions of dominance, one for each sex. At the locus for bald in some autosome the pair B^1B^1 results in baldness beginning at the crown of the head in both sexes, and homozygous B^2B^2 adult men and women are normally haired. The new principle in sex-influenced dominance is that heterozygous B^1B^2 adult men are bald while reproductively normal women have the usual hair (Table 16-1 bottom, left). Thus allele B^1 is dominant over B^2 in the presence of the male hormones, and B^2 is dominant over B^1 in the presence of the normal female hormones. Ample evidence from the experimental breeding of cattle, sheep, jungle fowl, and other organisms establishes sex-influenced dominance as one type of complication to be reckoned with in the study of living things.

TABLE 16-1 Sex-influenced dominance and the possibility of segregation from any of the four phenotypic kinds of marriages

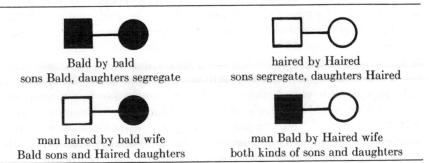

Bald by bald	haired by Haired
sons Bald, daughters segregate	sons segregate, daughters Haired
man haired by bald wife	man Bald by Haired wife
Bald sons and Haired daughters	both kinds of sons and daughters

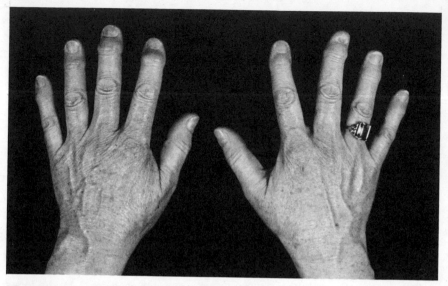

FIGURE 16-1 Heberden's nodes. Swellings due to bony growth at the distal interphalangeal joints of the fingers. Rare in men, more frequent in older women. Courtesy of R. M. Stecher, M. D.

The above theory has been tested in population data only once in recent years, by Snyder and Yingling. They tested whether the gene frequency of the bald allele and the gene frequency of the haired allele, as determined from observation of known homozygotes, would add up to one, the frequency of all alleles at the *B* locus. In their collection of data they found, as expected, that the square root of the frequency of bald women plus the square root of the frequency of the normally haired men did equal approximately one. Each of these two groups was the homozygous recessive class within the specified sex. If similar studies could be made of the total of supposed allele frequencies as computed from populations where the frequency of bald persons is greater than that found in the central United States and from other populations where baldness is rarer, each such study would serve as an independent test of the hypothesis. A one-factor pair determination with dominance reversed according to sex of the heterozygote is consistent with several published studies.

As an opposite example the distal finger joints may show a nonpainful swelling known as Heberden's nodes, named after an eminent eighteenth century physician, which appears more often in older women than in older men (Figure 16-1). It seems to be independent of several other forms of arthritis. Stecher and Hersh have proposed that this phenotype is determined by a single pair of genes with autosomal transmission but with dominance influenced according to sex. Thus heterozygous males retain the normal size of knuckles at ages when their heterozygous female relatives show the distinct bony swellings in several fingers. Heberden's nodes appear in women within a few years of the menopause, but some cases are diagnosable long before that time and others have not yet appeared by age 60. Although suitable corrections for the age must be made, the ideal expectations for the offspring of two heterozygous parents (normal male by female who eventually develops Heberden's nodes) are given separately for the two sexes. Because of the dominance of Heberden's nodes only in the female the daughters would tend to segregate 3 : 1 phenotypically while the sons would segregate 1 : 3 as adults. Study Figure 16-2 using the solid line boundary. This pattern of inheritance is often confused

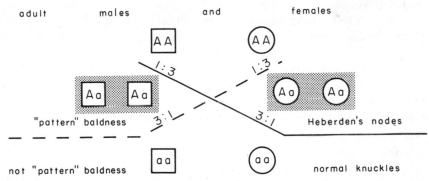

FIGURE 16-2 Sex-influenced dominance in a F_2-type sibship. Genes are in autosomes. Ratio of genotypes is 1 : 2 : 1 in each sex of sibs; heterozygotes shown shaded. Expression at a suitably advanced age is 3 : 1 among males (square symbols) and 1 : 3 among females (circles) if allele A is dominant only in males (left dashed boundary); the opposite ratios for those phenotypes where A is dominant only in females (right, solid boundary line).

by the uninitiated with that described in Chapter 12. Note that for any sex-influenced phenotype neither kind of inbred parent pair will always breed true: normal by normal may have some abnormal of one sex, and abnormal by abnormal may have normal among some of the opposite sex. (See Table 16-1 again.)

A disease of the nervous system called Kuru by the natives of the central mountains in New Guinea is a progressive debilitation which causes the death of some one percent of the population, more of them women, the remainder young girls and boys. Motor control of the legs is first lost, in the course of several months the victims cannot move around then cannot sit up, and in about nine months from the first tremor symptoms they are dead. No correlation with diet or geographical influences seems to be adequate to explain the incidence of the disease, and no signs of infective agents have been found during the first five years of study of the tribe in which there is the highest incidence of Kuru. Cases are rather closely related to each other suggesting Dominant gene determination among the female victims. The ages at death among females make a bimodal curve with a peak at about eight years and another around 33 years of age. The children thus appear to be homozygotes for the Kuru gene, and the mature women seem to be heterozygotes. Homozygous males also develop Kuru and die of it, but their modal age at death is 14 years. Thus this gene which is rare elsewhere around the world seems to be Dominant in females but recessive in males and acts slightly later among the male children who are homozygotes.

An emigration restriction has been placed on all persons from the region where Kuru is found, namely among the Fore group of natives. It had been the custom for many of the men to leave the mountain homes during several months of the year when there was poor subsistence and to work as far away as the coast before returning. The danger of spreading a distinctly undesirable gene was considered sufficiently great by the Australian government to inaugurate the first eugenic population law said to be based on a single gene.

SEX-LIMITED EXPRESSION

Not all phenotypic differences in the human species can be studied in both sexes, although the genes underlying them can be transmitted by both parents. Differences in the incidence of breast cancer among the relatives at different genetic steps away from index cases have been studied, naturally among only the female relatives. An investigation of the incidence of prostatitis would have to concentrate on the diagnosis among men, although the relation of each to an index case of this common abnormality of the prostate gland could be traced through female as well as male relatives. Corresponding characters which are important economically and appear in only one sex have been studied in animals, and a clear demonstration of sex-limited expression of the genotype has emerged. Thus differences in any aspect of egg laying would be examples of sex-limited expression of the genotypes of chickens, and differences in beef production between breeds or among hybrids obtained from various crossbreeds would be measured as if sex-limited to the more muscular male sex.

The model from sex-limited expression, as obtained from studies of mammals, birds and butterflies, in its simplest form would be the following monohybrid situation. Note that the same two or three genotypes are found in both sexes, but the genotype makes a difference in only one of the sexes.

aa	aA	AA	phenotypes alike in one sex
aa	aA	AA	in other sex, segregation

Thus both sexes can transmit the different alleles, but only one sex can show segregation into two or more phenotypic classes. It was at one time supposed erroneously that hemophilia was sex-limited to males for any expression as well as sex-linked in inheritance; but at that time females with classical hemophilia were merely too rare to be encountered with any regularity. They were statistically unlikely and not biologically impossible

QUANTITATIVE FACTORS AND THRESHOLDS

Some genetic conditions which do not seem to be under the control of a single gene occur more in one sex than in the other. *Pyloric stenosis* among infants is such an example. This severe constriction (stenosis) at the valve between stomach and intestine caused nutritional disorders and death in many infants until after 1917 when the use of Ramstedt's operation saved many of them for mature life. A variety of influences in addition to sex affect the incidence of pyloric stenosis and the time of onset of symptoms. By way of background we may point out from a study in England that it is three times more frequent among firstborn than among fourth born and later children. Also onset of symptoms is later in children who have been on 4-hour feedings than among those on 3-hour feedings. In addition, the hospital-born children also have later onset of pyloric stenosis than do the home-born. The big difference, however, is the sex incidence. Per 1000 live births the expectation is 5 males to 1 female to develop pyloric stenosis during the second or third month of life.

The fraction of near relatives who have the same condition depends not only on the sex of the relative but also on the sex of the index case. More sibs and children of female index cases are similarly affected than are the corresponding relatives one step removed from male pyloric stenosis index cases. Carter reports that the male and female close relatives of 147 male patients have 5 percent and 2 percent of secondary cases among them, or 10 times and 20 times the population frequencies for males and females, respectively. Starting from 48 female index cases the corresponding risks for sibs and children are 17 ± 4 percent and 7 ± 3 percent, or 35 times and 70 times the frequency among males and females, respectively, in the general population. This contrast suggests that the few female babies which develop pyloric stenosis are much more stringently selected than are males; therefore a greater proportion of their relatives (especially their male relatives) would have genotypes within a susceptible range beyond a *threshold* (Figure 16-3). This concept is used also on other phenotypes. Depending on where the threshold is, a larger or a smaller fraction of the

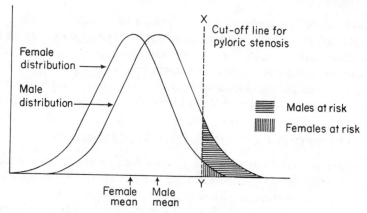

FIGURE 16-3 Hypothetical   distribution   of   multifactorial genotypes contributing to pyloric stenosis in males and females. From C. O. Carter, Brit. Med. Bull., **17**: 253 (1961).

general population would be expected to show some disease or some rare condition while all persons with genotypes placing them below the threshold would remain normal. In respect to pyloric stenosis the threshold seems to be located farther to the right on the population curve of females than it is on the curve for males, far enough so that the area under the curve and beyond the threshold among females is only one-fifth that of the corresponding part of the curve for males. Brothers and sisters would be expected to be genotypically in the same general part of the normal distribution curve plotted for the total contribution of many gene pairs toward susceptibility, toward predisposition or even toward some continuously measurable variable like height (Chapter 10). However, that genetic similarity on the curve may fall on different sides of the thresholds and result in phenotypic differences recognizable as sex-influenced.

The frequency of many other phenotypes is not the same in the two sexes and may eventually be explained in some similar fashion. Congenital dislocation of the hip is about five times more frequent in girls than in boys, although the hip socket defect which leads up to it is not as disproportionate. An open ductus arteriosus is found three times more often in girls than in boys, and this is one cause of a blue baby at birth. Rheumatic fever among girls is about double what it is in numbers of cases among boys. Cleft palate alone occurs more in girls in a similar ratio; but the genetically different harelip which sometimes is accompanied by cleft palate has a slight excess (10 percent) among males. Club foot cases among males are twice as frequent as among females. Spondylitis (Marie Strumpell arthritis of the spine) is nine times more common among males than among females, yet some males transmit it from father to son as if autosomal genes were in the main responsible for the disease. Hersh pointed out that female index cases led to a higher incidence of additional cases of spondylitis than male index cases, and he described affected females as a stabilizing influence. The situation is rather similar to the analysis of the pyloric stenosis distribution between the sexes, and it might turn out to be multifactorial with thresholds at different levels of cumulative genes before phenotypic expression, higher for the rarer female spondylitics and lower for the more numerous male cases.

SUMMARY

Sex can affect the phenotypic expression of genetic ratios in at least four ways. Inheritance itself has special rules only for the transmission of sex-linked genes and for distribution in a modified Hardy-Weinberg equilibrium as described in an earlier chapter, while the other kinds of examples in this chapter involve predominantly the autosomally carried genes. Dominance may be different for the heterozygotes of the two sexes in the phenomenon called sex-influenced dominance, while the two kinds of homozygotes are easily recognizable in both of the sexes. By contrast in sex-limited expression one sex may be phenotypically uniform but yet transmit genes which do result in phenotypic differences in their children of the other sex. Finally and at the multihybrid level the cumulatively acting genes may be required to reach different levels before some physiological threshold in the male or some different physiological threshold in the female is exceeded with phenotypic segregation being simply two classes, variously reached.

SUGGESTED READING

Anderson, R. C., Causative factors underlying congenital heart malformations. Pediatrics 14: 143–152 (1954).

Anderson, V. E., H. O. Goodman and S. C. Reed, *Variables Related to Human Breast Cancer*, Minneapolis, University of Minnesota Press, 1958, 172 pp.

Kellgren, J. H., Heberden oration. Ann. Rheum. Dis. **23**: 109–122 (1964). A readable review of genic and environmental influences on spondylitic males and females, on Heberden's nodes in the two sexes, on gout and on other rheumatoid diseases.

McArthur, Norma, The age incidence of kuru. Ann Hum. Genet. **27**: 341–352 (1964). Reconsiders the hypothesis of single gene determination on the basis of population incidence separately in males and females.

Slatis, H., and A. Apelbaum, Hairy pinna of the ear in Israeli populations. Amer. J. Hum. Genet. **15**: 74–85 (1963). Study of a phenotype formerly attributed to a single gene on the Y-chromosome.

Snyder, L. H., and P. R. David, *The Principles of Heredity* 5th ed., Boston, Heath, 1957, 507 pp. Chapter 9 explains the classic examples of sex influences with many photographic illustrations.

Stern, C., *Principles of Human Genetics* 2nd ed., San Francisco, Freeman, 1960, 753 pp. His Chapter 16, on variations in the expression of genes, is highly recommended.

PROBLEMS

16–1 If the frequency of a single allele causing Kuru in adult women and in homozygous children of both sexes were .005, what proportion of diseased persons would you expect to find
   (a) Among males?
   (b) Among young females?
   (c) Among mature women?

16–2 If a man developes Heberden's nodes but his wife does not have any by age 65, what would you predict for his sons and for his daughters when they reach the same age?

16–3 What would be the genotypes of parents whose sons were normal but one of whose daughters developed Heberden's nodes?

16–4 Define and distinguish from each other:
   sex-linked inheritance
   sex-limited inheritance
   sex-influenced inheritance
   simple linkage

16–6 (a) If pyloric stenosis occurs more often in male than in female infants, affected babies of which sex have genotypes with more of the extreme alleles?
   (b) What are the consequences of these inferred genotypes on the expected occurrence of pyloric stenosis among persons closely related to affected individuals?

chapter 17

Reduced Penetrance and
Varied Expressivity

The sex influences upon dominance and upon expression as described in the preceding chapter are special examples of a more general situation. There are other seeming exceptions to the basic rules of inheritance as expounded in Part One and in Chapter 12 in which specific reasons for the apparent exceptions are less easy to define. Wherever adequate information about either the primary effect of a gene substitution or the pleiotropic effects of this primary action is unavailable, the scientist may find a poor correlation between the final phenotype and the possession of certain genes. He may even need to describe that phenotype as being under the partial control of a "leaky" gene.

In choosing examples demonstrating the basic laws of genetics, first preference has been given to those genotypes each of which has a regular relation to one phenotype, and the less complete associations have been postponed to this chapter. However, some borderline examples have been used merely as examples of monohybrid segregation. For exacting genetic studies like estimating the degree of linkage in dihybrid sibships, Penrose has pointed out that it is hardly feasible to use the loci of eye color, handedness, ear lobe, tongue curling ability or the presence of middigital hair on the backs of the fingers, most of which have been mentioned earlier but not emphasized. Other phenotypes which run in families are even less easy to explain as dominant, recessive, monohybrid or dihybrid, yet they have some basis in inheritance.

EXPRESSIVITY AMONG POLYDACTYLOUS PERSONS

Variation within an abnormal phenotypic class will help to make plausible the failure of some other phenotype to reveal the true genotypes

245

of all individuals. Phenotypic expression may be slight or intermediate or severe, and this *expressivity* may be described in either qualitative or quantitative terms. In kindreds of Polydactyly an extra digit may be large or grade down to very small, and the expressivity may further vary as to whether hands and feet both have extra digits and whether right and left appendages both have the sixth finger or sixth toe. In the few instances where a child of a Polydactylous parent has only 20 digits (and did not have any removed surgically while an infant) but yet transmits his parent's dominant gene to an offspring, we have an example of zero expression of the phenotype. If a wide range of expressivity does not overlap the normal phenotype, it is said that the phenotype shows full penetrance as defined below.

PENETRANCE IN INBRED ANIMALS

Penetrance is complete when all of the homozygous recessives show one phenotype, when all of the homozygous dominants show another phenotype and when all of the heterozygous individuals are like each other. If less than 100 percent of the individuals of a certain genotype show that phenotype by which the class is recognized, there is *reduced penetrance*. Among experimental animals many examples of reduced penetrance have been described from very low values up to almost full penetrance.

Several leukemic strains of mice have been established by inbreeding from various affected individuals, but the strains show different degrees of penetrance. One inbred strain shows leukemia in 90 percent of the individuals by a certain age. Another strain reveals leukemia among only 5 percent of the individuals which have reached a certain age. Selection of leukemic or nonleukemic individuals within the strain for further breeding does not change these penetrance figures, which would have responded to selection if much heterozygosity had remained in the inbred strains. Crosses between the two strains produce an F_1 generation of obviously uniform genotype but with only about 40 to 45 percent penetrance of the leukemic phenotype. Where other simple hypotheses may be ruled out and no characteristic expression can be found in some individuals the idea of reduced penetrance may be invoked.

REDUCED PENETRANCE IN MAN

A rare human syndrome of *blue sclerotics, brittle bones* and eventual deafness shows reduced penetrance as a complete syndrome and also reduced penetrance for its several aspects. A single gene dominant to the normal allele is at work. The bluish eyeballs are found among a high proportion of the heterozygotes, both those diagnosed by some other aspect of the syndrome and those diagnosed by their affected progeny. Penetrance of brittle bones among the heterozygous class is not as high, and the skeletal weakness has produced many bizarre accidents as well as being a severe handicap for individuals and families. As a consequence of the bone defect an otosclerotic kind of deafness may develop, and this aspect of the phenotype has a lower penetrance within the genotype which might show it than have the other signs of the syndrome. It is in only a minority of the genotype that the complete syndrome shows its effects. Although a single gene seems to be primarily responsible in different kindreds and even in different races, the existence of different degrees of penetrance for the phenotypic components in different kindreds suggests that the genetic background of modifying genes may be important.

Among the several kinds of rickets are one or more skeletal changes which are not prevented by the early feeding of vitamin D in cold and cloudy climates. *Vitamin-D-resistant rickets* behaves like a dominant phenotype due to an X-linked gene, except that it fails to show in some females. Therefore as regards the skeletal changes penetrance is incomplete. A search for other accompaniments which might lead up to rickets revealed, however, that for all ages within affected kindreds there was a regular class of individuals who could be designated as having an abnormally low phosphorus content of the blood stream. This condition of *Hypophosphatemia* shows full penetrance among the class of genotypically abnormal individuals. Regular dominant sex-linked transmission is clearly demonstrated in the numerous pedigrees when inorganic blood phosphate is measured. It will not be surprising if other incompletely penetrant phenotypes of conspicuous nature are redefined in the near future by biochemical abnormalities which are fully penetrant.

Description of the degree of penetrance is much easier in experimental animals, which may be selectively inbred, than is a determination of the penetrance percentage among people. Yet if the phenotype is common enough to involve many pairs of monozygotic twins, measurement of the percentage of discordant MZ pairs is satisfactory. If only genetically different twins and singly born persons are available for study, estimation must rest on alternative assumptions. One may figure with perhaps equal justification a low penetrance percentage for an assumed dominant allele or a higher penetrance of an assumed recessive phenotype within the same collection of data. Thus penetrance figures as applied to singly born humans are more descriptive of a general situation than they are diagnostic of a mode of inheritance.

The application of the idea of reduced penetrance of a dominant character and separately of a recessive has been set forth for both assumptions by Hersh and his colleagues in a study of *ankylosing spondylitis*. They made a careful study of this rheumatoid disease which stiffens the joints between vertebrae, especially those of the lower back or lumbar region. Cases of spondylitis were found in significantly higher frequency among the first-degree relatives of spondylitics than among the closest relatives of several kinds of controls, namely, persons having gout, Heberden's nodes on the last finger joints or rheumatoid arthritis. Such findings indicate some influence of heredity, simple or complex, and perhaps of the familial environment. The genetic, or familial, influence was nevertheless weak, in that only seven additional cases were found among 247 adult relatives of 50 spondylitis index cases.

This incidence of almost 3 percent among relatives one genetic step removed from the index cases is far above the incidence of this arthritis of the spine in the general population, yet it is also farther below the expectations based on either of the two simplest genetic assumptions, single dominant determination or homozygous recessive determination. If the substitution of a single dominant allele were enough to cause spondylitis, then about 50 percent of sibs, parents and adult offspring would be expected to be spondylitic, but this basic figure must be corrected for the total individuals in each sibship. The 50 index spondylitis cases were not evenly divided between the sexes. There were 46 men and only 4 women, a rather representative distribution for this particular disability which occurs in men some ten times more often than in women. Therefore the mathematical analysis was done four times, starting from affected men and again from affected women and then proceeding on the dominant and recessive hypotheses separately.

The calculations on the dominant hypothesis are presented in Table 17-1 both as a general method of analysis and as they pertain to spondylitis. The corrective factors in the fifth column are standard for the ascertainment of all 1 : 1 segregations. Different numerical corrections would be used for the missed all-normal families under a 3 : 1 segregation (from the center column of Table 7-7). Careful study of these two tables and a review of Figure 3-4 at this juncture will be most appropriate. Because the observed cases were below the properly calculated expectations, we may at least describe the situation by saying that the phenotype has a reduced penetrance among individuals of the monohybrid genotype. Thus from Table 17-1 we may say that there is 68 percent penetrance of a detectable degree of expression of spondylitis among the genotypically *Sp/sp* heterozygous males of suitable age (20 years or older in this study). Similar calculations on a much smaller number of sibships with the index case a spondylitic woman gave a penetrance description of 90 to 100 percent, a result which the investigators called surprising in view of the low overall occurrence of this particular disease in women. Still other calculations by the same authors on the assumption of recessive determination of spondylitis showed discrepancies between observed and expected cases after correction for sibship sizes. In using these discrepancies as measures of penetrance, Hersh, Stecher and colleagues derived a slightly higher penetrance figure for males under recessive determination, namely 72 percent.

TABLE 17-1 Comparison of affected among sibships with theoretical expectation on basis of a simple autosomal dominant (1 : 1). Corrected for total males in sibship assuming complete penetrance[a]

SIBSHIPS ASCERTAINED			Observed spondylitics	Corrective factor	Expected affected
Size	Number	Persons			
1	14	14	14		14.000
2	11	22	11	1.333	14.663
3	12	36	14	1.715	20.580
4	3	12	3	2.134	6.402
5	5	25	6	2.581	12.905
6	1	6	1	3.047	3.047
Totals	46	115	49		71.597

Discrepancy, 49/71.6, ascribable to penetrance being 68 percent among males of spondylitic genotype over age 20 years.

[a]From A. H. Hersh et al., Amer. J. Hum. Genet., **2**: 391–408 (1950).

Without giving further comparisons we may summarize by saying that sibship data may be "explained" or better described by figuring a lower percentage of penetrance with dominant determination or a higher penetrance among homozygous recessive individuals. Such ambiguity of sibship calculations calls for other independent evidence as to the mode of inheritance. Recessive inheritance of the rarer conditions implies cousin marriages among the parents of homozygotes; and cousin marriages were absent among the parents of these 50 spondylitics. Under either dominant or recessive or complex genetic determination the members of identical twin pairs should show the same incidence of the condition, but they often do not. This observation among human twins and conclusions from many investigations in experimental animals point to the validity of the concept of reduced penetrance, but the calculation of the degree of penetrance may be fraught with difficulties in choosing the genetic hypothesis to be tested, except where twin data are extensively available.

THEORY OF ANTICIPATION

Diseases which have a variable age of onset lead to a curious compilation of data which have given rise to the idea of anticipation. It is frequently concluded that the age of onset among children is earlier than the average age of onset of the same condition among their parents. The idea has been proposed for several kinds of mental illness, diabetes, glaucoma, Huntington's chorea and for three kinds of muscle dystrophy which act late enough to allow many of these phenotypes to have children. The common feature of all of them is a widely variable range of ages of onset. The effect of this variability will be illustrated particularly in regard to just one of these.

The nervous disorder *Huntington's chorea* has such a wide range of onset that penetrance is zero in the first two or three years of life and by age 70 penetrance is still a little below 100 percent. The disease itself runs a long course lasting several years before the patient dies. The first symptoms are persistent muscle twitchings of the legs and later in other muscles. Eventually the person cannot control himself, cannot feed himself, and his mind deteriorates as he becomes a complete invalid. The modal age of onset is in the thirties and the forties, but some children become invalid with it in their teens and other people not until their sixties. It is therefore no surprise that many persons who run the risk of having the single abnormal gene may begin raising a family before it becomes evident that half of these persons actually did inherit Huntington's chorea. A certain kindred in Minnesota is already conspicuous because there are more than 19 persons with Huntington's chorea already manifest. Yet this is rather like the visible part of the iceberg, for there are over 716 descendants of the one immigrant who brought the dominant gene into that territory. Although some of these descendants are in lines of descent which segregated free of the chorea gene, the estimate has been made by S. C. Reed and J. D. Palm that some 101 of these persons now living will eventually succumb from the dread nervous disease. Even the ones which are not possible transmitters cannot be determined unless studies of brain wave patterns with the electroencephalograph continue to be indicative, as they are presently reported to be. Because only one to three new cases per year can be compared with previous brain wave information, decades will be required to check on the accuracy of predictions about the absence of a gene with such reduced penetrance and delayed expression.

When the data for parents and for their children are compiled in order to obtain the mean ages of onset two biases are at once introduced. The group labeled "parents" is selective against those individuals of the total affected group who had early onset and particularly against those with early death. Therefore the mean age of onset of those persons who were successful in becoming parents would be greater than that of the unselected population. This is indicated by the dashed line to the right of the true mean in Figure 17-1. Another bias results from the ascertainment of some of the secondary cases after having found the index case. Where the parent is

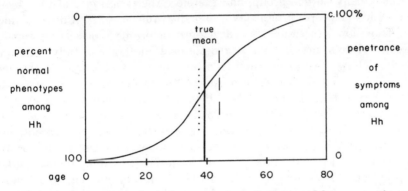

FIGURE 17-1 Hypothetical curve to show the source of data suggesting "anticipation" in regard to a phenotype with widely spread ages of onset. Assuming the true mean age of onset of all cases of Huntington's chorea to be 39 years, the mean among all "parents" within this group, dashed line, would be higher. The mean of the "children" category, dotted line, would be lower (see text).

known to be affected, observation of the children is a little more intense and diagnosis of onset in that generation is made a little earlier than in the total of all cases, some of whom come from parents who appeared normal until death. Where the child is the index case, he sometimes leads to a new diagnosis of a parent as affected, which contributes one item of late onset to the parental group and to the population as a whole. Thus the mean age of onset for "children" is lower because of quicker diagnosis and because of their opportunity to point to additional cases of late onset among their own parents. (See dotted line of Figure 17-1.)

Since these biases are inevitable, it should be no surprise that many examples have been published of diseases which seem to show anticipation among the children. It has been suggested for Huntington's chorea and many other genetic disabilities. However, no clear demonstration has withstood critical review.

SUMMARY

Although some strongly inherited phenotypes are under the clear control of genes with reliable, switch-like effects, many other characteristics and diseases seem to be under the partial influence of "leaky" genes. This means that some persons who are genotypically abnormal remain among the phenotypically normal group, and therefore the penetrance of the phenotype within its proper group may be less than 100 percent. A disease which may show low penetrance as a developed deformity, such as vitamin-D-resistant rickets, may be discovered to have another and fully penetrant effect, such as Hypophosphatemia which precedes rickets. Other genes with pleiotropic effects may also show different degrees of penetrance by different aspects of the phenotype. Penetrance may also increase with the age of the individual, as in the nervous disease Huntington's chorea. The ages of onset in different generations seem to be the same in parents and offspring for this and other diseases after allowances are made for the biases which get into the tabulating of the data. Describing the percentage of penetrance is relatively easy among laboratory animals and among human monozygotic twins. Satisfactory penetrance figures for those rarer human traits are difficult to arrive at because of the scarcity of genetically identical twins whose phenotypes may then be compared.

SUGGESTED READING

Berglin, C. G., Some penetrance formulae in recessive proband material. Acta Genet. Med. (Gemello) **6**: 451–458 (1957).

Hersh, A. H., R. M. Stecher, W. M. Solomon, R. Wolpaw, and H. Hauser, Heredity in ankylosing spondylitis. Amer. J. Hum. Genet. **2**: 391–408 (1950). The data are considered on both dominant and recessive monofactorial hypotheses with appropriate estimates of penetrance for each assumption.

Sang, James H., Penetrance, expressivity and thresholds. J. Hered. **54**: 143–151 (1963). A generalized mathematical treatment based on studies in *Drosophila* and in several mammals.

Stutz, H. C., Within-penetrance, between-penetrance and expressivity. J. Hered. **53**: 66–71 (1962). In rye plants variation within the same plant (as between left and right sides of the vertebrate body) may be compared with penetrance variation between sibling plants.

PROBLEMS

17-1   What would be the penetrance of a gene for Polydactyly in a line of descent where an individual with the normal 20 digits had a Polydactylous mother and grandfather if his only son and only grandson were Polydactylous?

17-2   Rare phenotypes which occasionally skip a generation as in Problem 17-1 have been called "irregular dominants."
(a) Would you describe vitamin-D-resistant rickets to be in that category?
(b) How would you describe the action of the gene mainly responsible for vitamin-D-resistant rickets?

17-3   A stiff little finger has been described as a genetic condition due to a single dominant gene with 50 to 75 percent penetrance. If a woman shows this condition in both hands but her husband does not, what would be a reasonable expectation for the occurrence of this condition among her children?

17-4   If a man who has five children develops Huntington's chorea in his early fifties, what is the chance that none of these children has received the Dominant abnormal allele from the father?

17-5   What effect would early death from other causes have upon the average age of onset of Huntington's chorea among the "parent group" and among the "children group"?

chapter 18

Marker Genes and Disease Risks

The discovery of an association of a certain disease and a certain blood group or other marker gene could have one of several meanings. First and most hopefully a causal relation might be indicated. For instance, the blood group *A* gene might have in addition to its early and reliable effect on the antigen reaction system a pleiotropic effect which predisposes to a particular disease later in life. Such information might be of some assistance in diagnosing early stages of the disease or in recommending extra precautions to minimize chances of that disease. Second and more often the observed correlation might be spurious, merely the outcome of small numbers in the study or else the result of observations from two different groups instead of from within one homogeneous group. A third and more remote possibility is that the association might indicate chromosomal linkage (Chapter 11) in two merging populations which have not yet come to genetic equilibrium. Better demonstrations of chromosomal linkage emerge as a degree of positive association in coupling sibships being matched by the same degree of negative association in repulsion sibships. As an aid to estimating the disease risks for one person, knowledge of any pleiotropic effects is directly usable, whereas knowledge of linkage of a disease locus and a marker locus requires further information about the genotypes of the parents, whether in coupling or in repulsion phase. Knowing a correlation which is spurious is perhaps worse than ignorance. Because this area of study is being actively pursued at the present time, full awareness of the several possible meanings of association assists the student in the acquisition of new knowledge.

Why humans remain polymorphic rather than uniform in their blood antigens and in a few other characters such as PTC tasting has remained a mystery for many years. In 1930 Fisher showed mathematically that the continuation of intermediate gene frequencies for many generations would be most unusual, unless there were selective forces acting for one genotype or against another. Although investigations into this possibility were pursued, the genetic evidence for many years indicated only that the ABO blood system was neutral as far as survival and reproduction were concerned. This was our assumption in earlier chapters introducing the principles of Hardy-Weinberg equilibrium. Not until 1953 was it shown clearly, by Aird and colleagues, that two different diseases of the stomach were associated with different blood phenotypes. Persons with gastric carcinoma were preferentially of blood type A, and persons with peptic ulcer were of type O more often than were persons from suitable control samples.

METHODOLOGY

Because the disease risks of different groups are not strikingly dissimilar, adherence to good methodology becomes very important in all studies. Large numbers of patients are required, and the need for large numbers can sometimes lead to amassing the data inappropriately — without due regard for the influence of ascertainment on the resulting proportions (Chapter 7). The mathematics of comparisons of relative risk, the sampling errors involved and the appropriate tests for heterogeneity among different studies have been conveniently described by B. Woolf. With these methods the evaluation of the distribution of numbers becomes very precise; the origins of the data are often a larger uncertainty. The unwitting combining of data from two groups which are each randomly composed can introduce spurious correlations. Two such examples for quantitative characteristics are presented in Figure 18-1, and the same principle applies to dihybrid segrega-

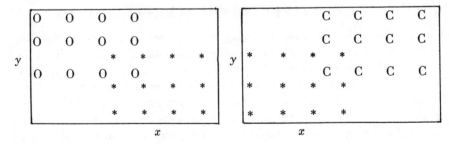

FIGURE 18-1 Spurious correlations. Combined data, * and O, or * and C, show correlation, yet the combined data have come from two separate and displaced (stratified) populations in neither of which is there any correlation between x and y.

tion and assortment into four groups. Artifactual correlation may be found in assembled data which are said to be *stratified*, because they are samples drawn from different populations rather than from the same source population. Spurious correlation usually disappears when the study is redesigned to eliminate the stratification caused by the mixture of sources. For instance, in a comparison of the blood group distribution of leukemic patients with that from the complete list of blood donors at a Brooklyn hospital MacMahon and Folusiak at first noted a significant association. However, they realized that leukemia is more often found in some races than in others among those included in the large sample and that blood group alleles also show racial differences. A better comparison was possible, partly because of the custom of allowing transfusion patients to repay the volume of blood received by means of donations from among their relatives and friends. Friends would usually be of the same racial group and relatives almost always would belong to the same population as the leukemic patient who required the transfusion. When the control group was limited to those blood donors whose last names matched the last names of the leukemic persons, the distribution of the blood groups was homogeneous among the sick and among the nonleukemics.

An even more exacting comparison was suggested by Penrose and has been used in many recent studies. The control population consists of the sibs of the patients, and thus genetic variability and stratification between patients and controls are greatly reduced. The minor chance that at a later time a sib will come down with the same rare disease is too small to invalidate the comparison. Many pioneer studies did not use this sib method and are therefore subject to review and reappraisal.

DISEASES ASSOCIATED WITH MARKER ALLELES

Associations with Blood Group A. In a recent study by Aird and colleagues on pancreatic cancer the blood group A among 620 patients was significantly more common than among nonpatient controls. Two other kinds of growths investigated at the same time showed no excess association, either among patients with cancer of the esophagus or with pituitary adenoma. It is of course no surprise that the three conditions did not distribute in the same way, because their genetic bases seem from other studies to be distinct.

Pernicious anemia also shows a preferential association with blood group A persons. Fraser Roberts has reviewed the reports from 12 different centers of study comprising a total of 1498 cases of pernicious anemia plus suitable controls and has found a significant departure from random expectation. The evidence indicated that persons in blood group A had a risk of developing pernicious anemia 1.26 times the risk for persons within blood group O. Furthermore, the 12 separate studies showed no evidence of statistical heterogeneity (Chapter 7) although they were made in different cities of England, Denmark and the United States. Thus their addition into a single comparison of patients with controls seems appropriate.

Suspecting a relationship between tumors of the stomach and epithelial cells anterior to it, Osborne and De George reviewed the records of a large number of patients having salivary gland tumors either benign or malignant. Although benign tumors occurred more often in females and malignant tumors of the salivary glands were found more often in males, totals of both sexes were alike in containing an excess of patients in blood group A. The risk of A persons was apparently 1.35 times the risk of O blood group persons in developing some cancer of the salivary glands. This association was more pronounced among the large number of parotid gland tumor cases and less among the smaller number of submaxillary gland tumor patients. In a separate subdivision according to histological tumor types the mucoepidermoid tumors included not only the excess of A persons just mentioned but also indicated an even higher representation of blood type B patients. The control sample included 4738 individuals, of which 2029 were in blood group O. The incidence of salivary gland tumors in the latter group was taken as the base for comparison both in this study and in the next.

Neoplastic diseases of the ovary were subsequently studied by Osborne and De George (1963) and compared with the above large group of controls. Blood group A persons were encountered more often than expected in the data as a whole and in a few of the dermoid subtypes. Over 10 subtypes were distinguished among 260 benign ovarian tumors, and a similarly large number of kinds of malignant tumors was found among 453 other patients. Their excess of type A persons was similar to the excess found among 1300 German patients reviewed by Helmbold. For the benign dermoid type of ovarian cyst the risk to group A persons was computed to be 2.4 times the risk for group O persons, and in the most extreme difference encountered the risk for a certain malignant type in group A was 6 times the risk in group O. As a generalization Osborne and De George found that the papillary types of tumors were associated with group A persons more often than were the solid tumor types. This was similar to their earlier observation that papillomas among the salivary gland tumors followed the distribution with group A here repeated among the ovarian tumors.

Associations with Blood Group O. Unlike the above cancers the ulcers of the stomach and the ulcers of the duodenum show significantly high associations with type O persons. Buchwalter has recently studied this and other possible associations while using the refinement of control populations composed of the sibs of the respective kinds of ulcer patients. Duodenal ulcer patients were in blood group O more frequently than were their non-ulcerous sibs. Gastric ulcer patients were likewise of blood type O more often than were their nonaffected sibs. Both of these conclusions confirm and extend earlier studies, including the pioneer finding of Aird. Heterogeneity among the separate studies on gastric ulcer was not found, but there did seem to be a lack of homogeneity among the studies of the more numerous duodenal ulcer cases.

Associations with Nonsecretors of ABH. The secretor locus causes a polymorphism which did not assort randomly in the above investigation. In persons who are *Secretors* the ABO blood type may be determined from a sample of saliva or other body secretions, but this cannot be done from the saliva of persons in the recessive *nonsecretor* class. To secrete a water-soluble form of antigen A in the saliva, a person must have the genes i^A and *Se* and must also have at least one other dominant gene called *H* which produces antigen H in saliva only. To secrete water-soluble B and H antigens in the saliva a person must have the genes i^B, *H* and *Se* in all tissues. Antigen H is not detected on the red blood cells, but it is present in the saliva of all H Se persons even those of blood group O. Hence references to ABH type reflects the outcome of tests on antigens in the salivary secretions.

The nonsecretors were found at a frequency significantly above the control expectation among the patients with duodenal ulcer; and nonsecretors among the peptic ulcer patients also were above expectation although not to a significant extent.

Secretor and Lewis Interactions. Duodenal ulcer is associated with the rare Lewis(a + b−) antigenic reaction as well as with group O and with nonsecretors. Ball has demonstrated this in a Nigerian population where this uncommon Lewis type is considerably more frequent than elsewhere. The *Lewis blood groups* are complex and interact epistatically with the secretor and perhaps other systems. The theory of Grubb and Ceppellini states in part that the Lewis recessives, *le le*, have red blood cells not reacting with Lewis antibody, a phenotype described as Le(a−b−), whereas the phenotype of Lewis dominant depends also on the secretor locus. Under this hypothesis persons who are nonsecretor Lewis, *se se Le* heterozygotes or homozygotes, have the red blood cell reactions symbolized by Le(a+b−). The converse blood cell reaction, Le(a−b+), results from the combination Secretor Lewis whether either dominant is heterozygous or homozygous. Although these same double dominant individuals secrete salivary antigens of both Lewis types, no red blood cells reacting to both Lewis antisera have been found yet. The Le(a−b+) type is very common among Caucasians.

Ball found elevated risks of duodenal ulcer in regard to alleles at three different marker loci, *i*, *se* and *Le*. The risk among Nigerians of type O was 1.43 times the control risk; and among the nonsecretors it was a little higher, 1.74 times the control risk of duodenal ulcers. The risk for the rare Le(a+b−) type of Nigerian was 2.26 times the control, and Ball pointed out that these Lewis types contributed all the excess found among the nonsecretor group. Such an interaction in respect to duodenal ulcer will doubtlessly receive further study in other populations.

Spurious Association with a Dominant Rhesus Type. One of the more common rhesus dominants, R_1R_2, seemed to be associated with both duodenal and gastric ulcers in a commendably large study. However, a *transfusion* effect was temporarily adding antigens to the blood stream of many of the ulcer patients. The blood transfused was usually matched only for the ABO isoagglutinogen type but, in the case of males, not for rhesus and other blood antigens. When the blood phenotypes of persons having received any transfusion in the previous 90 days were omitted from the total of patients, the spurious association between rhesus type and ulcers disappeared. In this case the asking of a more specific question produced a more typical although less exciting answer.

Associations with the Taster Differences. One of the many genetic causes of blindness in adults is *glaucoma*, actually a group of diseases which exists in several subtypes. Becker and Morton have found two kinds of glaucoma patients noteworthy for divergent distributions in regard to the ability to taste phenylthiocarbamide. Among 446 eye clinic patients without glaucoma tabulated as controls there were 72 percent Tasters of PTC. Yet among 211 persons with primary open-angle glaucoma there were only 47 percent Tasters. Another 155 angle-closure glaucoma cases included 83 percent in the Taster class. The frequency of Tasters among cases of each of these anomalies was significantly above or significantly below the expected frequency of Tasters of PTC.

Diseases of the thyroid gland also are of many kinds and result from a variety of causes both nutritional and genetic. Kitchin and coworkers in Liverpool have found unexpected associations of two large categories of goiter with polymorphism for the PTC taste sensitivity. *Exophthalmic goiter* (Graves's disease) has long been known to have some hereditary basis, and among 133 patients an excess of Taster individuals was found. Conversely, among 246 cases of *adenomatous goiter* Tasters were below the expected frequency especially among male patients. In all the categories of goiter studied at Liverpool there were no remarkable findings in regard to secretor status or isoagglutinogen reaction.

SOME NONSIGNIFICANT ASSOCIATIONS

The possibility of discovering genetic linkage as well as pleiotropic association was one of the reasons for investigating the association of marker genes and disease. Cytogenetic studies are particularly appropriate among children with Down's Syndrome (mongolian idiots who have extra chromosomal material, Chapters 22 and 23) and among their sibs and near relatives. Several teams of workers have made studies which clearly indicate that the gene locus for ABO is not linked to mongolism. In Pennsylvania Kaplan and co-workers in 1964 reported merely random distributions after comparing the ABO blood groups among 290 mongoloids at the Polk School and among three control groups. The latter were a large series of school children in Pittsburgh, a large list of blood donors in the same city and several thousand visitors at an Allegheny County Fair. From their failure to find fewer recessives (type O children) among the Down's Syndrome idiots, they concluded that the locus for ABO was not situated in the extra material of chromosome 21 which these severely impaired children always have. If the extra chromosomal material had contained the isoagglutinogen locus, more persons in the abnormal category would have contained at least one A allele or at least one B allele in the total of three loci, and conversely, fewer would have contained the recessive i allele at all three chromosomal loci (see Trisomy, Chapter 22).

Some studies of diabetes mellitus have reported an association while other studies, often larger, have found only the expected distribution. Because diabetics (frequency 4/1000 persons) are found in many large kindreds and because the disease is seventh highest of the causes of death, further genetic and epidemiological studies on diabetes will doubtlessly be made. In a review of six studies made to include nine geographical locations, Macafee found a heterogeneity of distributions but did not find a consistent association with any of three markers. In regard to MN type, over 400 persons were distributed randomly; the expected fraction of some 600 diabetics were Secretors; and over 800 diabetics followed the expected proportions in their ABO blood antigens. For a contrary result a clear association between diabetes mellitus and group A was shown in four consistent studies having more than 2000 diabetics. The reasons for the discrepancy are not understood at this writing.

The various cancers must be considered separately by types and subtypes. Cancer of the breast has a genetic predisposition in some kindreds, and investigation of the genetic basis and environmental influences on breast cancer is difficult and complex. No blood group association of significance has been shown although the summarization of over 2000 cases from six different studies showed the A : O ratio slightly above expectation. A summary of a still larger number of patients having had cancer of the colon and rectum showed only a slight elevation of the A : O expectation ratio. The blood types of lung cancer cases showed the least deviations from expectation among two large groups of A and O persons.

Explanations for the associations where detected and not due to faulty design of the study may be expected to be various depending on the disease and perhaps depending on the environment. In regard to the secretors it has been suggested that the substances secreted might have a protective effect in the stomach, although this is not the only possibility. In respect to the ABO type it has been suggested that the disease which may be chosen for study might be related to the blood type as second order effects. Since 1953 it has been known that there are incompatibility reactions between an A fetus or embryo and an O mother so that fewer A children are born. They are lost early in unsuspected pregnancies. This incompatibility effect and other selective effects will be described in the next chapter.

SUMMARY

Because some diseases are unevenly distributed among races, among nutritional classes or among common genetic phenotypes, the problem of spurious or meaningful correlation arises. Valid correlations are not only desired for practical reasons but are expected on theoretical grounds to explain the existence and persistence of intermediate gene frequencies and polymorphism. At the descriptive level a consistent association shows that individuals of blood group A have slightly elevated risks of having pancreatic cancer, pernicious anemia, salivary gland tumors and certain kinds of tumors of the ovary. Blood group O persons seem to have a slightly elevated risk of gastric ulcer and duodenal ulcer. The Lewis and Secretor phenotypes are said to interact in the incidence of gastric and duodenal ulcers. Persons who are Tasters of PTC seem to show elevated risks of having certain kinds of thyroid disease and one kind of glaucoma but show a reduced risk for another kind of glaucoma. Studies of marker gene incidence among patients and among the sibs of patients are superior to comparisons among unrelated control and patient populations which may tend to be stratified in respect to the frequency of each genetic difference.

SUGGESTED READING

Ball, P. A. J., Influence of the secretor and Lewis genes on susceptibility to duodenal ulcer. Brit. Med. J. **5310**: 948–950 (1962).

Becker, B., and W. R. Morton, Taste sensitivity to phenylthiourea in glaucoma. *Science* **144**: 1347–8 (1964).

Buchwalter, J. A., Peptic ulcer and blood groups. Ann. N. Y. Acad. Sci. **99**: 81–88 (1962). The higher risk phenotypes were group O and nonsecretors. A common dominant rhesus type was implicated only by recent blood transfusions.

Li, C. C., *Human Genetics: Principles and Methods*, New York, Blakiston Division, McGraw-Hill, 1961, 218 pp. His Chapter 6, Association and Relative Risk is crucial.

MacMahon, B., and J. C. Folusiak, Leukemia and the ABO blood groups. Amer. J. Hum. Genet. **10**: 287–293 (1958). An association which appeared when blood donors of several races were used as controls disappeared when the last names of diseased and control were matched. Such totals permitted the comparison to be made in a racially more homogeneous population.

Neel, J. V., Diabetes mellitus: A "thrifty" genotype rendered deterimental by "progress"? Amer. J. Hum. Genet. **14**: 353–362. (1962). A thought provoking article written from the long range medical point of view.

Osborne, R. H., and F. V. De George, The ABO blood groups in neoplastic disease of the ovary. Amer. J. Hum. Genet. **15**: 380–388 (1963).

Woolf, B., On estimating the relation between blood group and disease. Ann. Hum. Genet. **19**: 251–253 (1955).

Woolf, C. M., Investigations on the genetic aspects of carcinoma of the stomach and breast. Univ. Calif. Publ. Public Health **2**: 265–350 (1955). In this careful account the method of decision by sequential analysis is thoroughly illustrated.

PROBLEMS

18–1   (a) In a first comparison of the blood types of leukemic patients and blood donors, MacMahon and Folusiak found that among 1387 leukemics there were 561 type O, 519 type A, 223 type B and 84 type AB patients where 1967 blood donors at the same hospital were (in the same order) 900, 728, 261, and 78. Compute a homogeneity Chi-square for the distribution.

(b) When the same authors compared blood groups only among patients and blood donors whose surnames could be matched, there were among 1232 leukemics 507 type O, 455 type A, 193 type B and 77 type AB, while a similar number of blood donors on the revised list were 507 type O, 493 type A, 166 type B and 66 type AB. Compute a homogeneity Chi-square for this group and draw a conclusion.

18-2   In a large group of control persons Osborne and De George found that blood group A persons comprised .474 of the total of type O and type A persons and that women with various kinds of neoplasms of the ovary showed a slight or a significant excess of blood type A. Test the following distributions and state the probability that each might be a random deviation from the above expectation:

    (a) 22 persons with pseudomucinous cysts: 15 group A, 7 group O

    (b) 49 persons with endometriosis: 29 group A, 20 group O

    (c) 38 persons with dermoid cysts: 26 group A, 12 group O

chapter 19

Prenatal Interactions

In previous chapters it was seen that the expression of certain gene pairs varied with the body environment of hormones, sex, age and other unspecified internal variables. While the embryo and fetus are in the uterus, other more external variables have their effect on the development of certain kinds of genotypes. Sometimes the action is clearly two ways, between the phenotype of the fetus and that of the mother as in rhesus blood type incompatibility. It has even been suggested that the maternal environment at the time of impregnation in rats has an influence on the sex ratio in the litter, but this has not been confirmed. The later origin of sex ratio differences has been investigated in terms of the number of males and of females dying in the uterus.

MATERNAL-FETAL INCOMPATIBILITY

A kind of hemolytic disease of the newborn occurs chiefly among the later pregnancies of Rh-negative women, and the child subject to death at this time is always Rh-positive. Because of this eventual risk in large families the marriage of an Rh-positive man and an Rh-negative woman is said to be an Rh-incompatible marriage, and negative women usually have an Rh-positive husband, because most men are in that group. The earlier pregnancies from such a marriage are usually successful, unless the woman has been inadvertently sensitized by receiving transfusions of Rh-positive blood. There is no destruction of the blood cells of the fetus where the blood types of the mother and child are both rhesus negative, and compatible pregnancies occur about half of the time in a large group of incompatible marriages wherever the Rh-positive father is heterozygous and has an Rh-negative gene to transmit.

The disease *erythroblastosis fetalis* is the rapid destruction of the red blood cells of the fetus or newborn by antibodies which reach it from its mother.

The antibodies were previously developed by the mother in response to red cells of positive rhesus type which entered her blood stream during earlier pregnancies or transfusions. Usually the blood of the fetus and the blood of the mother remain separated by tissue in the placenta, but occasionally some blood cells from the fetus do get into the maternal circulation where they initiate the development of antibodies against their kind of cell. These antibodies are protective to the mother and do no harm unless they return in high titer to the same fetus or usually to a later one. The return is not necessarily by the same route in humans, but careful experiments in the rabbit show that the maternal antibodies pass in the placenta to the amniotic fluid and then into the fetal mouth and gut. This eventual concentration in the stomach has been confirmed in six other species of mammals and so may eventually be found to apply to humans.

The common immunizers are the rhesus alleles which give the D-positive serological test, and the common Rh-negative mothers thus immunized are those which have two chromosomes giving tests for c and for e and no D substance. During the course of pregnancy in an "incompatible" marriage, the level of antibody buildup, if any, in the mother can be followed. A sudden rise in titer may be an indication that delivery of the fetus should be speeded. Otherwise preparations may be made for a complete transfusion of blood to the child immediately upon birth. This saves many babies who would otherwise die. Normally, Rh-negative mothers do not get to nurse their Rh-positive babies.

The maternal-fetal interaction just described in regard to the rhesus D antigen is not merely between two aspects of the genotype; another incompatibility actually helps the situation. It was noted that hemolysis in rhesus incompatibility almost never occurs when the mother is also blood type O and the father type AB. Similarly, there is a less conspicuous amount of rhesus trouble when the mother is again type O but the father is A or is B. Independently it was noted by Matsunaga that A children and O children are not born equally often from the two reciprocal kinds of testcross marriages. The number of A children born to type O mothers was significantly below expectation, fully 10 percent below, as if there were some selection against that type.

The *ABO incompatibility* is that where a fetus develops an A or B antigen which the mother cannot also develop. It will be remembered that all persons except type AB have present in their blood plasma antibodies against A or against B or both (see Figure 8-1). These antibodies are therefore ready to act the first time that cells coated with A or B antigens enter the maternal circulation. The direct effect of this reaction in the mother's blood stream is usually nil, but the indirect effect of the early removal of foreign blood cells is helpful to the survival of a sequence of rhesus-positive fetuses in a rhesus-negative mother. The early destruction of Rh-positive A or B cells does not allow time enough for the mother to build up antibodies against the D antigen. Contrarily, among the ABO compatible marriages (in which the husband could be a blood donor to his wife as far as ABO matching is concerned) the regular frequencies of rhesus-erythroblastosis in the later and later pregnancies seem to occur. The direct results of ABO incompatibility seem to be the birth of fewer A children as noted above and perhaps of fewer B children as if there were early uterine selection against these genotypes. Occasionally there is a later effect, a definite erthyroblastosis fetalis due to the normal antibodies of the mother reaching the A or B fetus in large quantity.

Further incompatibilities have been sought within other blood group systems, but only two need be mentioned. *Kell incompatibility* sometimes causes erythroblastosis. Most individuals are kell-negative, but about 9 percent of persons are Kell-positive. The incompatible combination is a Kell-positive man and a kell-negative woman. The suggestion has been made that the common P alleles cause an early and severe reaction as reflected by early miscarriages. However, Sanger has pointed out that the P alleles are so common (above 99 percent) that they can easily be implicated when one is investigating the blood types of women who frequently have miscarriages.

PHENOCOPIES

The concept of a phenocopy arises from studies of laboratory animals and plants where a known change in the environment produces a phenotypic change easily confused with that produced by some known genotype. However, the offspring and F_2 generation from a phenocopy are normal in appearance provided that they are not again subjected to the same environmental change at a time in development like that which produced the phenocopy. Thus phenocopies are concerned with embryonic and fetal development and are not directly involved in inheritance. However, the study of laboratory animals has shown that different genotypes respond differently, if at all, to an environment capable of altering some phenotypes.

Rubella deafness and other defects result from a very few of the pregnancies where the mother has an infection with the virus of German measles during the second and third months of pregnancy (Table 19-1). This infection of adults is rare, but infection and fever are associated rather often with those cases of deafness which are sporadic, that is, isolated cases without additional deafness among large numbers of sibs and near relatives. Such a

TABLE 19-1   Relationship between time of infection and form of malformations in rubella embryopathy[a]

Infection during weeks of pregnancy	Malformations of the embryo
4–5	cataract
5–7	cardiac defects
6–14 (8–12)	damage of inner ear
8–9	defects of deciduous teeth

[a]From Widukind Lenz, *Medical Genetics*, Chicago, University of Chicago Press, 1963.

phenocopy married to a genetically deaf spouse usually has children all
with normal hearing, and this fact tends to distinguish it from the two major
kinds of recessive deafness (Chapter 10). A rubella infection also produces
another developmental abnormality, a cataract in the lens of the eye. Here
again the genetic forms of cataract are at least two, and the phenocopy is an
approximation of them rather than being an exact copy of some one genetic
type. It has been estimated following epidemics in Australia that among
women who had rubella infection during the first two months of pregnancy
there was close to 100 percent of births with some kind of congenital defect.
Following a 1955 epidemic in Montreal no deafness and only 19 percent
congenital abnormalities were found among 31 births; and 25 children
whose mothers had rubella during the first trimester remained normal.

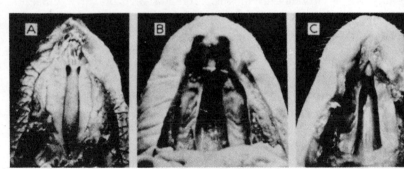

FIGURE 19-1   Cleft palates of different etiology. A. Mouse derived from strain
in which harelip and cleft palate were hereditary. B. Rat whose mother was
deficient in riboflavin. C. Rat whose mother was exposed to roentgen rays on day
15 of gestation. Reprinted with permission from Warkany, *Advances in Pediatrics*,
II, New York, Wiley, 1947.

In rodents cleft lip and cleft palate are known both as genetic types and
as phenocopies following known environmental change (Figure 19-1).
Among mice Reed has shown that cleft lip has a definite genetic basis seem-

ingly recessive but having variability in expression and also having reduced penetrance. A phenocopy with similar appearance has been demonstrated in the litters from normal mice by Steiniger, who injected the pregnant mice with anterior pituitary extract which increased the frequencies of cleft lip. Fraser and associates have found that cortisone given in large doses to pregnant mice results in considerable numbers of harelip offspring within the litter, and they further demonstrated that there were genetic differences in the abilities of different strains to react to excess of cortisone. Ingalls and his associates found that hypoxia, simulating the atmospheric pressure at 27,000 feet for five hours with slow return to normal, affected five strains of mice differently. Litters from all strains showed some malformations after reduced pressure on the 9th or on the 15th day of pregnancy, yet only four of the five genetic strains showed skeletal defects exceptionally. Only one strain responded by having umbilical hernia, only one strain had harelip above untreated litter frequencies, and a different strain had defective eyes or no eyes. The exact manner of application of this information from developmental studies and from genetics to the numerous cases of harelip babies is not yet evident. However, it seems closer to useful knowledge than does the old idea that pregnant women should not look at hares hung in the meat market for fear of impressing their fetuses!

Among rats cleft palate occurs sporadically, but the incidence is raised considerably by environmental means. Rats of any of three different genetic strains develop cleft palate readily if their mothers have been on a riboflavin-deficient diet up to the 15th day of the pregnancy (Figure 19-1 B) The fetuses seem to be normal in development up to day 13, and the critical decision for cleft palate or normal palate seems to be in the short interval between days 13 and 15. Other skeletal structures of the rat are also shortened as a result of the treatment in this same period. Cleft palate and other abnormalities including eye defects appear in litters of pigs from sows on a diet deficient in vitamin A during pregnancy. Conversely, excess vitamin A leads to similar abnormalities in mice. In cattle on a low carotene diet, blindness, weakness of calves at birth and stillbirths occur with high frequency.

Irradiation of the fetuses also produces many abnormalities depending on the time of exposure. L. B. Russell has made careful and extensive studies of litters of mice subjected to one of six different doses of X-rays on days 4 to 14 from conception. Many different kinds of skeletal abnormalities were found, and usually each kind was correlated with irradiation on a certain day of pregnancy or on the adjacent day or two. Cleft palate was one of the phenocopies among the many others whose possible genetic counterparts are not presently identifiable in mice.

Among humans it is known that cleft palate by itself is clearly different from harelip accompanied by cleft palate. In a nationwide Danish study Fogh-Andersen found low risks for each of these conditions among the later-born sibs of index cases. Both he and Fraser found that *simple cleft palate* cases were followed by a 2 to 4 percent recurrence among the younger sibs regardless of the phenotype of the parent. However, Reed found that when both a child and one parent had cleft palate the risk for later children was about 16 percent. Such an *empiric risk figure* is determined by direct observation, and it has no connotation as to mode of inheritance. Indeed, unless there is a significant contrast between risk figures for the different degrees of relation to index cases and unless this contrast is in the right direction — downwards with increasing genetic steps away — there is no indication of the fact of inheritance of the abnormality.

A second condition of humans, *harelip* whether with or without cleft palate, is slightly more frequent and is more definitely inherited than is simple cleft palate. The Drs. Metrakos studied or reviewed 86 pairs of twins with at least one having harelip to compare the concordance among the two types of twins. Both twins of eight pairs out of 19 monozygous twin pairs had harelip (42 percent concordance), but only four out of 67 dizygous pairs were alike in this respect (5 percent concordance). The latter figure is similar to that found by Reed (7 percent) for the younger sibs of harelip children from normal parents. He found indication of a genetic influence in the fact that when a child and a parent both had harelip the empiric risk among subsequent children was 16 percent for each child. Recently, Fraser Roberts determined the empiric risk figures starting from a harelip parent each with a normal spouse and found 10 harelip children among 303. However, most of the harelip offspring were boys, and most of these came from harelip mothers. This increase among the most affected sex when the parent is of the sex less often affected should recall the similar patterns shown by pyloric stenosis and by spondylitis as described in Chapter 16.

A sudden increase in the incidence of babies with reduced or absent hands and feet was noted in 1960 particularly in Germany and also in other European countries. These babies had flipper-like appendages, a condition whose inheritance in man is not definitely known but which resembles a recessive phenotype in the mouse called "phocomelia" which in turn is named for the normal condition of the flippers of the seal. More such children continued to be born at relatively high frequencies throughout the following year, but by November of 1961 Dr. Widukind Lenz pointed out that the phocomelia births were associated in time and place with the introduction of the drug thalidomide in certain sleeping pills, which were available without prescription in some countries but not cleared for unrestricted use in others, among them the United States. It was evident from the medical histories taken from many of the mothers that the malformed legs or arms followed the taking of thalidomide during early pregnancy, often when the fact of pregnancy was uncertain or even unsuspected. After thalidomide was removed from the market and after widespread warnings were made not to use pills already purchased, it was expected that the occurrence of this type of deformity would drop dramatically by the following August. The actual outcome in Hamburg, Germany, may be seen in Table 19-2.

TABLE 19-2   Total number of births and number of thalidomide-type malformations at 18 Hamburg obstetric hospitals from January 1960 to October 1962[a]

	1960	1961	Jan–July 1962	Aug–Oct 1962	Total
Total births	19,052	19,917	13,326	5,542	57,837
Thalidomide-type Malformations					
Extremities	22	53	30	2	107
Ears or internal Organs only	6	7	10	—	23
Total	28	60	40	2	130
History					
Thalidomide taken	13	46	33	2	94
No Evidence of intake of Thalidomide	0	5	1	0	6
No history taken	15	9	6	0	30

[a]From W. Lenz, *Congenital Malformations*, New York, The International Medical Congress, Ltd., 1964.

Thalidomide and many other drugs are not uniformly damaging to different species of test animals, and this is perhaps no surprise in view of strain differences of response within species. Rabbits are not damaged by thalidomide until given a dose that is 20 times that formerly recommended as a daily therapeutic dose in man. Cortisone, insulin and even caffeine are damaging to one or more species of laboratory animal but only in doses much higher than any person is apt to take (Table 19-3). Thus there appears to be a safe dose level for the ingestion of some drugs but not for others and not for irradiation of the germ line as we shall point out in Chapter 25.

The diagnosis of individuals without good knowledge of the family history and the history of pregnancy is fraught with difficulty. Phenocopies of genetic conditions and mimic genes among the inherited conditions mean

TABLE 19-3 **Ratio of teratogenic dose in animals to therapeutic daily dose in man for various drugs**[a]

Drug	Animal	Ratio
Caffeine	Mouse	35
Cortisone	Rat	—
	Mouse	400
	Rabbit	20
Insulin	Rat	100
Meclozine	Rat	35
Na salicylate	Rat	3
Terramycin	Mouse	12
Tetracycline	Rat	1
Thyroxine	Rat	2
Thalidomide	Rabbit	20

[a]From F. C. Fraser, *Congenital Malformations*, New York, The International Medical Congress, Ltd., 1964.

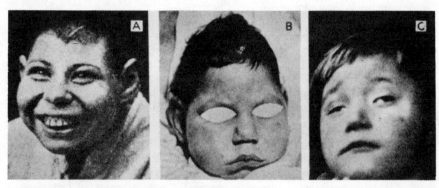

FIGURE 19-2 Microcephaly of different etiology. A. This microcephaly may be genetically determined; the boy had two sibs with microcephaly and three normal sibs, and a paternal grand-uncle who was mentally deficient. B. Microcephaly in a child with toxoplasmosis. C. Child of mother irradiated with roentgen rays during second and third months of pregnancy. Reprinted with permission from Warkany, *Advances in Pediatrics*, II, New York, Wiley, 1947.

that the first impression is apt to be only $\frac{1}{3}$ right and $\frac{2}{3}$ wrong. For instance, the malformed hands on a baby might be due to thalidomide or to a new dominant gene mutation or to the segregation of a rare recessive. Deafness may be due to rubella infection of the mother or to the presence of one or of another kind of recessive deafness, and Dominant deafness is known in connection with other pleiotropic effects. The three children pictured in Figure 19-2 may all be described as microcephalics because of the small cranial part of the head, yet the additional information about relatives and the course of pregnancy in each makes it very probable that the first is genetically microcephalic, that the second has been damaged by infection with Toxoplasma organisms long before birth and that the third has been altered by X-radiation in early pregnancy. Similarly, cataracts in various parts of the lens may be due to different genes or to irradiation. Some idea of the relative abundance of defects from clearly genetic sources and from interactions of environment and genotype may be gained from Table 19-4.

TABLE 19-4   **Frequencies in live born of certain groups of traits which are present at birth or manifest in later life**[a]

Group of traits	Frequency per 1,000 births
Malformations of complex genetic and environmental etiology	20
Malformations due to single-gene substitutions	5
Disorders associated with chromosomal aberrations	4
Single-gene traits determining disease	8
Erythroblastosis	4
Common disorders with genetic components in etiology	10
Total	51

[a]Courtesy of A.C. Stevenson, Brit. Med. Bull., 17: 257 (Sept., 1961).

In experimental animals one may search for chemical "cures" of an inherited phenotype. This means seeking a phenocopy of the normal in contrast to the foregoing, which was changing a developing animal of a normal strain to a phenotype not unlike that of some mutant genotype. The presence of cortisone in large amounts in a pregnant mouse works both ways. It is damaging to fetuses in several stages of growth, but it may restore the apparent normality of one aspect of the body. In mice the recessive lid gap phenotype allows the eyelids to be open at birth, with some subsequent damage through infection, and its penetrance is reduced to the level that only 77 percent of inbred *lg/lg* parents show the abnormally early eye opening. Watney and Miller have demonstrated that a small dose of cortisone late in pregnancy, on day 16, will result in only half as many lid gaps among the newborn, and that the same dose given one day earlier reduces the recessive phenotype to zero frequency. This is a highly specific response both in regard to time and to tissue. Unfortunately, some undiagnosed effects elsewhere result in death of most or all of the litter within a few days after birth. However, it is significant that treatment of the pregnant female may result in change away from normal or toward normal depending upon drug, time, and genotype.

THE FORMATION OF DIZYGOUS TWINS

Although single births are the rule for humans, horses, sheep, lions and many other species, multiple births from multiple ovulation are routine among cats, dogs, rats, mice, pigs, rabbits and a host of other mammals. When a woman has twins of different sex or of other inherited differences we may assume that there has been ovulation of two eggs from the same or opposite ovaries. In rare instances more eggs may be ovulated, and the children may differ in hair color, sitting height and facial features as well as sex. The Diligenti quintuplets from Argentina illustrate these differences and others, so that they must have come from five separate zygotes (Figure 19-3). There is no special genetic problem about fraternal twins, or dizygotic twins, DZ, as they are properly called. Environmentally, however,

FIGURE 19-3 The Diligenti quintuplets on their 15th birthday. No two of the girls are identical; neither are the boys. Courtesy of Wide World Photos.

they may crowd each other and be smaller than average at birth, and twins are generally not as long lived as are singly born persons.

Occasionally, there may be lasting influences of one twin upon another. When the fetal period is reached, the placental blood vessels of one may rarely make contact with those of the other and thus allow the exchange of hormones or of blood corpuscles. An anastomosis, or intercommunication, of the blood vessels of the twins is required for the transfer of red and white blood cells. The hormonal influence in cattle from the growing male to the female co-twin has long been known to biologists as well as to farmers ever since F. R. Lillie in 1916 advanced this explanation of the immature nature of the female, called a freemartin. Such a female cow is sterile, due to a stunting of ovarian growth by the hormones from the more rapidly developing testes of the male twin. A corresponding effect in sheep was described in 1953 in *Science* by Stormont, Weir, and Lane, where again the male twin became fertile while the female remained sterile as a freemartin sheep. The situation seems unknown among the many pairs of boy-girl twins and multiple births in humans, although a few examples of blood cell mosaicism show that hormones, if present, could be exchanged.

Blood chimerism is the presence of genetically different kinds of blood corpuscles in one individual. A woman reported by Race and Sanger in 1962 was found to have antigenic differences among her red blood cells in regard to the A, Kell and Kidd antigens. The knowledge of investigations in cattle by Owen in 1945 prompted the question of whether the woman had been twin-born, and she was the one survivor of fraternal twins. About 61 percent of her corpuscles were genetically her own, but some 39 percent stemmed from her brother, who had died as an infant. Her children, as we understand from Owen's studies in cattle, would inherit only from her own genotype and would not include other genes represented in her brother's corpuscles but lacking in her own ovaries. The discarded pangenesis theory of Charles Darwin would have called for some contribution from these acquired cells.

A two-way exchange of blood cells between twins has been reported several times in humans and many times in hoofed animals. One of two such pedigrees from Race and Sanger has been summarized in Table 19-5. All five members of the family were alike in Lutheran, Kell and Lewis antigens, but segregation was exhibited for the characters included in the table. The male twin had 86 percent of his corpuscles of one kind and 14 percent of a kind differing in four genetic respects. Both of his lines of blood cells differed in one or two respects from those of his older brother, but each of the two kinds was present in the bloodstream of his twin sister. She had 1 percent of her corpuscles which matched the major population of her twin brother's blood in three segregating respects and perhaps also in MS genotypes. The recognition of the person's "own" corpuscles depends, not on the majority of blood cells found but rather by means of the secretor phenotype, because the antigens secreted in the saliva come via epithelial cells which do not, so far as is known, have an opportunity to circulate in the

TABLE 19-5 Blood chimeras in fraternal twins

Father	β serum	A_1O	MS/Ms	CDe/cde	Fy^b/Fy^b	Jk^a/Jk^a	sec. A, H, Le^a
Mother	$\alpha\beta$ serum	O O	MS/Ms	CDe/cDE	Fy^a/Fy^b	Jk^a/Jk^b	sec. H, Le^a
Older son	β serum	A_1O	MMS.	CDe/CDe	Fy^a/Fy^b		
$\male$ twin	86%	A_1O	MS/Ms	CDe/cde	Fy^b/Fy^b	Jk^a/Jk^b	sec. A, H, Le^a
β serum	14%	O O	MS/MS	cDE/cde	Fy^a/Fy^b		
$\female$ twin	99%	O O	MS/MS	cDE/cde	Fy^a/Fy^b	Jk^a/Jk^a	sec. H, Le^a
β serum	1%	A_1O	MMS.	CDe/cde	Fy^b/Fy^b		

[a]Data from R.R. Race and Ruth Sanger, *Blood Groups in Man*, Philadelphia, F.A. Davis, 1962, (C) Blackwell Scientific Publications.

blood stream. Because the saliva of the male twin did contain the A substance, his type O corpuscles were diagnosed as introduced. Similarly, the failure of the salivary secretions of the girl to show antigen A reveals that the type A corpuscles which are included in her circulation came from outside her body originally. They could not have come from her mother who had several differences of genotype and therefore must have come from her twin brother.

THE FORMATION OF ONE-EGG TWINS

The less common type of twins in most races is the one-egg kind. Such twins almost invariably come from fertilization by a single sperm and are therefore truly monozygotic. However, a remote third possibility is foreshadowed by a human mosaic traceable to two kinds of sperm from his father and by several insect mosaics also from dispermy. If fertilization of one egg by two sperm should be followed by twinning, a new category of twins would emerge, twins resembling each other more than DZ twins but less than MZ twins. The MZ twins occur with rather uniform frequency around the world, at about $\frac{1}{3}$ of 1 percent of all births. This frequency, although low, helped to answer a question about common diseases and abnormalities, whether there is or is not an influential genetic component. For rare phenotypes, MZ twins and DZ twins are of little help in detecting genetic influences; for conditions near or below 1 percent in frequency consanguinity studies (Chapter 9) are more useful.

An understanding of the modes of formation of multiple human births from a single zygote comes from the study of other members of the animal kingdom. Separation of the cells or tissues to bring about twinning may come as early as the two-cell stage of cleavage, or at about the time the morula stage changes into a blastocyst having either one or two inner cell masses. Even as late as the embryonic shield stage two body axes may result from the concentration of cells which form two primitive streaks instead of merely one, or four instead of two. (These possibilities are all included in Figure 13-4.) Experimental separation of the two-cell stage is effective in forming complete embryos and adults in some species of amphibia and some invertebrates, although it produces incomplete and lethal twins in other invertebrates, whose cells are differentiated very early. The latest time of multiple embryo formation has been investigated in a species of armadillos which regularly produces litters of only one sex, usually three, four, or five in number. This absence of random samples for sex prompted J. T. Patterson to make a study of pregnancy and embryogeny in the nine-banded armadillo, which mates in the fall, hibernates during a few weeks in the winter and produces identically sexed triplets, quadruplets or quintuplets in the spring. Patterson found only one blastocyst in each pregnant animal, and this progressed to the embryonic shield stage before the lower temperature of hibernation arrested development in that stage. Only after the body temperature rose again to normal in the spring did concentrations of cells for the primitive streak of the body axis appear in several places out from the center of the embryonic shield. It is postulated that the drop in temperature is, for the armadillo, the occasion for the diffusion of chemical substances or cell aggregates out from a single concentration gradient to such an extent that reorganization is possible only locally at about four foci instead of at the original center. The observed result of a concentration of embryonic shield or germinal disk cells is the formation of one primitive streak and initiation of one embryo in line with the streak. If primitive streaks are not sufficiently separated at this time, conjoined twins or "Siamese twins" are the result. If the two primitive streaks are very unevenly spaced within the embryonic shield, one embryo may avail itself of much more material than the other; hence monozygotic twins may not always be identical in respect to size or degree of development.

CONCORDANCE OF ONE-EGG AND TWO-EGG TWINS

Monozygotic twins are always alike in regard to marker gene characteristics such as the blood groups but not always alike for phenotypes having poor penetrance. Full sibs are alike on the average only half of the time in regard to those examples of monofactorial segregation preferred for discussion in Part One of this text. Sibs are alike at lower frequencies when either free assortment or reduced penetrance is involved. Hence the illuminating observation is the comparison of the number of pairs of twins concordant for a single trait within each of the two twin categories, MZ and DZ as established by other criteria (Chapter 13). If the monozygotic twin pairs are no more alike in one respect than are the dizygotic twin pairs, then inheritance can have little to do with the particular difference, and accidents in the pregnancy can be crucial. However, if MZ twin pairs are alike significantly more often than are DZ pairs, the finger of the investigator may point to heredity as an active agent. Beyond this conclusion nothing may be decided about the number of gene pairs acting unless sibs are compared with their parents as well as with each other and until studies on the uniformity or variability of the environment may be undertaken.

Congenital Clubfoot. This inturning of one or both feet is present in about one birth per 1000, but among twins the monozygotic pairs are alike for clubfoot much more often than are other pairs. Monozygotic pairs are

33 percent concordant, whereas dizygotic pairs are only 3 percent concordant. Evidently reduced penetrance is at work, or all MZ pairs would be concordant. Since both feet are affected in only half of the clubfooted persons in the general population, it should be no surprise that at least half of MZ twin pairs would be dissimilar in this respect. Another comparison is consistent: the incidence of clubfoot among all children in the families of normal parents having at least one affected child is also 3 percent, which is the same as the concordance figure for DZ twins but far above the population incidence. A third indication of some contribution of heredity is that the subdivision of parents who are also first cousins has an elevated risk of further clubfoot among subsequent children, a 27 percent repeat risk. The phenotype of clubfoot would seem to be the product of some environmental forces interacting with several genic influences.

Aspects of Congenital Heart Disease. Many abnormalities are probably included under this one heading, and it is barely profitable to examine them as a mixed group. Dr. R. C. Anderson concentrated his investigation on those infants who had a persistence of the ductus arterosus, which is normally open in the fetus until birth and which rapidly narrows and closes in a few days after birth. A *patent ductus arteriosus* was sometimes found in a child with other circulatory defects and was sometimes found in mothers who had rubella infection early in pregnancy, but 105 cases of uncomplicated open ductus remained for investigation as a more uniform group. Although their occurrence was only 3/1000 in the general population, it was 14/1000 among the sibs subsequent to the index case, a figure later confirmed in another study by Polani. With such a low repeat frequency from the same parents it is little surprise that four pairs of monozygous twins were all discordant pairs. Patent ductus arteriosus also is a condition which affects the sexes unequally (page 243); females have this short vessel open three times as often as do males. Few of either sex survive to age ten and fewer still become parents, so most cases arise from two normal parents.

Congenital Dislocation of the Hip. This condition may appear at birth, especially if it was a breach presentation, or more likely during the first two years of life or even later. This suggests that it is the result of environmental forces and inheritance interacting, and such is clearly the case. Actual dislocation is rare being found in about 1/1000 children but unevenly distributed by sex; about six times as many girls as boys have dislocations. Only 40 percent of cases in one study had both hips affected, and among the remainder more had the left hip dislocated than had the right subluxated. Monozygotic twins were concordant only 42 percent of the time where less than 3 percent of dizygotic twins in the same study were concordant. Later sibs of index cases were in agreement with the DZ frequency being from 3 to 5 percent affected by actual dislocation.

The physical basis for dislocation is known to be a *shallow acetabular socket* in the pelvis holding the thigh bone less securely than in normal hip joints. This feature seems to be present in the patients and in half of their sibs and in one parent. Hence it may be said that the predisposition to early dislocation of the hip is inherited as a Dominant phenotype, the poor growth of the lip of the acetabulum. Environmental forces at birth or when a toddler or later in life cause about 10 percent of persons with faulty hip joints of this type to suffer an actual dislocation. Children in such families should be examined radiologically, and the susceptible babies deserve a little extra care and attention in regard to falls.

Some Novel Experiments. Just as necessity and love have sometimes moved children into foster homes after birth, necessity and curiosity have made some changes before birth. Several decades ago rabbit eggs were induced to grow without fertilization by any sperm. More recently human egg cells have been saved from the Fallopian tubes which were being excised and even from the ovary for the purpose of studying the normal sequence of growth and maturation in live material. If such eggs are placed on fragments of oviduct they can then be fertilized, and human development will proceed past two of the times of possible twinning. In other mammals many eggs in these stages have been implanted either in the uterus of the female parent or a foster parent, and development has continued successfully. In 1962 blastocysts of comparable ages from rat and from mouse were transplanted and grew in a convenient location under the kidney capsule. It is surprising that the exchanged tissues would grow, until one remembers that these were very young stages, before the time at which antigens begin to form. A similar early tolerance of foreign cells from a fraternal twin, received before antigen-antibody reactions develop, has been described above (Table 19-5) as an example of blood cell mosaicism. Not long after birth the skin of one person will not tolerate and maintain a skin graft from a genetically different person, even from a fraternal twin. The usual rule is that only monozygotic twins may exchange skin grafts or receive a whole organ, such as a kidney (see Figure 13-5). A wide range of investigations may greatly amplify our understanding of early normal and abnormal development and make possible the alleviation of the latter.

SUMMARY

The genotypes of fetuses in different mothers are not autonomous in their development. Rather some phenotypes result from interactions between known antibodies in the mother and known antigens in the tissues of the fetus or embryo. Rhesus incompatibility in rh-negative mothers and ABO incompatibility particularly in O mothers are two such examples. Because the latter acts rapidly and early in pregnancy, it protects against the build-up of rhesus antibodies in mothers otherwise subject to risks from the former. Red blood cells of types A, B or AB invading the maternal circulation are killed quickly if she has anti-A or anti-B in her serum. Blood vessel anastomoses which occasionally form between fraternal twins may occasionally exchange cells before antibodies may be formed in the twins and may give lasting mosaicism to the circulating blood.

Reactions of an unknown specificity also occur in the uterus with enough regularity to mimic or to make phenocopies of certain inherited conditions. Depending on the time during pregnancy when the mother is infected, German measles can cause deafness or cataract or other defects or else no observed change. Again depending on the time of ingestion the drug thalidomide in certain sleeping pills can cause abnormalities of the arms and legs or of the ears, or it may be without effect. Still other environmental assaults have other regular outcomes depending on the time of treatment and on the species and often on the genetic strains of the animals being investigated.

The existence of monozygous and dizygous twins affords a special method of screening for genetic effects. Where the genotype is influential, MZ twins will be concordant for a characteristic under investigation more often than DZ twins will agree. Analysis of harelip, clubfoot and some other defects indicates the presence of genetic differences but does not tell the particular mode of inheritance. The twin method is also used in screening postnatal differences for any single or cumulative genetic effect.

SUGGESTED READING

Edwards, J. H., "The Epidemiology of Congenital Malformations," pp. 297–305 in *Proceedings of the Second International Conference on Congenital Malformations*, New York, International Medical Congress, 1964, 442 pp.

Lenz, W., "Chemicals and Malformations in Man," pp. 263–276, ibid. This is a detailed and first-hand account of the thalidomide disaster by its diagnostician.

Newcombe, H. B., Risks of fetal death to mothers of different ABO and Rh blood types. Amer. J. Hum. Genet. 15: 449–464 (1963). Based on a large study in New York City.

Potter, Edith L., *Rh: Its Relation to Congenital Hemolytic Disease and to Intragroup Transfusion Reactions*, Chicago, Chicago Year Book Publishers, 1947, 344 pp. A clear and well-illustrated summary written six years after the demonstration of the genetic basis of rhesus incompatibility.

Woolf, C. M., Paternal age effect for cleft lip and palate. Amer. J. Hum. Genet.
15: 389–393 (1963). The greater risk for cleft lip with or without cleft palate
is associated with greater paternal age regardless of maternal age as shown by
covariance analysis.

PROBLEMS

19–1 How frequent are Rhesus-incompatible marriages among marriages at
random in a population where the gene frequency of the rh-negative allele
is .4? .2? .3?

19–2 If the gene frequency of the rh-negative allele is .4 in a population, what
percent of all rhesus incompatible marriages will be *Rh/rh* man by *rh/rh*
wife?

19–3 What fraction of the families of the genotypes stated in Problem 19–2 may
expect to have among their first three children
(a) Only *rh/rh*?
(b) The first two *rh/rh*?
(c) Only the third *Rh/rh*?
(d) Any 2 of the first 3 *rh/rh*?

19–4 Why is the deafness caused by rubella infection of the mother a more typical
example of a phenocopy than is the absence of fingers which often follows
the taking of thalidomide?

19–5 (a) What is the relation of vitamin A intake to cleft palate in pigs?
(b) In mice?

19–6 What was the pangenesis theory of Charles Darwin?

19–7 (a) Describe three substantially different times of origin of monozygous
twins.
(b) Are such twins invariably equal at birth?

chapter 20

Heredity, Environment and Phenotype

The terms *congenital* and *inherited* are not equivalent, as has been pointed out in a previous chapter. Some congenital abnormalities showing at birth are the result of unusual environmental assaults upon the growing embryo or fetus. Drugs or infections rather than genes may produce such deviations. Conversely, not all inherited characteristics are present at birth, but many of them will appear within certain time periods of later life. For some physical characteristics this is readily demonstrated (see Gardner's syndrome, page 74). For other characteristics the question of determination being mainly by heredity or mainly by environment will be debatable. After birth the environmental forces of a changing and perhaps erratic nature are acting more vigorously and with more variable outcomes than were possible prenatally. The term phenocopy (page 266) implies that the phenotype can be mistaken for another similar but genetically determined phenotype.

Doubtlessly the normal genotype has a range of possible outcomes, one of which is the rarely reached phenocopy. While the phenotype is developing, particularly during the embryonic period, the range of possible outcomes is narrowed for many of the physical outcomes of the genotype. An epigenetic landscape model of Waddington was designed to show the narrowing fates of cells of the embryo, but the idea of switchpoints passed and of specializations not undertaken has application to the fate of the individual in childhood and in part of adult life. The environment has favored some forms of behavior and has interposed barriers to others. Eventually training encounters limits or seems to reach insurmountable obstacles; and still later senescence may set in, partly from inherent design and partly from the wear and tear of experience. How much of each is determining? That question is often asked and has received many answers, but the answers vary widely and perhaps must long remain matters of conjecture and opinion.

A main problem for the individual is to recognize his opportunities and to avail himself of them while he is also recognizing his limitations and protecting his shortcomings from undue stress. Perhaps the handicaps, like crooked teeth, can be remedied more or less permanently; but in other instances continual treatment is necessary to approach normality, as in the insulin injections and proper management of eating and exercise required by diabetics. If certain environments are able to change a person, we would like to know in advance about the treatments and about the expected changes. If, however, a certain ability is lacking or a certain defect is incorrigible, both patient and doctor would like to forego the futility of seeking immediate training or therapy until further research has accomplished what has been called impossible. However, to find a brand new treatment or prophylaxis requires a method of measuring success; and likewise the continuation of an existing custom of education may depend on some review and new demonstration of the superiority of that method. Hence, when both external training and inherited developmental patterns are tending in the same direction, recognition of a major effect of one of them becomes especially difficult.

FINDING EXTERNAL AND INTERNAL MODIFIERS

A scientific procedure here is more easily stated than applied: one merely holds the environment constant and observes the effect of varied genotypes, then one holds the genotype constant and observes the effect of various environments. In studying human genetics one finds that environments are always varying and that people are not alike except in limited aspects of their phenotype. Among humans only monozygous twins, MZ twins, are completely alike in genotype, but by the time of birth they may be unequal in weight and in development due to a competition in the placental circulation or due to a quantitatively unequal division of tissues if twinning began late (see Figure 13-4). After birth the MZ twins tend to remain together, and the few who are separated do not ordinarily reside in the numerous kinds of contrasting environments which the scientist or the administrator is particularly interested in evaluating. The converse attempt, to study the two types of twins in the same environment, also runs into difficulty. The dizygous twins, DZ, tend to go their separate ways because they are genetically different, whereas the MZ twins tend to remain together more of the time. Hence any comparisons of the demonstrable differences within twin pairs cannot rightly attribute the greater difference within DZ pairs compared with the differences within MZ pairs as entirely due to the genetic differences within the DZ pairs. The environmental differences have varied concurrently with the genetic changes from uniformity to diversity, and so heredity and environment have been confounded. Population studies fortunately may be used to supplement the twin studies.

Twin Studies and Common Traits. Because twins comprise such a small part of the human population their use in the study of common differences is much more feasible than their use to investigate rare abnormalities. Twin pairs are produced in only 1 percent of all pregnancies carried to term, and a somewhat higher mortality than the singly born experience cuts down the number of surviving pairs during the early years of life. The MZ pairs are a minor fraction of this total frequency, and unless one can find a few dozen such pairs showing at least one case in each of the conditions to be investigated the resulting differences may have little numerical meaning. Affected DZ twins are easier to find, but full sibs are 50 times as available.

The method of comparison among twins or other uniform groupings is the classification of pairs as concordant for the abnormality or else discordant. If both have the disease under study, they are concordant. If only one has the disease, the pair is discordant. Normal pairs are omitted at the start of the study. At first thought one might suppose that all pairs of MZ twins would be concordant pairs if in a uniform environment, but this would be true only for the primary product of the genes directly involved and not for the typical phenotype produced later or at least revealed much later. Discordant pairs of MZ twins will be recorded wherever one twin shows the phenotype relatively early while the co-twin remains normal until some later date. A numerical example of this reduced concordance, to be expected because of the variable age of onset of an entirely genetic condition, has been prepared by Anderson, Goodman and Reed as an introduction to their search for the extent of genetic risks in the development of mammary cancer (Table 20-1). Breast cancer seems to involve only a slight increase of incidence among the near relatives (sisters, mothers and daughters), and the contributing environmental factors have not been pinpointed. However low the concordance among the MZ twin pairs may be, even lower concordance is to be expected among the DZ twins of the same age distributions whenever the genotype is important in the disease. If the genotype is unimportant in determining who gets the disease, the concordance figures would not differ significantly for the two types of twins. Comparison of the sizes of metric differences in MZ twins and in DZ twins can be very helpful in detecting whether there is a large difference due to heredity among the inevitable differences due to the environment.

Among twin pairs containing at least one schizophrenic the MZ co-twins are also schizophrenic much more often than are the DZ co-twins of patients.

TABLE 20-1 Concordance expected among monozygotic twin pairs for a phenotype assumed to be entirely genetic but (like breast cancer) with variable age of onset[a]

Age at diagnosis in proposita	Number of co-twins assumed to be MZ	Passed cumulative risk of developing breast cancer, %	Expected No. of co-twins concordant
20–34	19	1.84	0.35
35–49	171	12.33	21.08
50–64	196	39.90	78.22
65–84	155	73.93	114.59
85 up	3	98.11	2.94
	544		217.18

[a]Modified from V. E. Anderson, H. O. Goodman and S. C. Reed, *Variables Related to Human Breast Cancer*, Minneapolis, University Minnesota Press, 1958.

An example of the trend is presented from a study by Slater in Table 20-2. Note that the concordant pairs comprise less than 100 percent of the MZ group; hence we may conclude that the phenotype being observed is not entirely determined by the genotype at the time of classification. The DZ twin pairs show far less concordance, but the 11 percent incidence among fraternal co-twins of cases is far above the 1 percent level characteristic of the general population. Thus an influence of the genotype on schizophrenia is demonstrated, provided that we may assume that the environments of the two types of twins are sufficiently uniform. Nevertheless the exact manner of inheritance is seldom, if ever, indicated by twin studies alone.

TABLE 20-2 Comparison of concordance among monozygous and among dizygous twin pairs ascertained because at least one member of each pair was schizophrenic[a]

	MZ twins	DZ twins	Totals
concordant	28 (65%)	13 (11%)	41
discordant	15	102	117
Totals	43	115	158

[a]After E. Slater, Med. Res. Counc. Spec. Rep. (Lond.), **278**: 1–385 (1953) by permission.

Still other studies have shown that the details of an illness or of a disease and not merely its presence or absence are more often alike in MZ than in DZ twin pairs. Schizophrenia may have a sudden onset or a gradual onset. If it is sudden in one twin it is much more often sudden than gradual in the other member of MZ pairs. A gradual onset in one twin is more often matched by a gradual onset in an MZ co-twin than in a DZ co-twin. This is evidence that there is a genetic component acting directly or indirectly in determining the manner of onset. Another comparison among schizophrenic individuals is their having merely one attack or having several attacks. Monozygotic twin pairs are more often concordant than are dizygous twin pairs in both having a single attack or in both having more than one attack. Again this information shows an effective influence of the genotype but does not indicate the numbers or kinds of genes acting to produce the higher concordance in the genetically identical twins.

A considerable influence of the environment seems plausible in the development of manic-depressive psychoses, yet twin studies suggest an hereditary component also. Manic-depressive psychoses are common enough so that many twin pairs have been located for study by different investigators. A summary of 227 twin pairs from four different published studies has been compiled by Stern and is presented in Table 20-3. Monozygous twins are concordant in 77 percent of the pairs, yet dizygous twins are concordant in only 19 percent of their pairs. If the environment were the main influence in causing this psychosis, particularly among adults, one would expect the concordance figures to be about the same in these two kinds of twins.

TABLE 20-3   Manic-depressive psychosis in twin pairs[a]

	Monozygous	Dizygous	Totals
concordant	48 (77%)	31 (19%)	79
discordant	14	134	148
Totals	62	165	227

[a]After *Principles of Human Genetics*, 2nd edition, by Curt Stern.   San Francisco: W. H. Freeman and Company, 1960.

If aspects of the personality are strongly influenced by the environment, MZ twins raised apart in different homes and schools would show differences which other MZ twins remaining together during childhood would not show. In England recently a BBC broadcast was helpful in locating 44 pairs of monozygotic twins and also a few dizygotic pairs which had been separated as infants or young children. These were studied and compared with an equal number of MZ pairs remaining together and matched by sex and by age distribution with the separated pairs. The results of tests and interviews have been published by Shields in book form including case studies of his own material and summaries of previous studies on separated monozygous twins. Although the study of twins is fascinating, some geneticists have questioned whether it is worth the effort especially for investigating the rarer traits. As limitations of the twin study method are pointed out, other methods of study in population genetics should be considered, for instance, Newcombe's comparison in Figure 13-1.

Rarer Traits and Relatives. A more inclusive procedure than merely studying twins is appropriate for the less common traits. Sibs of cases are more numerous than are twins of cases, and uncles, aunts and first cousins are still more numerous. The various near and distant relatives may be categorized as being one, two, three or more genetic steps away from an index case. For instance, a monozygotic co-twin is zero genetic steps removed, and the genotypic resemblance of the pair is complete. At one genetic step (parents, offspring and sibs including any dizygous twin) the genetic resemblance is on the average 50 percent. At two genetic steps removed (grandparents, aunts and uncles, half-sibs, nephews and nieces, grandchildren) the average genotypic resemblance is 25 percent. At three genetic steps (first cousins and the equivalent, Figure 9-1) the genetic resemblance is $\frac{1}{8}$ among large numbers, and this is also the chance that any rare allele possessed by the index case will be found in a specified relative three genetic steps away. Purely environmental effects may occur uniformly among all these degrees of relatives, but whatever effects may be aided by the genotype or determined by it may be expected to show levels of incidence corresponding to the degree of genetic relationship. Therefore a comparison of rare conditions at successive genetic steps (not merely in a single category of "relatives" of unknown total number) may give indications of the influence of genetic factors in the phenotype.

The incidence of tuberculosis among different relatives of twins who had received attention at tuberculosis hospitals or clinics in New York City and State during a five year period has been studied by Kallmann and Reisner. At that time the incidence in the control population was above 1 percent, the incidence in MZ co-twins was 87 percent, and other members of the family showed intermediate frequencies of this disease (Table 20-4). Note that suggestions of graded genetic differences and of graded environmental differences appear in this table. The half-sibs show a rate well below the morbidity rate of those relatives only one genetic step from the index cases, and the spouses show a rate decidedly above that of a control population of the same age distribution. It is interesting to recall that at one time in history tuberculosis was believed to be a constitutional and hereditary condition, then it was found to require bacterial infection, and now it is widely recognized that both heredity and infection are involved together.

TABLE 20-4   **Tuberculosis morbidity rates in close relatives of index cases who are twins and in controls of comparable ages**[a]

Relationship to index	Percent affected
monozygotic co-twin	87.3
dizygotic, same sexed, co-twin	30.2
dizygotic, opposite sexed	20.5
full sibs	25.5
parents	16.9
half-sibs	11.9
spouses	7.1
none (control population)	1.4

[a]After Kallmann and Reisner, J. Hered. 34:294 (1943) by permission.

Schizophrenia among near relatives at zero, one and two genetic steps from index cases has been studied by Kallmann in the United States and by independent investigators in Germany. From a high of 86 percent schizophrenics among MZ co-twins the incidence fell to about 15 percent at one genetic step and fell further to below 5 percent among grandchildren, nephews and nieces at two genetic steps removed. Somewhat paradoxically the half-sibs, who are also at the two step distance, showed a higher frequency whereas step-sibs and spouses included only 2 percent schizophrenics. The population level of the schizophrenias is about 1 percent. To the extent of reliance on the assumption that stresses in a family are felt by all and that the dangers in civil life are communicated to all, the observed differences may be said to indicate a genetic component in the production of schizophrenia. Conversely, where categories within the same genetic step may show significantly different incidences, some environmental influences including age and selection are doubtlessly at work.

The causes of such bizarre accidents as shown in Figure 20-1 remain an enigma. In appreciation of the foregoing difficulties we shall not attempt to assign relative weights to the genotype and to features of the environment. Rather we shall consider some obvious avenues of influence upon the resultant phenotype just as in Parts One and Two of this text we have considered some of the clearest examples of genic influence from among the estimated thousands of genes in the whole genotype.

AVENUES OF RESTORATION AND PROPHYLAXIS

The developing child is constantly being exposed to influences in school and home and from outdoor advertising which will to some extent change his behavior and perhaps his health. Our purpose is not to repeat the contributions of other learned fields of human endeavor toward the demonstra-

FIGURE 20-1 Twin mishaps. Richard and Robert broke their left arms within a few days of each other. Coincidence or some predisposition? Courtesy of Wide World Photos.

tion of the value of one educational device or another; that had best be left to other authors. Rather we shall concentrate on the more recent contributions from the disciplines of genetics and medicine in maintaining the genetically diseased person on a path of development close to or even within the normal range of potentialities. The examples will be few but typical. The search for therapeutic treatments of disease regardless of origin goes on all the time, even on genetically determined conditions like the several muscle dystrophies. Strains of mice and of fowl with genically determined muscle dystrophy afford opportunities to try out altered diets, injections and other treatments one of which may obviate the development of the genetic defect in a person otherwise doomed to death in childhood. Some of the better known and partly explored avenues of therapeutic influence over genetic disease will be considered.

Nutrition. The food intake will have an obvious effect on the phenotype if there is not enough to eat. Not only is weight affected directly, but height in growing children is stunted by prolonged malnutrition such as has frequently accompanied war. Excess nutrition may endanger a constitutionally weak heart. Still other variations of nutrition are more specific. Vitamin D intake (or its manufacture in the skin under ultraviolet light) is an example of treatment to avoid the more common kind of rickets, that which is correctable by administration of modest amounts of vitamin D. In the development or avoidance of pyloric stenosis during the first one-third year of life there are other influences than merely the sex difference described in Chapter 16. A postponement in the time of appearance of pyloric stenosis was noted among those infants who were born in hospitals rather than at home. A similar delay in the need for surgery was noted among those children fed on a four-hour schedule rather than on a three-hour routine. If the delay of symptoms can be prolonged to the end of the fourth month, the danger period for the appearance of this constriction would be safely passed, and a major operation would be unnecessary.

Normal intelligence may be maintained in spite of certain faulty genotypes by following specific dietary precautions in some instances but not in others. At this writing the Downs syndrome mongoloids seem to be uncorrected by present practices, although the ingenious prescription of dried embryonic cells has long been recommended with the hope of aiding the growth of the brain and tissues generally. Attempts to alleviate the sensory defect of red-green color blindness by the eating of generous amounts of carrots have not been uniformly successful. Fortunately, the low phenylalanine diet now available has maintained and has allowed normal mental growth to many babies who would have become PKU idiots on a normal diet (page 59). A much simpler prescription exists for the child with sex-linked diabetes insipidus; the patient needs lots of water, otherwise a subnormal mentality usually results. As another instance, removal of lactose sugars from the diet of children with the recessive phenotype galactosemia permits normal growth. If the usual milk sugar remains in the diet during the first weeks of life, malnutrition and liver enlargement result. Among those who survive the liver damage, cataracts and mental retardation are noted.

Hormone Therapy. The classic example of the hormonal correction or alleviation of a genetic defect is the injection of the correct amounts of insulin by persons with diabetes mellitus. The dosage must be adjusted to the amount of physical exertion and to the anticipated food intake in order to maintain the carbohydrate reserves high enough to avoid coma, yet keep the hormone level low enough to avoid insulin shock. In this instance an alleviation of a genetic disease has been achieved rather than a cure. Likewise the taking of cortisone in regular doses by patients with rheumatoid arthritis is an aid to the maintenance of joint mobility and tends to arrest or to postpone further degenerative changes in the joints. Aspirin and mild exercise are a further assist in the same direction. Some of the steroids are used to combat metastasizing cancer cells. Steroids may also be used to diagnose the early stage of hereditary glaucoma, which is high internal pressure in the eyeball leading to eventual blindness unless the pressure is surgically relieved.

Fever. Heat alone has demonstrable effects on the phenotype of experimental animals, but heat associated with certain viral infections may be merely correlated and not causal. The household Siamese cat and the similarly shaded Himalayan rabbit have darker fur on their cold extremities and lighter colored fur centrally on their bodies. In the Himalayan strain of rabbits the contrast is sharp. Ears, nose, tail and feet are black while most areas of the body and head are white. However, black fur may be made to appear in the white part of the body if some hair is plucked and if the plucked spot is covered with an ice pack during the regrowth of fur. Other examples of the direct responses of experimental animals, plants and insects to various temperatures are well established.

Season of Birth. From time to time evidence is published showing a slight correlation of season of birth with one or another rare or common genetic condition. It has been questioned whether these signify cause and effect relations or whether the observed correlations are secondary. One viewpoint is that mothers pregnant at different times of the year are subject to different kinds of seasonal infections, and perhaps to other stresses, and that one or more of these specific events rather than merely seasons as such may be responsible for the observed increase in a type of defect or perhaps genius. A correct decision as to any large and consistent seasonal influences awaits further study.

PROBLEMS FOR THE NEAR FUTURE

Postnatal improvements of the normal and of the gifted are of crucial importance today, yet little is known about the inheritance either of normal or of special abilities. It is a matter of faith, but reasonably founded faith, that especially favorable characteristics are inherited. Improvement programs for cattle, for chickens, for hogs, for rabbits and for silkworms, wheat, corn, garden vegetables and a host of other organisms have demonstrated that desirable biological characteristics are inherited. Concurrently, animal and horticultural sciences have demonstrated that the use of a suitable environment and of well-chosen culture methods have a tremendous effect in increasing the desired yields. In any given state or area the practical problem is choosing the appropriate seeds and breeds for the climate and the appropriate culture methods both for the genetic strain and for the changing hazards and opportunities of the environment. Human genetics and education can differ from this experience only in detail, not in the necessity of adjusting and matching genotype and the (largely) man-made environment. We have made little or no progress in fathoming the manner of inheritance of the specific primary mental abilities defined by Thurstone and colleagues. Instead we have made solid progress by studying rare defects, usually physical, yet often biochemical and sometimes behavioral. Conjecture and opinion have wide range in the last category, but scientific progress is a possible reward for effort in this direction. It can proceed on the basis of classic lessons learned on experimental animals and plants and on the intensive investigation of human characteristics for reasons of therapy or of classification. No other species has been as well observed or as well studied by man as has the human species.

Returning to the problem of the subnormal, we note that unsolved problems relate to changes in pressure and perhaps temperature, to which astronauts and others may become exposed. New phenocopies, or old ones at an increased frequency, may appear from exposure to low pressures, or from living at high pressures far beneath the seas. Long term genetic changes may also result from these pressure changes and more likely from any temperature of hibernation which might be invoked for a long journey between this planet and another.

Among the census records of 5,000,000 births there lurks a slight influence of the age of the father on the sex ratio of offspring. Other effects of the age of the mother or father will be pointed out in the next chapters in connection with mutation to the trisomy of Down's syndrome (mongolism) and to the dominant gene mutation of achondroplastic dwarfism.

SUMMARY

Heredity and environment overlap extensively in the shaping of the adult phenotype. A role for heredity is indicated when the closer relatives of an index case with a rare condition show a greater incidence of secondary examples than do the more distant grades of relatives. For more common abnormalities it is sometimes possible to find index cases each having a twin, so that the degrees of relationship may be extended to genetic identity. Even with data from many pairs of MZ and DZ twins the apportionment of outcomes partly to heredity and partly to the environment cannot be designated except in the broadest of terms. For any genetic diseases eventually appearing in both twins during a wide span of years in adult life concordance is necessarily less than 100 percent even among MZ twins. For DZ twins also concordance will be less at the time of investigation than in some later year. In spite of these limitations some phenotypes, like manic-depressive psychoses, appear more often among the MZ co-twins than among the DZ co-twins of patients. The schizophrenias also show higher concordance among MZ than among DZ co-twins or other sibs, and concordance for the time of appearance and for the numbers of attacks tends to be highest among the genetically identical pairs.

Education, it is hoped, can mould or change many phenotypes. Diet can do this in particular ways for some people, not for others. The results of genetic defect can be avoided in the PKU child if he receives a special diet, in the child with diabetes insipidus if he receives large amounts of water regularly, and in the galactosemic infant if milk sugars are removed from his diet. Hormone therapy is a modern necessity for diabetics and for certain other deficiencies with an inherited basis. Other avenues of favorably influencing the phenotype may at intervals be discovered as investigations into the effects of the above, of aging processes and of temperature and pressure changes are pursued.

SUGGESTED READING

Anderson, V. E., H. O. Goodman, and S. C. Reed, *Variables Related to Human Breast Cancer*, Minneapolis, University of Minnesota Press, 1958, 172 pp.

Edwards, J. H., The genetic basis of common disease, Amer. J. Med. **34:** 627–638 (1963). Demonstrates the merging of the "nature-nurture dichotomy" and reviews various methodologies.

Fuller, John L., and W. Robert Thompson, *Behavior Genetics*, New York, Wiley, 1960, 396 pp.

Reed, S. C., *Counseling in Medical Genetics* 2nd ed., Philadelphia, Saunders, 1963, 278 pp. This short book has separate chapters on twins, schizophrenias, manic depressive psychoses, convulsive seizures and "cures" for seven genetic diseases.

Shields, James, *Monozygotic Twins*, London, Oxford University Press, 1962, 267 pp. Includes personal and objective ratings of 44 MZ twins raised apart, 44 other MZ pairs raised together and 11 DZ pairs raised apart.

Slater, Eliot, Psychotic and neurotic illnesses in twins. Med. Res. Counc. Spec. Rep. (Lond.) **278**: 1–385 (1953).

Stern, C., *Principles of Human Genetics*, 2nd ed., San Francisco, Freeman, 1960, 753 pp. Three detailed and well-illustrated chapters explore the interactions of heredity and environment in regard to physical, physiological and mental traits.

PROBLEMS

20–1   List and briefly describe several ways in which MZ twins may become different during infancy, during childhood and during later life.

20–2   Describe ways in which DZ twins may be raised under conditions which are not as uniform as the conditions under which MZ twins grow and mature.

20–3   If in a certain study DZ twins are concordant for schizophrenia in 12 percent of pairs, what frequency of concordance (higher, same, lower) would you expect among MZ twins and among other sib pairs on the assumption
(a) Of a strong environmental influence during infancy?
(b) Of a strong genetical influence?

20–4   (a) Apply a homogeneity Chi-square test to the data from Slater as presented in Table 20-2.
(b) Could this distribution be due to chance?

20–5   Are convulsive seizures in the sibs of affected cases influenced by the fact of seizures in one parent in the following data? A collection of normal parent pairs produced 498 normal sibs and 52 with convulsive seizures while a collection of parents of other seizure cases with one parent having seizures produced 671 normal sibs and 105 with seizures.

part four

Mutation and Evolution

We pass now from the common genetic events of gamete forma-tion and zygotic development to the equally important rare muta-tions and gradual selection of certain types. In all earlier chapters of this text the events described were happening in each generation — segregation and recombination, sex-linked trans-mission, DNA replication and RNA readout, biochemical suppression, epistasis, sex-influences on the expression of certain genotypes, penetrance, hormonal and other intrauterine modifica-tions and, finally, postnatal influences such as infection of the individual. In the next chapters we shall deal with new muta-tions, which arise in some but certainly not in all individuals or families. Mutational events will be rare in contrast to the content of the foregoing text, where mutant genes were used but mutation was left to unnamed ancestors.

Among large numbers of individuals mutations of one kind or another take place. A certain gene suddenly forms a mutant allele of itself. A certain chromatid fails to move correctly along the mitotic spindle, and such a nondisjunction produces a mutant daughter cell or even two opposite mutants with new numbers of chromosomes. Breakage in one or more chromosomes of some gamete and subsequent rearrangements may establish various kinds of stable structural mutants. All such mutations occur spontaneously at a low frequency to which may be added muta-tions induced by the action of irradiation or of chemical mutagens. Mutations occur more frequently at the time of gamete formation, but because mutation may occur at any time in the life cycle some persons are mosaic rather than genotypically uniform. Mosaicism reaches its highest frequency in normal females and in those few male mammals having two X-chromosomes.

Survival is not exactly uniform for all phenotypes, and this contributes to evolutionary change. Some genotypes never live to reproduce; others leave fewer than the average number of offspring. The effects of rare mutation and of mild selection have presented us with racial differences which favor one race or another depending on the time and on the location. The genotype and the environment are difficult to analyze independently, and the distinction between the two tends to break down when the biological environment of an organism is considered. For instance, an external, dormant virus may become an internal agent of disease, or it may become attached to a chromosome and then be inherited as regularly as is a gene. Selective forces within and exterior to the individual seem to have been aiding those genotypes and environments which interact more favorably with each other.

chapter 21

Spontaneous Gene Mutation

The study of genetics would begin here, with the study of mutation, were it not for the existence of sexual reproduction. In an historical and evolutionary sense mutations have provided us with all of the genetic differences which we have been comparing before this chapter. A *mutation* may be defined as a sudden change in the genetic material, a change which is handed on to daughter cells and even to the next generation to produce a *mutant* cell or *mutant* individual. If the descendant cells give rise only to blood cells or pigment cells or cancerous cells or to any other somatic cells, a *somatic mutant* spot or area may result. Alternatively, a mutation in the germ line may pass by way of a gamete into the next generation, where an entire individual will then have a new mutant constitution both in his body cells and in his germ cells. This is what is usually meant by the term mutant individual, the product of a *germinal mutation.* The methods of investigating germinal and somatic mutation are naturally different, but the same process is being studied, sudden heritable change in the composition of the chromosomes.

Mutation in the broad sense may include (A) change in the number of whole chromosomes, (B) gain or loss of parts of chromosomes, or (C) rearrangements of parts of chromosomes or merely (D) changed chemical composition of a locus. The last is the simplest and classic variety of mutation. In their initial appearance within a pedigree (or mass of tissue) most new mutants behave like *gene mutants* or *point mutants.* Later studies, which often depend on the observations of cytologists, show that some apparently simple mutants are in reality *chromosomal* mutants or chromosomal *aberrations.* The known chromosomal aberrations already recognized in man will be described in the next two chapters, and those which presently pass as simple gene mutants (type D) will be discussed in this chapter.

If a new mutant produces a definite phenotypic effect when it is present in single dose, it is said to be a *Dominant* mutant; but if it is not recognized in single dose and shows a phenotypic effect only in individuals with the double dose, it is a *recessive* mutant. The distinction is a practical one rather than a fundamental one. As the biochemistry of cells becomes better known, many genes now known to us only by recessive phenotypic effects will be found to have other phenotypic effects observable in the heterozygote. For instance, the Duchenne type of muscle dystrophy was long recognized only as a recessive and sex-linked phenotype of muscle degeneration; recently the discovery has been made that an elevated activity of the enzyme serum creatine kinase identifies many of the heterozygotes. In other words, the mutant allele is partially dominant in this chemical manifestation although recessive anatomically. New mutants with a Dominant effect are easier to recognize than are new recessive mutants in man; however, studies upon experimental animals indicate that the numbers of new mutant recessives are much more numerous than are new Dominants. Evidently the normal phenotype is protected against the conspicuous and often adverse effects of gene change in single dose. This stability of the normal phenotype possessing one or more mutant alleles at different loci is what one would expect as a product of continued natural selection of man and of his animal ancestors. However, the very rarity of Dominant mutants in man makes their origin more readily detectable.

AUTOSOMAL DOMINANT MUTATION RATES

Direct Method. Estimation of a mutation rate directly is sometimes possible depending on several assumptions. One is that large numbers of individuals will be uniformly observed. Another is that persons will be consistently diagnosed as normal or mutant of the specified variety. A third assumption is that the constitution of the two parents is correctly known. If the new mutant is rare and is a Dominant thus appearing as an offspring of two normal parents, the determination of the mutation rate is easier than in other situations. Several rare Dominant phenotypes have been studied in this manner.

Chondrodystrophy, a Dominant phenotype of shortened limbs on a normal trunk, is easy to distinguish from other kinds of dwarfs and is known around the world. In Denmark the mutation rate of this gene locus was studied by Mørch in 1941 based on the records of a large hospital. There were 12 Chondrodystrophics reported among 94,075 births, but only two of these had a Dwarf parent from which the gene could have been received by ordinary autosomal transmission. Thus the 10 Dwarfs from normal parents represented cases of new mutation in one or the other of the two germ cells received from the parents. The mutation rate from this material was therefore 10/188,150 or 0.000053 gamete, conveniently expressed as 5.3×10^{-5} of the germ cells. In another study by Neel and Schull in Japan a significantly higher frequency of new cases, 17/69,464, led the authors to the conjecture that more than one kind of Dwarf mutant had been recorded in their data.

Indirect Method. A more widely applicable method of estimating mutation rates is the indirect method. Births are not always recorded with uniform regard to the phenotype under investigation; or genetically different babies may delay in showing the mutant phenotype (i.e., Retinoblastoma or cystic kidneys) until a later age. In these and other diseases which are eventually clearly classifiable the estimations may be made on the assumption of equilibrium between new mutations and elimination of the previously existing mutant alleles. It is a matter of record that Chondrodystrophics have fewer children than do their normal brothers and sisters; not many of the male Chondrodystrophics have families, and even fewer of the women do. Thus the old sources of Chondrodystrophic genes diminish in each generation and the phenotype would not be seen were it not for additional new mutations of the normal allele. Conversely, new mutation would raise the frequency of Dwarfs to very high frequencies (50 percent or above) if the above counteracting tendency toward elimination were not at work. It has therefore been assumed that the level of cases of the phenotype in the population is the result of a balance between the origin of new mutant genes and their elimination over the next several generations. For a severely handicapping gene causing death in childhood or at least before reproduction, the prevalence of the phenotype in the population would also be the mutation rate per generation. For a new gene transmissible on the average down through many generations the mutation rate would be considerably smaller than the frequency of mutant individuals among the population at any given time.

The equilibrium between new mutant alleles and the loss of older mutant alleles through lessened reproduction may be visualized in Figure 21-1. It is assumed that in a large population there are no mutants of a certain kind initially. If the first generation included 200 new mutants of whom some live, reproduce and thus contribute some of their mutant genes to the next generation, the fraction of persons in the population mutant for that kind of Dominant gene would increase for several generations from our assumed starting point. However, a gene which is handicapping in the reproductive sense cannot replace the normal allele, so eventually an equilibrium must be reached. With survival of 50 percent uniformly in each generation, an equilibrium is reached at the level of 400 mutant alleles in the population after some five or six generations. A second example may be considered. If

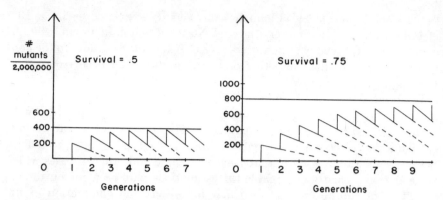

FIGURE 21-1   Model for equilibrium level of total mutants. Vertical lines, new mutations at constant rate in each generation; slanting lines, average reproductive survival of mutant gene.

the reproductive survival of these mutant alleles, old and new, is 75 percent per generation, the equilibrium will be higher and will take more generations to attain from our assumed zero starting level. At the level of 800 mutants there will be a balance between the 200 new mutations and the loss of that 25 percent of the total which on the average do not survive. Other uniform fractions of survival and other uniform mutation rates would move a population to equilibrium in a manner similar to that shown in Figure 21-1.

The equilibrium formula used in the indirect method of estimating mutation rate for the above examples and for any allele with Dominant phenotypic effect follows. The number of new Dominant cases depends on the mutation rate, m, on the number of persons, N, times 2 for the diploid constitution of each person. The number of eliminated cases depends on the number of persons, N, and on the proportion of mutant persons, x, among them and on the selective disadvantage, $1 - f$, where f is the reproductive fitness. The equilibrium equation is, for a new Dominant mutant

$$2\ mN = (1 - f)\ xN$$

which becomes

$$m = \tfrac{1}{2}\ (1 - f)x$$

The value of x is observable if the phenotype is conspicuous. The value of f is the ratio of the (potentially) affected children per affected parent to the total children per sibs of affected cases. In a large Danish study the fitness factor, f, was computed as follows:

$$108 \text{ Dwarfs had 27 children receiving } 13\tfrac{1}{2} \; D \text{ genes} = \cfrac{\cfrac{13.5}{108}}{\cfrac{582}{914}} = f$$

$$457 \; dd \text{ sibs had 582 children receiving 582 } d \text{ or } d \text{ genes} =$$

If the observed x which is to balance this loss is 10 Chondrodystrophics among 94,075 births or (1.063×10^{-4}), the mutation rate, m, turns out to be 4×10^{-5} with a wide standard error. This is within agreement of the direct method of estimation above. Other measured spontaneous mutation rates are in this same order of magnitude.

AUTOSOMAL RECESSIVE MUTATION RATES

The indirect method for estimating mutation rates to autosomal recessives may be formally stated, but it is difficult to apply. Both the observed cases and the eliminated cases involve two doses of the gene, and so the previous factor of $\tfrac{1}{2}$ drops out and the equation is simply $m = (1 - f)x$. To use this equation, however, requires the assumption that all of the reduced fertility affects the homozygotes and almost none of the handicap involves the heterozygote. As little as 2 percent selection against the heterozygote for a deleterious recessive of low gene frequency can severely upset the estimation. A direct method of estimating the rate of new recessive gene mutations seems impossible. Only the ready detection of an effect in single dose would allow us to record the mutation to a new allele, and then by definition of the fact of detection we would be dealing with a partially dominant gene

SEX-LINKED MUTATION RATES

For sex-linked genes the indirect method of estimating the mutation rate to a recessive allele again becomes applicable. If the detectably mutant individuals are measured only among males, the mutation frequency is $\tfrac{1}{3}$ the fitness loss times the frequency among males:

$$m = \tfrac{1}{3} (1 - f)x$$

Estimates of the mutation rates resulting in hemophilia and in muscle dystrophy have been published by several geneticists during the past two decades as large enough bodies of data have been accumulated. Rates of from 2 to 9×10^{-5} gametes have been reported, and these may be considered as not inconsistent with each other or with the rate given for the autosomal Dominant allele of Chondrodystrophy. However, we now know that the earlier data did not distinguish all cases of hemophilia A from the milder and rarer hemophilia B; so those rates separately would be lower than the previous estimate.

TOTALITY OF MUTATIONS PER GAMETE

Although the mutation rates at single loci may seem small, the aggregate of mutations per gamete is appreciable. A first consideration before extrapolating from a few measurements is to recognize that the loci first studied were perhaps selectively those having the higher mutation rates. Mutation rates in plants have been found to vary over a range of two orders of magnitude, over 100-fold. In a review of genetically different but somewhat similar muscle dystrophy phenotypes Morton and Chung found different mutation rates ranging from 9×10^{-5} for the sex-linked recessive form, through 3×10^{-5} for autosomal recessive limb-girdle muscle dystrophy down to less than $\frac{1}{2} \times 10^{-5}$ for the dominant Fascioscapulohumeral type. However, if any of the above is the average mutation rate for 10,000 genes then the mutation rate per gamete will be high enough to make a large minority of eggs or sperm contain a new mutant gene. Muller has pointed out in *Our Load of Mutations* that perhaps as many as every other individual, on the average, carries a new mutant allele not possessed by his father or his mother. The estimate of 10,000 loci came in part from *Drosophila* material where hundreds of loci with visible effects have been identified per chromosome and where more than a thousand genes with lethal effects have been estimated for each of the three long chromosomes of the haploid set.

A direct estimate of the total number of loci in a person is now possible. Our knowledge of genes in any one human chromosome is being paced by the X-chromosome, where at the time of estimation between 12 and 20 loci were already well known. Because this chromosome comprises 5.4 percent of the visible length of all chromosomes of the haploid set we may, for our estimation, predict that there are at least 222 and perhaps 370 gene loci in the gamete capable of showing a phenotypically detectable mutation. If other more necessary genes which mutate only to lethal alleles outnumber the visible mutations, say 2 : 1, a total of 1000 gene loci per gamete is indicated. A higher number of gene loci would be estimated if the ratio of lethal mutations to visible mutations is 10 : 1, as seems to be justified by the vast amount of experimental work on fruit flies. Therefore mutation in general is a common genetic event, if we consider the whole picture; mutation is rare only in a single chromosome or in respect to a single phenotype.

The possibility of an effect of age or of sex upon mutation rate has been investigated, but only one example remains in the category of a point mutation as distinct from larger aberrations to be described in the next chapter. Achondroplastic dwarf mutations were studied by Penrose using the methods of simple correlation and of partial correlation. He found a strong positive correlation between increasing age of the parent's totaled ages and mutation rate among the children, $+0.79 \pm .04$; and simple correlation between mutant offspring and the age of one parent, ignoring the other, gave lower correlations of $+0.39 \pm .09$ with the father's age and $+ 0.28 \pm .10$ with the mother's age, as if each sex were influential on the result. However, by the method of *partial correlation* (holding maternal ages fixed and getting correlation coefficients between father and offspring within fixed maternal age intervals) the age effect was attributable to the father, $+ 0.29 \pm .09$ while by contrast partial correlation between maternal age and Chondrodystrophics became insignificantly negative among fathers of constant age groups. This genic mutation relationship to age is not nearly as pronounced as the chromosomal mutation involving mongolism (see next chapter).

ENZYMATIC CATEGORIES OF GENE MUTATION

The qualitative differences in mutant genes have been categorized by Muller as including amorphs, hypomorphs and neomorphs, among others. The amorphic mutants produce none of the enzyme which the gene at that locus normally produces, the hypomorph produces less of the enzyme or a less efficient form of the enzyme than would its normal allele, and the neomorph produces an enzyme yielding new products not readily predictable from a simple knowledge of what the normal allele has been doing. As a consequence these qualitatively different kinds of mutants may be expected to react differently in respect to dominance in the ordinary heterozygote and in respect to expression in double dose and in triple dose, where the last becomes possible through trisomy and duplication (see next two chapters). Different rates of mutation to neomorphs and to amorphs have been proposed by Frota-Pessoa and Wajntal in regard to the abnormal hemoglobin alleles. They suggest that whereas amorphic mutants form on the order of the foregoing frequencies, 10^{-5}, the neomorphic alleles arise with frequencies of about 10^{-8}, or only $1/1000$ as often as the mutants which do nothing within the cell. This is consistent with the observation of geneticists that in both plant and animal material it is a rare mutation indeed which improves rather than handicaps the individual in which it is acting.

SUMMARY

The point mutations are a particular and common variety of genetic mutations to be distinguished from the larger mutations called chromosomal in contrast to genic mutations. A majority of mutations are probably lethal to the organism rather than merely detrimental and therefore visible. The detrimental mutants of humans which come to attention are mainly recessive to the standard type as we presently and superficially observe phenotypes; however, a few mutants are to Dominant alleles. Most mutants are in autosomes, but a small fraction are sex-linked and these have figured conspicuously in the discoveries of human genetics. Mutation rates of the order of a few dozens per million have been estimated in three categories of new alleles, autosomal Dominants, autosomal recessives and sex-linked recessives. Considering all kinds of chromosomes (X and autosomal), loci with mutant visible phenotypic effects, and loci which are lethal in early stages, Muller has made estimates that from 10 to over 50 percent of zygotes contain at least one new mutant allele not possessed by either parent. Different loci have different mutation rates, and for at least one locus the rate changes with the age of the parent.

SUGGESTED READING

Hobaek, Andreas, Problems of Hereditary Chondrodysplasias, Boston, Oslo University Press, 1961, 175 pp. Mainly for the medical specialist but describing over a dozen inherited abnormalities of skeletal growth.

Kosower, N., R. Christiansen, and N. E. Morton, Sporadic cases of hemophilia and the question of a possible sex difference in mutation rates. Amer. J. Hum. Genet. 14: 159–169 (1962). A mathematical analysis of previous mutation rate estimates for hemophilia and for Duchenne muscle dystrophy. A wide range of possibilities still remains considering the limited size of the available data.

Lenz, W., *Medical Genetics* (translated by Elisabeth F. Lanzl), Chicago, University of Chicago Press, 1963, 218 pp. The gene mutation section of Chapter 4 may best be read now and the remainder deferred until after the next several chapters.

Morton, N. E., C. S. Chung, and H. A. Peters, "Genetics of muscle dystrophy," pp. 323–365 in G. H. Bourne and M. N. Golarz, ed., *Muscular Dystrophy in Man and Animals*, Basel, Switz., S. Karger, 1963. A comprehensive article, of concern here with the question of differentiating mutations at a sex-linked locus from mutations in autosomes.

Morton, N. E., J. F. Crow, and H. J. Muller. An estimate of the mutational damage in man from data on consanguineous marriages. Proc. Nat. Acad. Sci. U.S.A. 42: 855–863 (1956). Derives an estimate of the spontaneous mutation rate from data on mortality during the late fetal to late adolescent period.

Zamenhof, Stephen, Mutations. Amer. J. Med. 34: 609–626 (1963). A review chapter in a special issue on human genetics.

PROBLEMS

21–1   How soon after the mutation has occurred and in what sibs would you expect
to detect each of the following kinds of mutants:
(a) Autosomal Dominant?
(b) X-linked Dominant egg?
(c) X-linked Dominant sperm?
(d) X-linked recessive egg?
(e) X-linked recessive sperm?
(f) Autosomal recessive?

21–2   Discuss the possibilities of detecting somatic mutation to
(a) Dominant autosomal muscular dystrophy
(b) recessive albinism
(c) recessive deuteranomaly

21–3   What would be the mutation rate to the allele for Duchenne muscular
dystrophy if males of this constitution (who die before leaving any offspring)
comprise .00018 of the male population?

21–4   What would be the mutation rate to recessive protan alleles if males of these
constitutions have .99 fitness and comprise .02 of the male population (and
if we arbitrarily assume an equilibrium of mutation to elimination)?

21–5   Retinoblostoma involves progressive blindness in one or both eyes of young
children who usually die of metastasizing cancer in early childhood. In a
study of the occurrence of such cases diagnosed during a ten year period in
the whole state of Michigan, Neel and Falls found that there had been 49
affected children with only normal sibs among 1,054,985 births from normal
parents. What mutation rate does this suggest?

chapter 22

Abnormal Chromosome Numbers

The variations from the typical 46 chromosomes to be described in this chapter have been recently discovered and are sometimes few in number of examples. However, they rest on a solid scientific base composed of previous studies in animals and plants, particularly in the Jimson weed *Datura*. Although the interpretation of some of these mutant types may change, other more typical examples will probably be encountered. One of the phenotypes formerly thought to be due to a Dominant gene mutation, Down's syndrome, now is known to be due to a detectable (therefore Dominant) increase in chromosome number. Other phenotypes at first associated with an extra chromosome were later found to involve an extra length of chromosome attached to an abnormal position (see next chapter on broken chromosomes). In this chapter we shall outline the origin and action of extra whole chromosomes or of missing whole chromosomes.

POLYPLOIDY

Animals occasionally and plants more readily have whole sets of extra chromosomes, a condition called polyploidy. One extra of each kind of chromosome per cell makes a *triploid* individual, two extra sets make a *tetraploid* (Figure 22-1), and even higher multiples like hexaploids and octoploids are known among plants. All these numbers of chromosomes obtained as whole multiples of the haploid (or gametic) number are called *euploid numbers* for the particular species of plant, and they seem to cause less drastic changes in the phenotype than do the many possible departures from the euploid number. In man the first euploid individual reported was a triploid described by Böök and Santesson in 1960 with 69 chromosomes instead of the diploid number of 46. This triploid was male, XXY in constitution, and had a Barr body in the nuclei of cells, but he was

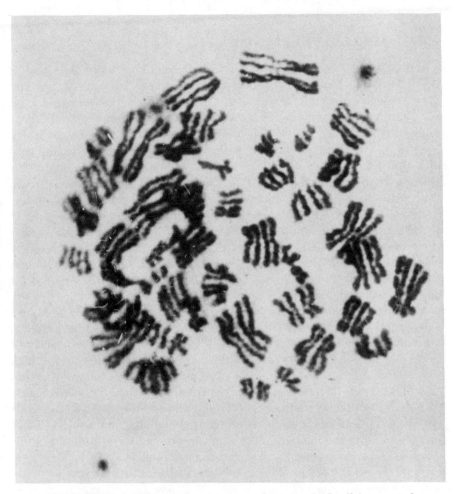

FIGURE 22-1 The 92 chromosomes of a tetraploid cell in arrested metaphase. From W. Zuelzer, Lancet Vol. ii: 1039 (1963, Nov. 16).

more typically male than is the XXY Klinefelter's syndrome on a diploid background. Nevertheless, the triploid showed abnormalities of cerebral development, had syndactyly of hands and feet, was small jawed and obese. It is not known whether such a type can reproduce; triploid *Drosophila* and triploid plants are noted for their poor fertility which often results from pairing difficulties of the chromosomes at meiosis. In view of the survival to birth of this male triploid it is to be expected that triploid females may be encountered at the same rare frequency.

AUTOSOMAL ANEUPLOIDY

Individuals having one, two or a few chromosomes more than or less than the euploid number have an *aneuploid* chromosome number and show various distinctive phenotypes. Those with one extra have a total of 47 chromosomes and are called *trisomic* individuals, but several different kinds of trisomics are known depending on the kind of chromosome which is extra. Thus there are persons with 47 chromosomes showing the condition of Trisomy 21 when the 21st chromosome is the extra one; other persons show Trisomy 17 when that slightly larger chromosome is extra. Still other people with 47 chromosomes show the Trisomy D syndrome involving some one chromosome of that size group, either an extra number 13 or number 14 or number 15 (Figure 2-2). Trisomies for the longer chromosomes have not been reported in the first few years of recently intensified research in human cytogenetics, except for extra X-chromosomes, which are not autosomes and are being conveniently deferred for discussion in a later section.

A distinct human anomaly formerly called mongolian idiocy is known among native peoples on four continents and was described as a clinical syndrome in 1866 by Langdon-Down of England. It involves a slant of the eyes which suggested its older name, and these mongoloids have a thick tongue and sagging mouth, unusual palm and sole prints, obesity, mental growth far slower than normal and minor differences in many tissues (Figure 22-2). These characteristics, collectively known now as typical *Down's syndrome*, appear sporadically from normal parents and usually affect just one child in the family, unlike a less severe and rarer form of it to be described later in Chapter 23. The incidence at birth is about 1/700 among Europeans, but the origin of these trisomics by mutation increases greatly with the increasing age of the mother. Of all the Down's syndrome cases recorded some 40 percent are born to women over 40 years of age, an age group which is producing only about 4 percent of all babies. Similarly, Penrose gives the mean age of mothers at all births as 28.5 years, but the mean age of mothers at the birth of all mongoloids is much higher, at 36.6 years. The life expectancy for these children of idiot mentality used to be about eight years, but Penrose found in 1949 that the life expectancy for the Down's syndrome children had risen to 12 years. Very few families are prepared either emotionally or financially to carry such a burden for even the shorter period of years.

The identification of the typical Langdon-Down syndrome with the presence of a very small 47th chromosome, an extra chromosome number

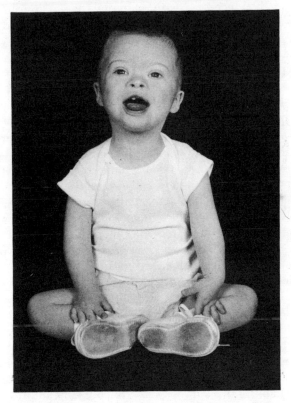

FIGURE 22-2 Boy of age 20 months showing some of the typical features of Down's syndrome: squat sitting posture, eye-fold, open mouth, furrowed tongue and a happy disposition.

21, was achieved by Lejeune, Gauthier and Turpin in 1959 in Paris. This suggests the synonym *Trisomy 21* instead of mongolism and leads in a new direction for the cause of the mutation. The fact that the potential egg cells of women and some other female mammals proceed to the first maturation division and halt in their development for many years may eventually help to explain the age difference of mothers in the production of Down's syndrome children. Meiosis in the egg is not completed until after ovulation and after the stimulation of sperm entrance has been received, and by this criterion the eggs of a woman over age 40 have been quiescent more than twice as long as were the eggs which she ovulated before age 20, when Trisomy babies are very rarely produced. Somehow *primary nondisjunction* of chromosome 21 increases with maternal age. Transmission of the extra chromosome to half of the offspring has been recorded for the very rare cases of eight Trisomy 21 women who bore a child. They were young, 30 or less, at the time they reproduced. Some of them had a normal child when the extra chromosome seems to have gone to a polar body as one consequence of *secondary nondisjunction*, the other women had Down's syndrome children as the alternative and equally likely consequence of separation of three chromosomes.

Other instances of trisomy in humans are much less numerous than the above kind. A single case involves a slightly larger chromosome but normality of phenotype. A 47-chromosome man of good mental ability was diagnosed as being 19-trisomic after his son came to the attention of the medical cytologist because the youngster was of the "mongol" phenotype. Until more examples of this same chromosomal constitution are described, the typical phenotype of the syndrome cannot be defined.

When the 47 chromosomes belonged to the *Trisomy 17* pattern cytologically, two female patients described separately in 1960 showed the same four anomalies. Patau and co-workers described a girl with a small mouth, low-set ears, heart defects and a flexion anomaly of the fingers and toes. Edwards and his co-workers described a girl with the same four abnormalities and also syndactyly, a malformed chest and a webbed neck. Both had the single Barr bodies and the XX-chromosomes of normal females and an extra chromosome of the size group which normally includes just the two number 17 and the two number 18 chromosomes. It may become necessary to change the name of this karyotype to *Trisomy 18* as additional experience is gained either by the cytologist, by the geneticist or by the diagnostician separately or together. Similar numbering difficulties exist within other size groups, such as the 21–22 group of smallest chromosomes described above, or the size D group to follow.

The largest autosome to be found in a viable trisomic mutant in the first four years of intensive karyological studies is some one member from the chromosome pairs 13–15. Because this group is the fourth longest in average size, it has been designated in the Denver system as the D group, and the genotype is better designated as *Trisomy D* or as Trisomy 13–15 rather than by any single number for the extra kind of chromosome among the 47 total. Individuals with Trisomy D were first described by Patau and coworkers in 1960 and by Therman and coworkers at the same laboratory in 1961. Although the patients had heart defects, they were unlike the previously described cases of other syndromes in that they had polydactyly, mental retardation, harelip and cleft palate and severely defective eyes. Thus this kind of trisomy is different from other trisomies as if each kind of chromosome were upsetting the balance of the normal diploid constitution in a different combination of ways.

From a knowledge of plant and animal genetics one may venture a few explanations and predictions in regard to the human aneuploids. The origin of trisomy by primary nondisjunction has been described in *Drosophila* by Bridges and in the Jimson weed by Blakeslee. Some of these trisomic insects live and reproduce in spite of their extra chromosome, all of the *Datura* trisomics do. With 12 kinds of chromosomes differing visibly in length in the haploid set of the Jimson weed, 12 kinds of trisomics were found to arise as new chromosomal mutant plants. In fact, the possibility of 12 kinds was predicted by Blakeslee before the last few were found, but the phenotypes of the trisomics could not be predicted until after the first examples of each had been seen (Figure 22-3). Evidently, so many typical normal genes are at work in each chromosome that they compose a syndrome which is not easily overridden by whatever few mutant alleles of low frequency may be in some of the specimens. Even the longest *Datura* chromosome has a viable and fertile trisomy syndrome, but the longest of the 12 chromosomes contains a very minor fraction of the whole chromosomal genome. In *Drosophila melanogaster* with only four pairs of chromosomes there is evidence (from the many infertile eggs of triploid females) that all kinds of trisomics probably form, but the only surviving trisomic flies have as an extra the very short fourth chromosome or the medium-sized X-chromosome or the long but probably empty Y-chromosome. It will thus not be surprising if humans trisomic for the longer autosomes are found less often and in less variety than trisomics for some or all of the shorter chromosomes. We may also be led to suspect that people may have greater latitude in departing from the customary X-Y complement than from the number of autosomes.

ABNORMAL NUMBERS OF THE X-Y PAIR

The sex chromosomes contribute to the aneuploid totals of chromosomes both downward to 45 and upward to 47 or more. The 45 chromosome variety is now recognized only as XO individuals. These are immature females with webbed neck described long ago as *Turner's syndrome* cases and now classified as *monosomic for X*. They occur in a frequency of about 2/10,000 as new chromosomal mutants. The corresponding monosomic, YO, is unreported among humans, mice and fruit flies.

With only one X-chromosome in the Turner's females the possibility of dominance of X alleles does not arise as in the usual female, and so recessive sex-linked phenotypes appear among the tested Turner's syndrome girls

FIGURE 22-3   Seed capsules on Jimson Weed plants having the usual 24 chromosomes (top center) or 25 chromosomes. A different phenotype characterizes each of the 12 different Trisomies according to the identity of the extra chromosome. The longest chromosome is named 1·2; the shortest is named the 23·24 chromosome. From Amos G. Avery, Sophie Satina, and Jacob Rietsema, *Blakeslee: The Genus Datura*. Copyright © 1959 The Ronald Press Company.

with the same frequency as among their brothers or among males in the population. For instance, about 8 percent of the XO girls show one or another form of color blindness, as do the males listed in Table 12-2. The Turner's syndrome girls either tend to show all the recessive sex-linked phenotypes of the father, if the X-chromosome is from him, or they tend to show all of the sex-linked characters of the X-chromosome (crossover or noncrossover) received from the mother. The XO monosomics seem to be distributed proportionately among all births and show no correlation with age of mother or with birth order, although Grell has in 1964 doubted this for good reasons. Survival of the XO karyotype seems to be poor; Twiesselmann and colleagues at Brussels have estimated that only about 1/14 of the XO zygotes survive and are diagnosed.

The aneuploid karyotype *Trisomy XXY* was demonstrated by Jacobs and Strong in 1959 in a very high percentage of cases previously described as having Klinefelter's syndrome. As boys such males are normal; as adults they are fairly normal physically but with the rounded proportions of a eunuchoid person and with a very low sperm count. Among live born males some 2 to 3 per 1000 have a Barr body in their nuclei and may be judged to be future Klinefelter's syndrome men and probably sterile. Among adult males of subnormal intelligence the frequency is ten times as great, or from 1 to 3 percent of that selected group. Among adult males attending infertility clinics, a similar 3 percent estimate of the frequency emerges. The syndrome is even more often associated with oligospermy, if the latter is defined as having a sperm count below 1,000,000 per milliliter. If such a person should reproduce, half of his offspring would be expected to receive one chromosome and the other half might receive any two out of the XXY group by secondary nondisjunction. Confirmation of either or both of these possibilities may have to wait for many years because of low fertility of the Klinefelter type.

The corresponding aneuploidy in the other sex is *XXX Trisomy*. Women of this type are normal in appearance, but many of them never menstruate. About 1/1000 live females at birth have the extra Barr body identifying them as XXX individuals. If the search is made among mentally defective females the frequency is about 7/1000; and among women complaining of never having menstruated the frequency of the Triple-X syndrome is about 40 percent. The cases are sometimes called "metafemales" by analogy with similarly trisomic-X *Drosophila*, which are also female in appearance but sterile. However, some of the human X-trisomics have reproduced, but the first 10 children to be reported were all normal instead of being distributed approximately equally among the two possible chromosomal classes, normal diploid and trisomic mutants. Perhaps the assumption of a uniform genotype from cheek lining and blood cells to include the ovary is faulty in these instances, and an alternative hypothesis of mosaicism will be considered in Chapter 24.

Several higher aneuploids among humans have been reported. A *tetrasomic* female is known to have 48 chromosomes including the XXXX constitution. Other kinds of tetrasomics having XXYY or XXXY are males and have one or two Barr bodies, respectively. The simplest rule is that Barr bodies number just one less than the number of X-chromosomes seen in dividing cells. Five known *pentasomics* of constitution XXXXY among 49 chromosomes are all males. These excesses of the sex chromosomes raise a question of what is happening to prevent these extra chromosomes from killing the individual before birth, and a possible answer will be discussed under the heading of the Lyon hypothesis in a section of Chapter 24 on regulatory mosaicism.

Sometimes the matching of chromosomes by length and by arm ratio indicates that a person with 48 chromosomes is not a tetrasomic but rather is a *double trisomic* for two different kinds of chromosomes. Uchida and Bowman have reported an individual with three X-chromosomes and three number 18 chromosomes. Ford and others have reported instances of a different combination trisomy, a male who had both Klinefelter's and Down's syndromes; his 48 chromosomes included three number 21 chromosomes and also XXY from the sex chromosome kind. (See Figure 23-4.)

A forecast should be made of the effect of simple trisomy on recessive phenotypic segregation from a testcross. Although persons with only one Dominant and two recessives in the trisomic "pair" will continue to show $1:1$ segregation in a testcross family, the meiotic segregation of a *DDd* genotype will usually produce only $\frac{1}{6}$ recessive gametes. The diploid phenotypes would be 1 *dd* to 2 *Dd*, and among the three trisomics complementary to the diploids all would have at least one dominant *D* allele. Thus the successful demonstration of a significant $5:1$ ratio from a known category of trisomics would demonstrate which chromosome pair (or size) carries the gene locus segregating in non-Mendelian fashion. The above altered transmission ratios of the three chromosomes after the extra chromosome has arisen in the germ line of an individual involve *secondary nondisjunction* of the set of three in contrast to the initial mutation in the chromosome number as described next.

PRIMARY NONDISJUNCTION

The origin of trisomics and of monosomics as new chromosomal mutants is usually due to nondisjunction of partner chromosomes. A failure of normal chromosomal separation although rare may occur in any cell division, during mitosis or during one of the divisions of meiosis. The result of either kind of rare event will be the formation of a daughter cell or cells with less than or more than the normal number of chromosomes. These cells will tend to perpetuate their kind by continued cell division, which usually reverts to following the normal rules of mitosis but with a mutant number of chromosomes to be copied and transmitted.

Mitotic nondisjunction is the simpler process. In it the replicated chromosomes, the two chromatids, fail to separate at anaphase fast enough to get into the nuclei of daughter cells. As a result of nondisjunction during mitosis, one daughter cell receives one less chromosome (in the simplest case) and the other daughter cell may receive an extra chromosome. Figure 22-4 shows the kinds of mutant and normal cells resulting from the nonseparation of the chromatids of one chromosome in a simplified cell

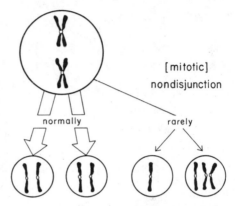

FIGURE 22-4 Products of mitotic nondisjunction in an embryo or in any later stage: cell with $2n - 1$ and cell with $2n + 1$ chromosomes.

diagram showing only two chromosomes as its typical euploid number. The resulting cells, if they survive and multiply, would give a mosaic of two or three different genotypes within one person at later times in life.

Meiotic nondisjunction is fundamentally similar to the above but may occur at either the first maturation division or at the second. Furthermore, the details of oogenesis and of spermatogenesis will not be the same. The results of irregular meiosis in the male are depicted in Figure 22-5 where attention is concentrated on the optically different heterosomic pair, the long X and the short Y-chromosome. If the homologous centromeres fail to segregate from each other at the first maturation division, the two kinds of secondary spermatocytes produced will have different numbers of chromosomes. One of them will transmit neither an X nor a Y to its two resulting sperm, and the other will be able to hand on both X and Y to the same sperm. Consequently, any zygote resulting from the "empty" sperm of Figure 22-5 would have the constitution of a Turner's syndrome, and any zygote from the other kind of nondisjunctional sperm would have the trisomic constitution of a Klinefelter's male. Such a male would inherit both a Y-chromosome and an X from his father, and in the posses-

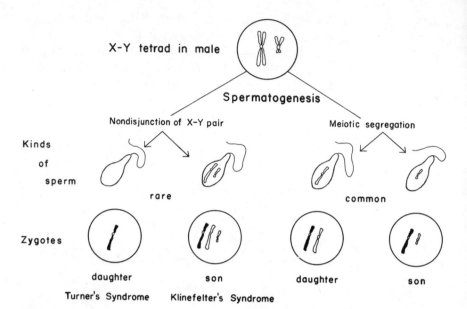

FIGURE 22-5 Consequences of nondisjunction in the male illustrated for the X-Y pair of chromosomes: a daughter monosomic in respect to X; a son trisomic XXY.

sion of a paternal X he would resemble his father for any Dominant alleles in that X-chromosome. The technical name for this phenotypic resemblance of father and son is *patroclinous inheritance*. Ordinarily, it is the Y-chromosome which shows patroclinous transmission generation after generation. It is unusual for any other chromosome to do so.

Meiotic nondisjunction in oogenesis similarly involves the production of a gamete with only 22 chromosomes or a gamete with 24 chromosomes, but the resulting zygotes are more varied. Figure 22-6 shows the consequences of the failure of first division segregation in the female. Except for the sperm drawn this diagram is applicable to primary nondisjunction of any pair of chromosomes either shorter or longer than the XX pair. After fertilization by the two kinds of sperm, the nondisjunctional eggs become four kinds of zygotes. Two of these are the Turner's type daughter and the Klinefelter son just as following X-Y nondisjunction in the male. One of the other zygote types is the metafemale having chromosomes XXX and two Barr bodies. The fourth and last possibility is the monosomic type YO, which has not been reported and is presumed to be lethal at an early stage of development both in mammals and in the fruit fly *Drosophila*.

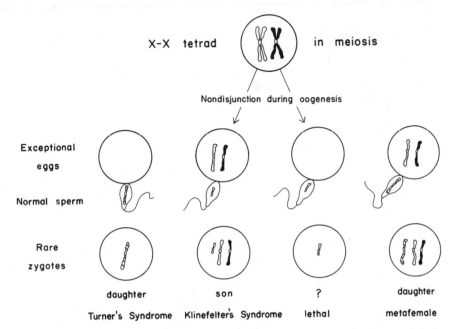

FIGURE 22-6 Products of nondisjunction during oogenesis illustrated with the X-X pair. Offspring of types XO, XXY and XXX have been observed, but the YO product remains undescribed.

It may be viewed as a particularly extreme kind of aneuploid, one which is *nullosomic* for X. Such a complete absence of a chromosome having many genes in it and customarily present twice or once is indeed a great departure from the usual diploid type. The short Y-chromosome can hardly be expected to substitute for the long X-chromosome in a YO embryo.

Only the first maturation division was assumed to be unusual in the above two paragraphs, but there is evidence for a normal meiosis I being followed by nondisjunction during meiosis II. Through this rare event a heterozygous but normal mother may give rise to a homozygous recessive son, and among Klinefelter's type sons such evidence for nondisjunction of the X-chromosomes during oogenesis has been obtained. The details of one manner of doubling an X are shown in Figure 22-7. If a woman is heterozygous for color blindness and if the *cb* half of the tetrad remains in the egg cytoplasm during the normal formation of polar body I, doubling by nondisjunction may take place in the next division. If the kinetochore holding the two chromatids of the dyad fails to split soon enough, both of the incipient X-chromosomes may remain in the egg (as shown) while

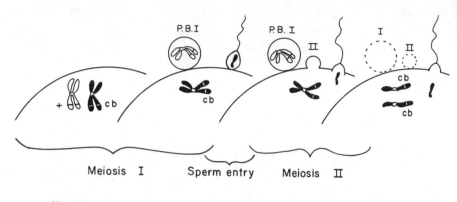

Meiosis I   Sperm entry   Meiosis II

X tetrad
of heterozygote

2 normal dyads

dyad delayed

X X chromosomes
of homozygote

FIGURE 22-7 One mode of origin of a homozygous color-blind son (XXY Klinefelter's syndrome) from a heterozygous mother and normal father, following nondisjunction during the second maturation division. Note that polar body II has received neither of the darkened chromosomes.

the rest of a normal set of chromosomes is going into polar body II (here shown empty of any X). This leaves the material for two separate X-chromosomes in the mature egg while polar bodies I and II degenerate. If a Y-chromosome sperm has entered this egg, the recessive alleles which are common to the two X-chromosomes will be able to show phenotypic effects. In Figure 22-7 the absence of crossing over in the region between the centromere and the *cb* locus during meiosis I is required for color blindness to appear in this Klinefelter's syndrome male.

Stern has pointed out that an alternative sequence of events can produce homozygous color-blind XXY sons from heterozygous mothers but in lower frequency than the above. If single crossing over occurs between the kinetochore and the locus of the recessive and if nondisjunction of these kinetochores also occurs in the first maturation division, then the random orientation of the regular and the extra dyads in the secondary oocyte will from half of such cells deliver two X-chromosomes homozygous in the region beyond the crossing over, one homozygous pair to polar body II, the other pair to the egg. Available evidence does not distinguish between the possible times of primary nondisjunction as being at the first or the second maturation divisions, but several cases of homozygous recessives already reported must have originated in the female rather than in the other parent. Ferguson-Smith and his colleagues have distinguished two XXY persons resulting from maternal nondisjunction and two persons resulting from failure of the paternal X and Y to segregate and point out the possibility that the former kind have older mothers than is usual.

Primary nondisjunction in more than one chromosome pair would result in double trisomy, or triple trisomy or perhaps in even more extreme aneuploids of inviable constitution. A complete failure of nuclear division during or before maturation in one parent could lead directly to a diploid gamete and hence a triploid zygote having 69 chromosomes. After zygote formation failure of anaphase separation could produce a tetraploid individual or a tetraploid clone of cells having 92 chromosomes in an otherwise diploid individual.

SUMMARY

Abnormal numbers of chromosomes such as 45, 47, 48 and 69 instead of the usual diploid number are occasionally found in persons who seem to have a Dominant mutant phenotype. These chromosome numbers arise either by the complete failure of a nuclear division before a gamete is formed, which can give rise to a triploid, or by primary nondisjunction of just one pair of chromosomes to produce a trisomic mutant with 47 chromosomes or a monosomic mutant with 45 chromosomes. If the trisomic should be fertile, its gametes would be the product of secondary nondisjunction and would be distributed in a 5 : 1 ratio for any locus with two Dominant and one recessive alleles present and simultaneously in a 1 : 1 ratio for the extra chromosome.

Several autosomal trisomies have been described, each kind involving a different one of the shorter chromosomes. The best known human trisomy coincides with the phenotype which used to be called mongolian idiocy and which is now preferably named for its discoverer Down's syndrome. Almost all Trisomy 21 cases arise as a chromosomal mutation from genotypically normal parents, and the mutant offspring rarely reproduce. New mutations to Trisomy 21 arise much more often in older mothers unlike most other mutations. Other chromosomal mutations from the normal euploid number of 46 chromosomes are also rarely formed, to Trisomy 17 (in the E group) and to Trisomy D (involving some member of the 13–15 group).

Fully as many aneuploid mutants are already known from the heterosomic normal pair. The Turner's syndrome female with sterility has only 45 chromosomes and is X-monosomic because of the lack of a partner sex chromosome. She shows the recessives carried in her one X as readily as a male would. Many Klinefelter's syndrome males who tend to be sterile as adults are now shown to be Trisomic XXY among their 47 chromosomes.

In such a person recessive phenotypes show less often than in males of the same population but more often than among the females who also have the usual two sex chromosomes. A few trisomic XYY males are known. Tetrasomic XXXY males with 48 and pentasomic XXXXY males with 49 chromosomes are also known rarities. Mixed trisomics having the same chromosome totals as the above are possible, and several XXY 21-21-21 double trisomic individuals have been described. Where trisomy is the cause of a certain syndrome, sibs and relatives with the normal number in the karyotype have no elevated risk of developing the syndrome of such a Dominant phenotype.

SUGGESTED READING

Avery, A. G., Sophie Satina, and J. Rietsema, *Blakeslee: The Genus Datura*, New York, Ronald Press, 1959, 289 pp. An exemplary study from plant genetics.

Brit. Med. Bull. 17 (No. 3): 179–212 (1961). Contains six excellent review articles on human cytogenetics by C. E. Ford, L. S. Penrose, W. M. Davidson, Bernard Lennox, P. E. Polani, and by D. G. Harnden and P. A. Jacobs.

Gustavson, K. H., B. Hagberg, S. C. Finley, and W. H. Finley, An apparently identical extra autosome in two severely retarded sisters with multiple malformations. Cytogenetics 1: 32–41 (1962). A detailed comparison of two sisters having almost the same constellation of characteristics with other individuals representing typical Trisomy D or Trisomy E.

Grell, Rhoda F., and J. I. Valencia. Disruptive pairing and aneuploidy in man. Science 145: 66–67 (1964). The authors suggest that the increasing number of associated aberrations in human families may find a precedent in the effects of crossing over upon disjunction in *Drosophila*.

Hauschka, T. S., J. E. Hasson, M. N. Goldstein, G. F. Koepf and A. A. Sandberg, Amer. J. Hum. Genet. 14: 22–30 (1962). Describes progeny of a fertile XYY male in which there was primary nondisjunction of another pair resulting in a Trisomy 21 daughter.

MacLean, N., D. G. Harnden, W. M. Court-Brown, J. Bond, and D. J. Mantle, Lancet Vol. i: 286–290 (1964, Feb. 8). Gives details on karyotypes of 37 babies found to have unusual numbers of Barr bodies among 20,725 babies born in hospitals in and around Edinburgh.

Penrose, L. S., Parental age in achondroplasia and mongolism. Amer. J. Hum. Genet. 9: 167–169 (1957). Shows by partial correlation methods that Achondroplasia mutants increase with age of father within uniform age grouping of mothers and that the reverse is true for Down's syndrome.

PROBLEMS

22–1   State which of the following involve an aneuploid number of chromosomes: diploidy, duplication, haploidy, nullosomic for X, tetraploidy, triplication, triploidy, Trisomy 21, Turner's syndrome, XXYY.

22-2 (a) Do you believe that the normal genes in chromosomes 15, 18 and 21 are fully dominant over common and rare recessives in the partner chromosomes?

(b) Why?

22-3 With each of the following five syndromes what chromosome may be suspected of being represented in abnormal number in an affected person?

(a) heart defects, polydactyly, low I. Q., small eyes, harelip and cleft palate

(b) heart defects, small mouth, low-set ears, flexion anomaly of fingers and toes

(c) girls with webbed neck, short stature, not maturing

(d) tongue thick and furrowed, squat posture, low I. Q., obliquely set eyes

(e) male appearance, low sperm count

22-4 (a) If a person having Trisomy 21 were to mature and to reproduce with a normal spouse, what ratio of normal to Down's syndrome children would you expect among the offspring?

(b) Would this be conspicuously affected among births to an older mongoloid parent?

22-5 Redraw the chief aspects of Figure 22-6 to show the several consequences of crossing over between the centromere of the X-chromosome and the locus of *cb* followed by nondisjunction in the first anaphase.

chapter **23**

Aberrations Arising from
Broken Chromosomes

Chromosomes are usually immutable in the sequence of their gene loci, but rarely they do break. If the broken pieces do not heal but instead join in a new order, a chromosomal *structural mutant* is the result. This structural Rearrangement of one or more chromosomes need not involve the mutation of any gene to a new allele, a category of mutations already defined as point mutations in an earlier chapter. Yet the phenotypic effects of these three kinds of mutants, genic mutants, numerical mutants and structural mutants, may overlap to a degree which annoys the scientist and those who consult him. Many a chromosomal mutant has successfully masqueraded as a Dominant genic mutant before its basic nature became known. The combined efforts of geneticists, cytologists and clinicians may be required to demonstrate that an assumed Dominant gene is really one or another form of chromosomal Aberration. Because a genic mutant does not involve any demonstrable length of chromosome such as two or more adjacent loci or a whole chromosome added or lost, point mutants are in practice defined by indirection. More cases of Dominant "genes" may in the future have to be renamed as Duplications, Deficiencies or other changes in number or in position of chromosomal loci.

CLASSIFICATION OF STRUCTURAL MUTANTS

The chromosomal mutants which do not directly and immediately involve an increase or decrease in chromosome number (previous chapter) all involve breakage of one or more chromosomes followed by Rearrangement of two or more parts. The most common types of structural mutants to be encountered are conveniently called Duplications, Deficiencies, Inversions and Translocations of one or more normal sequences of genes.

As the name implies, a *Duplication* individual has a length of extra material but not a whole extra chromosome as in a Trisomic person. The cells of a *Deletion* individual have a sequence of genes missing from part of a chromosome unlike a Monosomic aberration of a whole chromosome. An *Inversion* type has the order of some gene loci reversed within the chromosome; hence the four genes bordering the two break points each have one new neighbor after the breakage and reunion. Translocations usually form as two chromosomes bearing *reciprocal Translocations* after a two-way exchange of pieces. These distal pieces are usually unequal in length by mere chance, and almost always contain loci which are not homologous. In both respects Translocations, which are rare, differ from complementary crossovers, which are frequent and so were described earlier in Part Two. Combination cell types such as a Translocation, larger Duplication, small Deficiency are found.

Structural Aberrations of the above and still rarer types of chromosomal mutants may well be classified according to their mode of origin (Table

TABLE 23-1   Classification of some structural mutants

I. Originating from a single break in a chromosome
   A. terminal Deficiency and centric anaphase bridge, unstable mutant
      (See breakage-fusion-bridge cycle, Chapter 24, mosaic)
   B. *Isochromosomes:* equal-armed V and v from replicating J by transverse
      division of the centromere, or II, B, 1 below

II. Orginating from two available breaks per nucleus
   A. exchange between two different kinds of chromosomes
      1. *reciprocal Translocation* chromosomes (inheritable)
      2. anaphase bridge and distal fragment or fragments ($\pm$ lethal)
   B. exchange between homologous chromosomes
      1. *Isochromosomes:* two unequal arms exchanged
      2. *pseudocrossovers:* unequal exchange in same arm
             one Deficiency, one Duplication chromosome
      3. complementary crossovers without any aberrations (very common in
         meiosis, as rare as mutants during mitotic divisions)
   C. exchange within one chromosome
      1. one break in each arm: a. *pericentric Inversion*
                  b. *Ring chromosome* and terminal fragment
      2. both breaks in same arm: a. *paracentric Inversion*
                  b. *Deletion* or Deficiency and fragment

III. Originating from three or more breaks
   A. *Duplication* by insertion, and *Deletion*
   B. other combinations, e.g., Inversion and Translocation in same cell

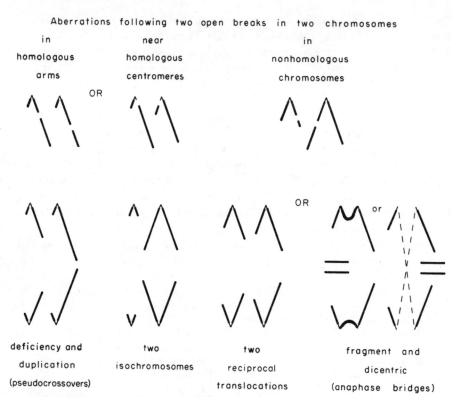

Aberrations following two open breaks in two chromosomes

in homologous arms

near homologous centromeres

in nonhomologous chromosomes

deficiency and duplication (pseudocrossovers)

two isochromosomes

two reciprocal translocations

fragment and dicentric (anaphase bridges)

FIGURE 23-1   Two-break Aberrations. Above, location of breaks. Below, anaphase appearance of the mutant chromosomes. The simpler but rarer situations are depicted at the left; the more representative breaks and their immediate products are shown at the right.

23-1). Surprisingly, a single break in a cell contributes very few viable Aberrations. The break either reheals (by *restitution* in technical language), or the replicating basal portion joins back on itself so that the two separating centromeres are tied together by a visible *anaphase bridge* which interferes with the next and any later cell division. An anaphase bridge tends to produce mosaicism if it survives and multiplies. The origin of *Isochromosomes*, any chromosome with an exactly median spindle attachment, is uncertain, but a misdivision of the centromere transversely, instead of longitudinally between the separating chromatids, would produce one equal-armed V chromosome, representing genes of the long arm twice, and another smaller V chromosome, containing Duplications of all the genes of the short arm of the ancestral chromosome. Each would also be Deficient for the loci formerly in the other arm of the chromosome as it existed before this kind of wholesale mutation.

The availability of two breaks open at the same time in a nucleus is sufficient for the formation of many kinds of two-way exchanges either between chromosomes (Figure 23-1) or within a single chromosome (Figure 23-2). Some of these new unions produce new but discrete chromo-

Some two—break aberrations formed in one chromosome

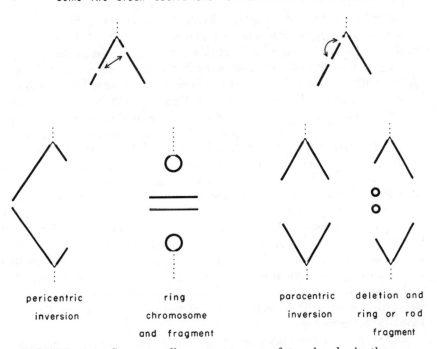

| pericentric inversion | ring chromosome and fragment | paracentric inversion | deletion and ring or rod fragment |

FIGURE 23-2 Some equally rare outcomes of two breaks in the same chromosome. Above, diagram of break locations before rearrangement. Below, stylized appearance at anaphase separation. One Inversion is unnoticed.

somes which can pass through cell division without mechanical difficulty, but other unions connect two basal portions of the chromosomes which will then form an anaphase bridge whenever their two centromeres start toward opposite poles of the mitotic spindle. The first or eucentric exchange attaches the free fragment of one chromosome to the basal portion and therefore spindle attachment of the other, and vice versa, to produce a mechanically workable arrangement which may be encountered in subsequent cells, tissues or generations of persons. Many different kinds of reciprocal Translocations will be formed when there are two or more breaks per cell, because there are so many available chromosomes to be broken.

In the rarer event that the two broken chromosomes are homologues which then exchange their free ends (in eucentric fashion) then there are certain special products. Two *Isochromosomes* might be formed in this manner, rather than by misdivision of the centromere described above, if the two breaks were in different arms of the chromosome and close to or equidistant from the centromere (see Figure 23-1). Thus a pair of J-shaped chromosomes would become a large V and a small v chromosome, the arm size of each corresponding to the length of the long arm or to the length of the short arm of the original J-shaped chromosome. More often the arm lengths would remain different. Other homologues which have breaks in the same arm and exchange the free ends would usually be unequal Translocations to the cytologist and Pseudocrossovers if discovered by genetic methods. The change in chromosome arm length characteristic of reciprocal Translocation is represented in Figure 23-3 for comparison with a similar but much more common and exact process, crossing over. Note that four chromatid strands are present when crossing over occurs, but that only two strands need to be present and broken for Translocation to take place. Although the cell in which the Translocation occurred has all of its gene loci present, the upper chromosome has become Deficient for the *C* region and the lower chromosome has a Duplication of the *C* locus and all intervening genes. Translocations in general may be represented in this same figure by substituting letters from another part of the alphabet for the chromosome of one of the colors, and for good measure one could start with the two chromosomes being of unequal lengths, and therefore obviously not homologous.

A single chromosome broken at two places can have its pieces recombine in four major formations which are new, as shown near the bottom of Table 23-1 and in Figure 23-2. It is assumed that neither break restitutes, for a restitution would take the cell back to a one-break situation. The four chromosomal mutants possible are two classes of Inversions, one internal Deficiency and a Ring chromosome plus fragments temporarily accompanying the last two. If the breaks are in separate arms and the free ends are exchanged a *pericentric Inversion* is produced; this usually changes the relative arm lengths. Breaks in the same position can, however, produce a *Ring chromosome* containing a centromere and leaving the two distal fragments separate or joined together. The Ring chromosome will necessarily be Deficient for the gene loci beyond the two breaks. If both breaks are in the same arm, the part between them can form a *paracentric*

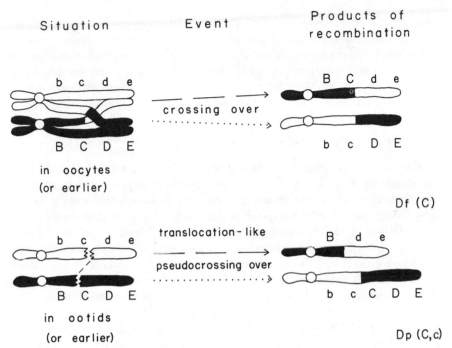

FIGURE 23-3 Common and rare methods of exchange between chromosomes, illustrated within one pair. Crossing over transposes exactly equal amounts of material which is homologous. As a rare mutational process the Translocation exchanges are usually unequal enough to produce new arm lengths of chromosomes and usually are between nonhomologues at random rather than as pictured above. Deficiencies and Duplications are products of Translocation but not of crossing over.

Inversion without changing the arm ratio. Alternatively, the part between the two breaks can be lost to the cytoplasm of the cell as a small ring or fragment, and the remaining two pieces can join to form a *Deletion* chromosome. Most chromosome Deficiencies are probably interstitial Deletions of this type rather than terminal Deficiencies, since a broken chromosome end tends to stick to another broken chromosome, as was noted above in regard to Aberrations from single breaks.

If more than two breaks per cell provide points for exchange or omission, various combinations of the above can form. A *Duplication* can be produced directly in a three-break cell, if two of the breaks cut out a piece from one arm of a chromosome and by luck that piece is inserted between the open ends at a third break. The secondary formation of Duplications during meiosis in a reciprocal Translocation heterozygote or in an Inversion heterozygote undergoing crossing over has been mentioned above. Other three-break Rearrangements are possible, such as a Translocation adjacent to an Inversion, or a progression of three broken ends transferred to three different centric portions of chromosomes. Such complications are of special concern to the student of induced mutation and of radiation effects.

GENETIC EFFECTS OF STRUCTURAL MUTANTS

The known structural mutants behave like Dominant factors in that they are recognizable in single dose in those rare heterozygotes who carry the aberrant chromosome or chromosomes. Each structural mutant is appropriately named with a capital initial letter to denote that Dominance, a numbering of the chromosomes involved (or a lettering for the chromosome size group involved) plus some unique designation as to its discoverer or its historical origin. Thus a Translocation between parts of chromosomes number 15 and number 21 would be designated Tr(15-21)a or b or c . . . by different discoverers. Where the size group rather than the chromosome number is described the symbol Tr(D-G) would include 15-21 Translocations, 15-22 Translocations, 14-21 or 14-22 which are genetically very distinct in the gene loci transposed but are at present cytologically difficult to diagnose in any greater detail. Inversions determined to be in chromosome 5 would be denoted as In(5) followed by a specific symbol of choice. An Inversion individual is understood to be In/+, that is, heterozygous for one chromosome partly inverted in respect to the gene order in the other, standard chromosome denoted by a single + sign for normal gene order. A Deficiency which is found to carry no rhesus allele would be called Df(R_1)1962 to distinguish a Deficiency known as to gene locus but not as to chromosome number and found in that certain year. By contrast the visibly shortened chromosome found in Philadelphia can be cytologically named by the designation Df(21)Ph[1], the first of such to be described at that laboratory. An Isochromosome can be thought of as a Deficiency but perhaps better as a certain Duplication, for instance, Dp(X/X)Li as described by Lindsten.

Each Aberration may have certain phenotypic effects which have led to its discovery as if it were a simple Dominant factor showing up against the usual genetic backgound, but, in addition, each category of Rearrangement shows special types of effects in the presence of one or more linked recessive genes. A Df/+ person would appear normal as regards all loci represented by + in the normal chromosome, but the same chromosome in a person heterozygous for a recessive, Df/r, would show that *r* phenotype even in single dose, much as a single hemophilia gene shows phenotypically in a male possessing it, because the usual male has no second H gene. If the Deletion should be opposite several closely linked recessives, those recessives in the normal chromosome would "shine through" in the heterozygous individual.

The second category, Duplications, would be harder to detect. A certain Duplication opposite an incompletely recessive gene might completely dominate the recessive phenotype in all such Duplication individuals, yet the same Duplication opposite another gene might act differently. The chief point is that three doses will not necessarily act like two doses in respect to phenotypic expression. However, the existence of Duplication of certain loci will have other genetic effects. Duplication of the locus for albinism would have effects on gene frequency calculations in one direction, but Duplication of a locus producing a different degree of pigment change might have genetic consequences in another direction.

The third category, Inversions, might have little or no phenotypic effect, but an Inversion opposite linked genes would show less than normal crossing over. For instance, in the short $Pt\text{-}i$ interval marked by the nail-patella syndrome and the ABO blood group locus, heterozygous $In/Pt\ i^A$ persons would show no crossing over. Also a long Inversion opposite loosely linked loci would show close linkage among the offspring of such a structural and genic heterozygote.

The fourth category, reciprocal Translocations, is a regular producer of Duplication and Deficiency gametes at meiosis as well as of Translocation and normal offspring. The specific phenotypic effects of some of these will be given later, and the general problem will be discussed here. One reciprocal Translocation in a person whose other chromosomes are normal may be viewed simply as a dihybrid situation. Let the normal partner to one translocation-bearing chromosome be designated by a and that Translocation with homologous spindle attachment be shown conspicuously as A', and let the reciprocal of the latter be B', and call its normal length partner, homologous at the centromere, small b. The meiotic segregation of homologues and the free assortment of centromeres will produce four kinds of gametes in equal numbers, ab, aB', $A'b$ and $A'B'$ gametes. The first contains normal chromosomes and may certainly be expected to survive. The last contains the same two newly mutated chromosomes which allowed and assisted the parent to survive and therefore will presumably allow $Tr/+$ offspring (abbreviation for $aA'bB'$) to live. The other two kinds of gametes contain untried or possibly lethal combinations of genes. The gamete with the A' chromosome of the Translocation would be described as Df(a)distally and Dp(b)distally, while that with the B' chromosome resulting from the previous Translocation process would similarly be deficient for the corresponding part of b material and duplicate in regard to some of the a chromosome. Thus the $aA'bb$ offspring of the Translocation could also be described as Df(a)distally and Dp(b)distally, a new combination of many genes which is often slightly abnormal in phenotype or even lethal. The complementary $aabB'$ offspring are another new combination of genes but unbalanced by Duplication and Deficiency in the opposite way and perhaps extreme enough to be lethal before birth. Thus the offspring from a translocation individual may be variously reduced, depending on the specific Translocation, from the simple four classes to three or only two kinds of survivors. One direct consequence would be spontaneous abortion or miscarriage and a tendency for fewer live births, unless there is replacement by the parents who are desirous of having an additional child. Where all pregnancies can be accounted for as in experimental animals, or where ovules may be counted as normal or degenerate, Translocation parents often reveal themselves by the fact of *Semisterility* before other signs are noticed. Another genetic consequence would be the absence of free assortment of genes on the chromosome pairs involved; the finding that only ab and $A'B'$ are transmitted to offspring would be called *Pseudolinkage* because of the absence of the other half of the possible combinations, those from the Duplication-Deficiency gametes, aB' and $A'b$.

Reciprocal Translocations may exchange such grossly unequal lengths of chromosomes that the smaller of the two products may be lost without drastic effect. Where such a *centric fragment* has been lost, the chromosome number for the cell becomes 45, an Aneuploid number for the species. Many persons have been described who have only 45 chromosomes and become parents in spite of the absence of the shorter fragments of two chromosomes. In such a person there are three different chromosomes to be divided two ways at gametogenesis. The best balanced division is for the remaining (long) Translocation chromosome to go one way and for the two unaltered chromosomes to go the other way. Either of these two kinds of gametes would lead to viable offspring, but other two-and-one divisions among the three would lead to very long Duplications of genes and even greater Deficiencies of loci. Therefore the simple Translocation individual with only 45 chromosomes would have only two major kinds of offspring, individuals like himself with 45 chromosomes and others with the normal 46 chromosome karyotype. He would expect even numbers of these two chromosomal classes, just as the reciprocal Translocation person with the full number of 46 chromosomes would have an equal expectation between his structurally normal and his reciprocal Translocation chromosome children.

CYTOGENETIC CORRELATIONS

Those cytogenetic correlations which involve a change in the total number of chromosomes are not easily overlooked, but a progression of difficulties may hide a structural Rearrangement. The possibility of identifying structural Rearrangements both genetically and cytologically depends on the size of the alteration and even on the position of an Inversion. Very unequal exchanges of parts of chromosomes in the formation of a Translocation and unequal exchanges between arms of a single chromosome in forming a pericentric Inversion may hopefully be detected in the karyotype. However, a paracentric Inversion will make no change of length in its arm of the chromosome, and small Deletions and small Insertions may likewise be present in chromosomes of apparently normal length. Should these Deletions or Insertions be large, the cell or individual with so many genes out of normal diploid balance might not survive to demonstrate its typical genetic effects. Even if a visible structural arrangement is handed on to several offspring, genetic demonstration requires the simultaneous presence of certain alleles or of certain linked alleles whose segregation or assortment ratios might show unusual classes or limited assortment. Such a reduction in assortment implies larger numbers of

TABLE 23-2 Possible cytogenetic correlations

Aberration		Cytological detection	Genetic detection
Reciprocal Translocation		two chromosomes of changed length, without equal partners	Semisterility and altered linkage; Duplication phenotype (Down's syndrome); Deficiency in an F_1
Pericentric Inversion		new arm ratio; Ring chromosome seen	linkage changes; Deficiency of terminal genes
Paracentric Inversion		no visible change until meiosis (anaphase bridge)	linkage changes
Isochromosome		equal arm ratio	Pseudodominance of linked recessives
Deletion	(large)	shorter chromosome	usually Lethal
	(small)	overlooked	removed loci don't dominate
Duplication	(large)	longer chromosome	perhaps Lethal
	(small)	overlooked	reduced recessive segregants

offspring than one family is apt to have. However, the difficulties enumerated above should not minimize the importance of the principles concerned. A condensed summary of the cytogenetics of structurally mutant chromosomes appears in Table 23-2.

Chromosomal Translocations. Some Translocation individuals have been discovered indirectly because of the inclusion of an abnormal offspring (Down's syndrome); other Translocation individuals have been found because they themselves are phenotypically abnormal (speech defect of Moorhead). The existence of a familial type of Down's syndrome was pointed out by Penrose, who showed that young mothers of mongoloids tended to have sisters who also had mongoloid children at the usual child-bearing ages. By contrast no familial relation was found among the group of mothers who first had mongoloid children after age 34. Later investigations by different workers showed that a variety of Translocations could result in Down's syndrome offspring.

Over a dozen different kindreds of *familial mongolism* (or *familial Down's syndrome*) were reported in 1960 and 1961 to be due to Translocation of the major arm of chromosome 21 to the former position of the tiny arm of some other acrocentric chromosome. In all kindreds the chromosome which was the chief donor of material was a number 21 chromosome, but its material had been exchanged for a small transfer from a chromosome of the D group in some kindreds, or for the small arm of another chromosome in the G group, either number 21 in some kindreds or number 22 in other families. A summary of these together with some Trisomies is given in Figure 23-4. Note that in only one example is the small centromere bearing the two shorter arms of the reciprocally translocated chromosomes of some ancestor still present. We may infer from the three or more varieties of Translocation types and from the Trisomic individuals that the genes whose extra presence (Duplication) results in the Langdon-Down syndrome are located in the long arm of chromosome 21.

A few mongols have borne children, of which half were again mongoloids, so in Mendelian terms inheritance followed the pattern of a rare Dominant factor. Similarly, the Translocation-bearing mother of a mongol has an unusually large chromosome which is handed on to half of her offspring like a rare Dominant in a testcross. Segregation of the small (or absent) Translocation from its still normal partner is also on the pattern of a rare Dominant factor, so that four kinds of gametes may be produced equally often by the Translocation mother, only one quarter of which will contain the two structurally normal chromosomes. Another quarter of her gametes will contain the long Translocation chromosome almost balanced genically even without the short reciprocal. This balanced combination may also

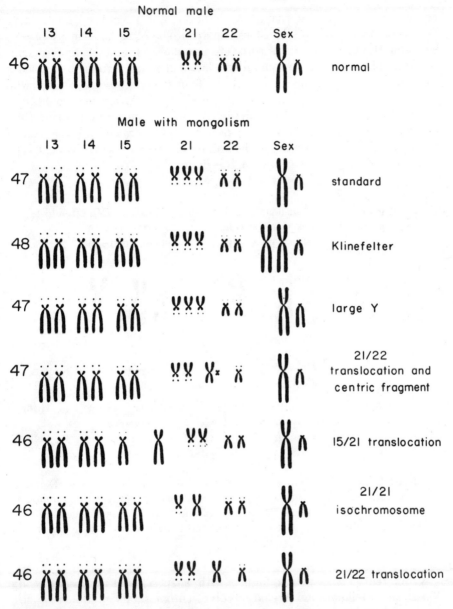

FIGURE 23-4 The acrocentric chromosomes plus the metacentric X-chromosome of a normal male and of Down's syndrome (mongoloid) males with a variety of karyotypes. Total chromosome counts are given at the left. After L. S. Penrose in Brit. Med. Bull. **17** (No. 3): 187 (1961).

occur in some of the maternal aunts. Another quarter of her gametes may be expected to show the Translocation syndrome of mongolism by possessing almost all of the genes of three chromosomes 21, and the final quarter remains unidentified and presumably is lethal in early pregnancy. Evidence for special rules of transmission through men and through women who are carriers of Tr(D/G) has been presented by Hamerton and colleagues; sex differences of a somewhat different nature are known in Translocation heterozygous plants. The basic expectations are drawn and symbolized in Figure 23-5 as a general example and for comparison with the next type which is shown right of center in the figure.

New mutant translocation (generalized)	Descendants without smaller product (G′), often lost:	
	This translocation, normal phenotype	This translocation, subnormal speech, low I. Q.

| D | D′ | G′ | G | | 15 | 15/21 | 21 | | 13 | 13/22 | 22 |

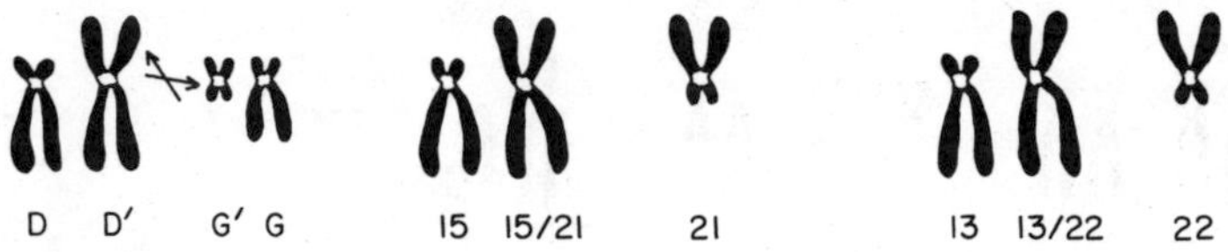

Types of gametes		Kinds of offspring	Generalized genotype	Kinds of offspring	Chromosome total	
D′	(G′)	transmitter	DD′G( )	*subnormal speech*	45	(46)
D′	G	*Down's syndrome*	DD′GG	unknown	46	
D	(G′)	unknown	DD G( )	unknown	45	(46)
D	G	normal	DD GG	normal	46	

FIGURE 23-5 Inheritance of different Translocations between sizes D and G chromosomes. The most conspicuously abnormal phenotypes are in italics. Although the chromosomes 21 and 22 of the G group are the same size, they are qualitatively different. (See the foregoing text and the next paragraph for details.)

A different Translocation family with a speech defect described by Moorhead, Mellman and Wenar involves chromosomes of the same size as the above but doubtless from different pairs because the phenotype associated with the aberration is different. *Delayed development of speech* and a lowered I.Q. among the older and testable children seem to characterize those persons who possess this particular translocation. The pedigree

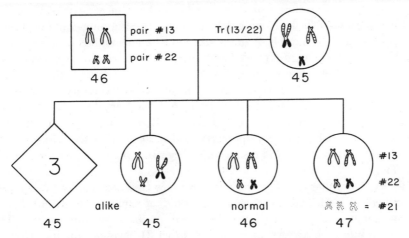

FIGURE 23-6 The 45 chromosomes and abnormal karyotypes involving a Translocation chromosome coming from the D and G size groups and provisionally numbered as 13 and 22. One Tr(13/22) was present in the mother and her first four children of both sexes; these children also had retarded speech and subnormal mentality. Fifth child normal. Sixth child without translocation but showing typical Trisomy 21 Down's syndrome. Data of Moorhead, Mellman and Wenar, Amer. J. Hum. Genet. **13:** 32–46 (1961).

is given in Figure 23-6, where the chromosomes of one D pair and of one G pair are represented in the two parents and in three different genotypes among the seven offspring. The first four children all had the same Translocation picture in a total of only 45 chromosomes as if the small product of reciprocal Translocation in some earlier generation had been lost for this line of descendants. This family differs in one important detail from the mongoloids described in the preceding paragraph and compared in the preceding figure. There the 45 chromosome translocation bearer was normal; here the 45 chromosome individuals have the abnormal phenotype of speech defect and lower I.Q. This fact indicates that different chromosomes were involved in the two kinds of Translocations, number 21 for the Langdon-Down syndrome, number 22 in this family. By a perhaps unusual coincidence in the family being investigated a sixth child with the typical Trisomy 21 Down's syndrome was born. There is the hypothesis, however, that the presence of one chromosomal abnormality may affect the otherwise normal behavior of other chromosome pairs. Any such increase is doubtlessly small if we may judge by studies in *Drosophila* on interchromosomal segregation effects.

Many other Translocations are possible but perhaps most of them are not compatible with development to infancy. A single example of Translocation between a number 2 and a size D chromosome has been described by Mercer. A single case of exchange between two of the latter resulting in a Tr(D-D) has been described by Walker. Translocation involving the Y and some other chromosome has been described by Lamy. The above three reports were all published in 1962, but the very first Translocation to be discovered in man also remains as another unique case, a vertebral column defect called polydysspondyly and associated with Translocation of the long arms of D/G chromosomes described by LeJeune and Turpin in 1959.

Twelve examples of iso-armed chromosomes (*Isochromosomes*) have been described or reviewed by Lindsten. Some of them seem to be iso-21 chromosomes; others have been described as iso-X chromosomes. The iso-21 chromosome was with a normal number 21 chromosome in a Down's syndrome child (see Figure 23-4). This type of replicated large arm represents simultaneously a large Duplication and a small Deficiency.

Duplications. The typical Duplication cell has merely a fraction of the length of one chromosome in a new position while also having the same loci in a complete normal pair. This condition (often called *Partial trisomy*) contrasts with two other Aberrations. These slightly different situations are typical Trisomy, where a whole chromosome is extra, and Duplication-deficiency as represented by the longer chromosome from a Translocation pair, that one which is simultaneously a long Duplication for material elsewhere in the cell and a small terminal deficiency for some of its own exchanged material. A simple Duplication is usually from a complex origin requiring three chromosome breaks simultaneously and the insertion of a piece of one chromosome into the opening in another without the loss of any material by the recipient chromosome. Insertional Duplications have been described by Patau and co-workers in a pedigree which included a carrier mother and daughter, several miscarriages and one living but affected daughter. They have reviewed the meaning of other Partial trisomics as compared with typical Trisomy 18, and they have proposed a map of the sequence of several normal gene loci as presented in Figure 23-7. Because the smaller Duplications are practically undetectible under the microscope and because the larger Duplications are likely to kill the cell, it is fortunate that the few cases recognizable as insertional Duplications in man can be compared in such a meaningful manner.

In mice a complete cytogenetic demonstration of an insertional Duplication has been provided by the work of Ohno and Cattanach. The X-chromosome of the mouse was visibly lengthened by the change, and in

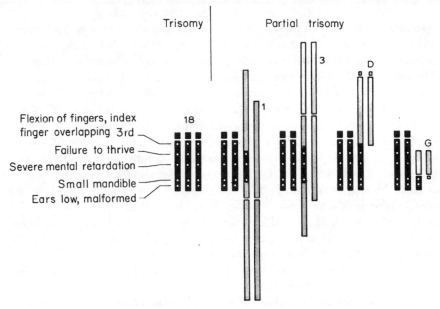

FIGURE 23-7 Diagram relating observed chromosome lengths and observed phenotypes of cases showing full or partial Trisomy 18 to the inferred locations of some normal genes having additive effects in triplicate (black regions). Extra genes are carried in typical Trisomy 18 (left), in insertional Duplication into chromosomes 1 or 3 (center) or by Translocation onto chromosomes of size D or size G (right). From K. Patau in *Proceedings of The Second International Conference on Congenital Malformations*, p. 58, New York, International Medical Congress, 1964.

the same line of descent two known linked loci from autosomal linkage group 1 showed sex-linkage. At these inserted loci wild type genes were present, and it turned out that one dose of each of these could dominate over the phenotypic effect of two doses of the recessive alleles at the usual place in the autosomes. Whereas normal X males having $pp\ c^{ch}c^{ch}$ showed the characteristic pink eye and chinchilla fur, those males having the autosomal Duplication inserted in their X were uniformly normal in pigmentation of the eye and of the skin. Similarly, X^{PCh}/O mice homozygous recessive in their normal autosomal pair for pink eye and for chinchilla failed to show either of these recessives. This uniform pigmentation of XY and of XO animals will be contrasted later with the mottled appearance of the XX animals during a discussion of the Lyon hypothesis in Chapter 24 on mosaicism. The origin of the unusually long X found by Cattanach is evidently the product of a three-break rearrangement in which the loci of *p* and *c* were broken out of one autosome and the piece was inserted as a one-way "translocation" into a gap between broken sections of the X-chromosome, which was visibly lengthened thereby. The break was found following chemical treatment of the parent mouse.

A chromosomal fragment having its own spindle attachment may also be considered to be a Duplication. Thus from the standpoint of the numbers of each kind of gene involved Duplications may be said to include (1) centric fragments, (2) true Trisomies where a chromosome of typical length is extra, (3) Partial trisomies in which much but not all has been translocated and (4) terminal Duplications from the foregoing or different origins. Migeon, Kaufmann and Young have described a child with such a centric fragment which was smaller than any other chromosome of his karyotype. The child showed very few of the features of Down's syndrome and has been described as a *paramongol* child. It is reasonable to suppose that a person with smaller fragments of chromosome 21 added to the diploid complement might show fewer of the Down's syndrome traits or might show those abnormal traits less definitely.

Chromosomal Deficiencies. Loss of a piece of a chromosome constitutes a cytogenetic deficiency or *deletion*, and this should be distinguished from enzyme deficiencies or other physiological deficiencies. These other deficiencies include such things as the failure of a gene to act at the g-6-P-d locus or the failure of demonstration of the usual varieties of C antigens in a rare rhesus homozygote, $r^G r^G$. True chromosomal Deletions in man undoubtedly exist, but present evidence is not yet conclusive.

If an extra chromosome is present, it is not always a complete one but in several instances has been a Deletion or a terminally Deficient extra chromosome. A shorter than usual chromosome has been described in two sisters who were severely retarded. Gustavson and co-workers in reporting this case suggested that it might be a number 18 chromosome after Deletion in the long arm, for the girls showed many similarities with trisomy of number 18. However, their phenotypic anomalies overlapped with some of those from D-trisomy cases, and therefore deletion of part of a number 15 chromosome was considered as an alternative possibility. In cases such as this one and that of the paramongol child mentioned under the heading of Duplications and that of the Philadelphia chromosome to follow, it is a matter of viewpoint whether the person with the extra but incomplete chromosome is classified as a Duplication (Partial trisomic) individual or as a deletion trisomic individual. The paradox may be resolved by reference to the standards available for comparison. The shortened extra chromosome makes the individual Partly trisomic and therefore

Duplication in respect to the lengths of chromosomes present. Thus the Langdon-Down syndrome cases are large Duplications in comparison with normals. However, there are many typical Trisomy 21 persons with which to compare the familial types of mongolism, and the differences found between these two kinds of mentally subnormal children may be attributed to the small deficiencies of material in the persons having just one translocation product. In the two possible deficiencies of chromosomes 13 or 18 there are not enough Trisomics of those two categories presently known to emphasize the deficiency aspects of the phenotype, although the chromosome is undoubtedly a deficient chromosome.

The possibility of a homozygous deletion at the rhesus locus has been raised but it is not readily settled. Most persons react to tests with the usual rhesus antisera by revealing the possession of one or two antigens of the C varieties, one or two of the E type antigens; and with newer tests even the small d antigen as well as the large D can be demonstrated. Blood showing no rhesus antigens has been taken several times from an aboriginal Australian who may be presumed to be lacking the length of the rhesus locus or loci in both of his chromosomes. If he is not Df(CDE) homozygously he could alternatively be physiologically devoid of some percursor substance out of which the rhesus region of the chromosome makes the various specific antigens. The one woman described by Vos and co-workers was the only such person among 450 aborigines examined within a tribe numbering around 2000 members. If a Df/+ relative can be found, he would give a positive antigenic reaction for one kind of C, one kind of E and only one D antigen on the chromosomal deficiency hypothesis. However, such a phenotype could result also from a homozygous rhesus genotype. Here again in the development of human genetics the best illustration of principles comes from an experimental animal.

An exemplary chromosomal Deletion was described in the mouse by Kidwell and co-workers in 1961 as a product of an irradiation experiment. The Deficiency was a loss of certain loci in linkage group VI of the mouse such that the genotype Df(VI)/*bt h* showed the recessive phenotypes belt and hairloss, although these recessives were present only in single dose in the heterozygote. By contrast a third locus in this linkage group (naked, n) was not affected in F_1 individuals; the Df(VI)/n individuals were normally furred due to the dominance of an n^+ allele remaining to one side of the deficient region. All F_1 animals which allowed the other two linked recessives, belt and hairloss, to shine through in single dose were mice of small size. When two Deficiency heterozygotes were bred together they produced some mice of normal size, +/+ for totality of loci, more mice which were again small like their two parents, Df/+, and one very small mouse which was presumed to be homozygous Df/Df. Thus this chromosomal Deficiency had a small size effect of its own even against a standard genic background, a more severe effect in mice homozygous for the Deficiency and a demonstrated lack of the normal dominant alleles bt^+ and h^+ at two linked loci. Furthermore, one limit of the deficiency was shown not to extend as far as the n locus of the same linkage group.

Inversions and Ring Chromosomes. Typical inversions will not change the length of the whole chromosome, and only the pericentric inversions will redistribute the ratio of arm lengths. However, several different reports of so-called inversion chromosomes or of probable inversion chromosomes complicated by other changes have appeared in the literature of human cytogenetics in which the mutant chromosome is described as being of greater than normal length. These initial cases are atypical.

Ring chromosomes are readily seen, and cases of the origin of Ring chromosomes by mutation are probable indications that pericentric Inversions are at least as numerous. Both products result from the same positions of breaks, one in each arm of a single chromosome. Joining of end to base results in the pericentric Inversion; joining of base to base makes a Ring chromosome which is deficient for gene loci distal to the two break points. Two unrelated children in Canada having one Ring chromosome among the usual total of 46 chromosomes in most of their cells give evidence for the transmission of this form of chromosome through mitosis. Both persons were from parent pairs which had normal acrocentric and metacentric chromosomes. One child had only five members of the D-size class present, so the ring chromosome was assumed to have formed from some one of the chromosomes 13–15. The other child had only five of the size E chromosomes visible as such, and that was the indication that one of these metacentrics, a number 16, 17 or 18, had been converted by breaks and rejoining into the Ring chromosome. The lost terminal pieces were considered by Wang and his co-authors to be small in view of the not very severe differences from normal children in phenotype; however, these minor differences involved six or more aspects of body structure or behavior.

Other reports of Ring chromosomes include two unrelated females with apparently ring-shaped X-chromosomes. One showed gonadal dysgenesis; both were mosaic as to the number of Rings and hence the total number of chromosomes in different cells of the body. Some cells had no ring and 45 chromosomes, other cells had one Ring and 46 chromosomes and still other cells had two Rings and 47 chromosomes. Other examples of mosaicism are described in Chapter 24.

Phenotypic Position Effects. Most of the above aberrations in human chromosomes produce phenotypes which are correlated with extra or missing material and hence may be thought of as mere dosage effects of genes having incomplete dominance. However, some Rearrangements in *Drosophila* seem to result in regular phenotypic change without evidence of gene mutation or gain or loss. If a section of chromosome has a different phenotypic expression in individuals carrying it in a new chromosomal location, the phenomenon is called a *position effect*. For instance, two closely linked wild type genes may be ineffective in repulsion linkage but effectually Dominant in the coupling phase of linkage. Until the demonstrated presence of two Dominant alleles reveals that their two recessives are *pseudoalleles*, those closely linked recessives which in repulsion have a recessive phenotype act as if they were true alleles. The phenotypic effects of some chromosomal Rearrangements may mimic the effects of simple genic mutation; therefore exceptionally good cytological studies may from time to time differentiate some structural Rearrangements from what formerly passed for simple point mutations.

SUMMARY

Structural rearrangement following breaks in the chromosome set may be followed by phenotypic change, by new monohybrid segregation, by altered dihybrid assortment and by visible change in the karyotype alone or in any combination. The usual structural mutants are Translocations, Inversions, Ring chromosomes, Duplications and Deficiencies singly or in combination. The changes in inheritance include the uncovering phenotypically of one or more recessives opposite a Deficiency, the failure of independent assortment following many examples of large reciprocal Translocations and the reduction of assortment of linked genes opposite an Inversion and sometimes the masking of two recessives in a homozygous normal pair by one Dominant in a Duplication elsewhere in the cell. An altered chromosome is usually passed on like a normal one, namely to almost all mitotically produced cells of the clone and to half of the gametes after meiosis. In this respect Rearrangements are like simple Dominant genetic factors, and offspring not receiving and showing the factor either cytologically or phenotypically will not transmit the chromosomal Rearrangement.

SUGGESTED READING

Atkins, L., M. A. O'Sullivan, and V. Pryles, Mongolism in three siblings with 46 chromosomes. New Engl. J. Med. **266:** 631–635 (1962). Has five karyograms and reports usual segregation of six antigenic loci unaffected by the translocation (without pseudolinkage).

Barnicot, N. A., J. R. Ellis, L. S. Penrose. Translocation and trisomic mongol sibs. Ann. Hum. Genet. **26:** 279–285 (1963). Discusses the alternative, centromeric fusion. Electron micrograph shows something unusual in the Tr chromosome (13/21 or 22).

Benirschke, K., L. Brownhill, D. Hoefnagel, and F. H. Allen Jr., Langdon-Down anomaly (mongolism) with 21/21 translocation and Klinefelter's syndrome in the same sibship. Cytogenetics **1:** 75–89 (1962).

Biesele, J. J., W. Schmid, C. H. Lee, and P. Smith, Translocation between acrocentric chromosomes in a 46-chromosome mongoloid and his 45-chromosome mother. Amer. J. Hum. Genet. **14:** 125–134 (1962). The excellent photographs of karyotypes include some from tetraploid cells.

Ellis, J. R., R. Marshall, and L. S. Penrose. An aberrant small acrocentric chromosome. Ann. Hum. Genet. **26:** 77–83 (1962). Describes a chromosome with satellites at both ends and its possible origin from an inversion followed by crossing over.

Hamerton, J. L., V. A. Cowie, F. Giannelli, S. M. Briggs, and P. E. Polani, Differential transmission of Down's syndrome (mongolism) through male and female translocation carriers. Lancet Vol. ii: 956–958 (1961). The 39 offspring of eight females were evenly distributed over three groups, but the 13 offspring from two male carriers were mostly carriers.

Lucas, M., N. H. Kemp, J. R. Ellis, R. Marshall. A small autosomal ring chromosome in a female infant with congenital malformations. Ann. Hum. Genet. **27:** 189–195 (1963). Mechanics of rings.

MacIntyre, M. N., W. I. Staples, A. G. Steinberg, and J. M. Hempel, Familial mongolism resulting from a "15/21" chromosome translocation in more than three generations of a large kindred. Amer. J. Hum. Genet. **14:** 335–344 (1962). Ten carriers, ten spontaneous abortions and three or four mongoloids give some additional evidence about transmission through males and through females.

Moorhead, P. S., W. J. Mellman, and C. Wenar. A familial chromosome translocation associated with speech and mental retardation. Amer. J. Hum. Genet. **13:** 32–46 (1961). The relationship of this translocation to other chromosomal mutants of different phenotype is evaluated.

Penrose, L. S., *Biology of Mental Defect*, 3rd ed. New York, Grune & Stratton, 1963, 374 pp.

Shaw, Margery, Familial mongolism. Cytogenetics **1:** 141–179 (1962). Pictorial pedigrees. Each translocation family was a separate problem phenotypically and cytologically.

PROBLEMS

23–1   In what ways could a cell with a pair of J-shaped chromosomes give rise to two equal-armed isochromosomes?

23–2   What are the various possible chromosomal aberrations directly responsible for the phenotype of Down's syndrome?

23–3 Which of the following genotypes, $i^A i^B Ph^1$, $i^A Ph^1$, $i^A i^A Ph^1$, $i^B Ph^1$, and $i^B i^B Ph^1$, would be possible in a diploid with 46 chromosomes
    (a) If the ABO locus were in the deleted part of the Ph^1 chromosome?
    (b) If the ABO locus were in another autosomal pair?
    (c) Rewrite the one or more crucial genotypes if the ABO locus were on the remaining part of the Philadelphia chromosome.

23–4 What kinds and proportions among live offspring would you expect from
    (a) A normal person with 45 chromosomes including a translocation of chromosomes 21 and 22? Why?
    (b) A person with subnormal speech and low I. Q. and 45 chromosomes including a translocation between chromosome 22 and a larger chromosome?

23–5 Outline the possible modes of origin of duplications of one or more gene loci and of deficiencies of one or more loci.

23–6 Distinguish between partial trisomy and typical trisomy.

chapter 24

Rare Mosaic Individuals

Multicellular individuals have been assumed to be uniform both in appearance and in genotype, but there may be exceptions. A woman may make her hair a *phenotypic mosaic* by the simple expedient of bleaching a streak of it. Similarly, the regenerating hair on a formerly white part of a Himalayan rabbit will come in black if a cold pack is kept over that spot during hair growth. Possibly a *physiological mosaicism* regularly exists involving a different active X-chromosome in adjacent cells as has been proposed by Dr. Mary Lyon, among others; and if this hypothesis is correct, alternative inactive X-chromosomes would cause a special type of mosaicism in all female mammals.

The established examples of rare mosaicism include many different subdivisions of *genotypic mosaicism*. The ancients wrote of a rare and imaginary animal called the chimera having the head of a lion, the body of a goat and the tail of a dragon. Current usage of the word *chimera* in biology means mixed tissues, but not from as remotely related animals. The existence of mosaicism of tissues of one species not only causes some change in phenotypic appearance, perhaps of small extent, but the prediction of kinds of offspring will be erroneous if the gonads are not of the same genotype as the somatic cells and if the gonads are not uniform throughout their tissue. Conversely, the discovery of two or more offspring showing a new mutant may indicate either early or late origin of a new mutation, either one whole generation earlier in the gamete from one of their grandparents or after zygote formation, say in some gonadal cell which gave rise to only a fraction of the parent's eggs or sperm. Enough examples of chromosomal mosaicism are known in man to show that uniformity cannot always be expected and that exceptions may not be so very rare.

ORIGINS OF GENETIC MOSAICS

A simple form of mosaic is the blood chimera formed by a mere *mixture* of mature red blood cells or of blood-forming cells. Because of small or large breaks in the placenta a mother may rather often receive blood cells from her fetus. Clarke has demonstrated this mixture microscopically both by agglutination techniques and by eluting the adult hemoglobin out of red cells leaving a few cells with fetal hemoglobin showing conspicuously among empty ghost cells (Figure 24-1). Mosaicism from a two-

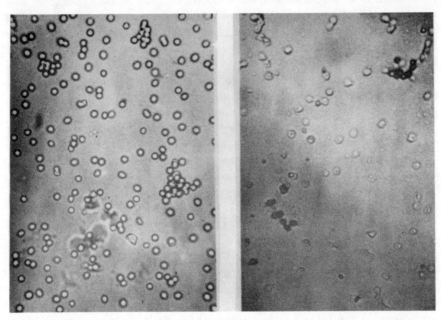

FIGURE 24-1 Fetal and maternal blood cells together in a woman's blood stream after an unusual hemorrhage of the baby. The two were ABO compatible. Left: drawn blood tested with Landsteiner anti-S serum agglutinates some cells (from the *Ss* fetus) but leaves other cells dispersed (from the *ss* mother). Right: elution of hemoglobin A leaves many ghost corpuscles (maternal) and a few intact corpuscles (containing fetal hemoglobin F). From C. A. Clarke, *Genetics for the Clinician* second edition, Plates 15-2, 15-3, Oxford, Blackwell Scientific Publications, Ltd., 1964.

way exchange between dizygotic twins was described earlier in Chapter 19 and Table 19-5. In neither of these instances would the gametes of the mother or of the growing twins be changed genetically by the foreign blood cells, nor does a gonadal change result from an intentional blood transfusion. The idea that transfusion could affect inheritance harks back in part to the hypothesis of pangenesis proposed by Darwin as a mechanism for producing evolutionary change and in part to the older expression "blood relative" as if blood were the essence of inheritance. In a new sense, however, blood is the key to inheritance thanks to its diversity, its normal fluidity and its laboratory agglutinability. Other kinds of mosaicism arise internally.

Somatic Gene Mutation. This type of mutation can produce lines of cells in various proportions with the mutant line usually being in the minority. All other genes of the individual except descendants from the one which has mutated would be alike. Considering that there are so many billions of blood cells in the body, Atwood conceived the idea of looking among the cells of group AB persons for mutant recessive cells having only antigen A or only antigen B on their surfaces. Similarly, he sought type O cells in large samples of blood from heterozygous A persons or from heterozygous B types. Technical difficulties prevented the completion of the program, which was aimed at measuring the relation between mutation and the process of aging.

Unsymmetrical persons with one brown iris and one blue iris might represent single gene mutation among other causes. A blue gene might have mutated to brown in one cell which multiplied and gave rise to the tissues of one eye; or else the brown allele in a heterozygote might have mutated to blue and thus allowed a blue phenotype in any descendent cells which might reach the proper location in the other eye. Persons with only a sector of the iris in one color could have become that way by either direction of gene mutation at a later time, as well as by other mechanisms to be described. The cells of such a sector constitute a *clone* within which all cells are alike. An individual color blind in one eye but normal in the other has been studied by Kalmus; he and his subject together produced a film showing in objective rather than verbal form what the world looks like to a color-blind man. While gene mutation doubtless accounts for many of the observed instances of mosaicism, any one example of change from the Dominant to the recessive phenotype could be due to the loss or removal of the Dominant allele by other than gene change. The other mechanisms which lead to the same phenotypic result are chromosomal Aberration and somatic crossing over, which will be discussed in turn.

Somatic Chromosomal Aberrations. In the numerous mitotic divisions of somatic cells there are many small chances for a change in chromosome number. It is a wonder that mosaicism does not result more often. If a whole nucleus stops in metaphase and its chromosomes have no chance to follow the usual plan of anaphase separation, a tetraploid nucleus will be the immediate result. Such larger cells later regain the ability to divide, and the next mitosis starts back from the beginning so that two daughter cells, each with 92 chromosomes, are the usual result. From this a volume of tetraploid tissue may grow, and perhaps whole organs will be affected. Tetraploidy is but one kind of aberration.

If mitosis proceeds normally for all chromosomes except one, then *nondisjunction* could readily establish descendent cell lines with monosomic and trisomic genotypes among the surrounding diploids. One such example is a girl with tissues composed of XXX, XX and XO and showing poor development of the gonads. At least eight persons of intermediate sex (*intersexes*) have been found to be mosaics of XY and XO tissues. Other persons are XYY/XO mosaics. Mosaicism for the number of chromosomes of pair 21 has been reported in individuals showing most of the features of the Down's syndrome. Trisomy of chromosome 18 has been found in some of the tissues, not in other tissues of the same individual. Mosaicism of an abnormal chromosome, in contrast to the above normals, has also been reported. Miller and colleagues have studied cells and cell cultures from a mosaic XO/XX′ woman whose second sex chromosome, called X′, was longer and equal armed as if composed of the two long arms of a normal X. This case is of special interest in connection with the Lyon hypothesis and will be considered in more detail below.

Similarly, if two chromosomes *break and exchange* (forming a Translocation) in the same cell in any mitotic division between that of the zygote and the next meiotic divisions, somatic mosaicism would be initiated. Deficiencies or Inversions could also arise within growing tissue of the individual (or his cultured tissues) and produce daughter cells and eventually a clone of identical descendent cells.

If a *chromatid tie* forms between two centromeres, varied kinds of mosaicism may appear among surviving descendant cells. McClintock has described the *breakage-fusion-bridge* cycle in the endosperm cells of corn kernels where mutant cell survival is good. Such endosperm cells are triploid and are less easily upset by aberrations in one chromosome. A single break in one chromosome can initiate the breakage-fusion-bridge cycle, provided the break remains open while the chromosome replicates up to it. Then the proximal strands often join each other and thus form a tie between the two centromeres. This kind of basal union after replication of the DNA is shown in Figures 23-1 and 25-1. Such a chromatid tie may again break at anaphase and the broken ends may again fuse with each other during DNA replication at interphase remaking a dicentric chromosome situation. Variety enters here because the second break may not be at the same location as the break in the previous mitotic cycle, so that Duplication and Deficiency cells will be formed. Some Duplication daughter cells may next give rise to a cell with a chromosome containing Triplications, at the expense of a sister cell, and this may continue during several other mitotic divisions. Thus the breakage-fusion-bridge cycle of McClintock leads to genetically different daughter chromosomes at each cell division for as long as the cells may live and divide.

If one individual can be a genetic mosaic, it is then no surprise that monozygotic twin pairs can be different. At least 12 pairs of one-egg twins have been diagnosed as genetic mosaics, and there is no preferred distribution of the two kinds of cells among the tissues of the twins. Some monozygotic twin pairs mosaic for XX and XO cells have been found where one twin was a normal female and the other had the characteristics of Turner's syndrome (ovarian dysgenesis) showing in spite of the possession of a few XX cells. Another pair of twins included an XO Turner's girl and an XY male. Yet because concordance was observed in many autosomal characteristics for which differences might have been expected among mere sibs, these twins of opposite sex were nevertheless judged to be monozygotic. Naturally, such dissimilar monozygous twin pairs will be very rare. From all the recorded dissimilar MZ twins it appears that the mosaicism can arise early or late in development. Mosaicism can arise in one twin after the folding and separation of the tissues for the two twins. It can arise long before separation and be sampled unevenly by the twin partners, or the allotment of kinds of cells might occasionally happen to be equivalent only to be followed by unequal growth of the two kinds of cells in each of the monozygous twins.

Somatic Segregation. A three-way mosaicism within an individual may follow the formation of adjacent twin spots by crossing over. Although crossing over is rare during mitosis, it does occur. If the point of crossing over is near the centromere, any and all heterozygous loci distal to the point of equal reciprocal exchange may show somatic segregation. This will happen whenever a crossover and a noncrossover strand from a tetrad go into one daughter cell and simultaneously the complementary crossover will be left to go with the homologous noncrossover into the other daughter cell. These daughter cells will be distally homozygous even though the centromeres are separating equationally. Such distal homozygosis probably follows after half of the occurrences of mitotic crossing over, and the other half of the time heterozygosity is maintained, in one daughter cell by the usual two noncrossover homologues and in the other daughter cell by the complementary crossover strands. Figure 24-2 illustrates the

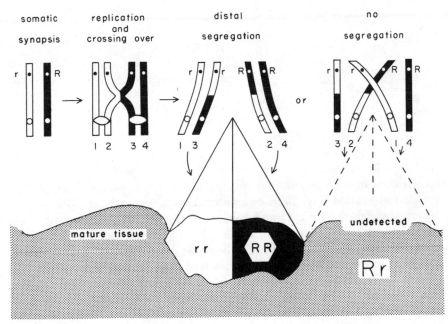

somatic synapsis   replication and crossing over   distal segregation   no segregation

FIGURE 24-2 Origin of homozygous twin spots in a heterozygous individual. The spindle attachments (numbered) separate the nearby identical genes equationally in mitosis. Genes beyond a point of mitotic crossing over (uppermost) may or may not undergo somatic segregation.

chromosomal results of somatic crossing over. Depending on the recessive genes carried and the competence of the tissue to express visible phenotypes a single spot will show in some instances and occasionally the ideal twin spotting will become apparent. The classical demonstration of twin spotting being the result of crossing over within a chromosome pair was performed by Stern in *Drosophila* dihybrids having long gray bristles over most of the body and known to be heterozygous for recessive yellow bristles and also for recessive singed bristles and hairs. Single yellow spots were found numerous times and so were single singed spots; much more often than by chance a yellow spot was touching a singed spot in a background which showed neither recessive phenotype.

Double Fertilization. Several recessive characters controlled by un-linked genes may show in as much as half of a person's tissues, if he arose from double fertilization. The previous explanations can readily account for the observation that one or two or a very few loci are involved. However, if the mosaicism concerns gene differences in several different pairs of chromosomes, the source can best be sought by assuming polar body

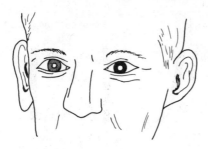

FIGURE 24-3 Dissimilar eyes and ears. The right eye is probably the genetic recessive blue, and the left ear resembles the recessive attached ear lobe. For a wide choice of genic and chromosomal origins see text.

retention at meiosis and polyspermy at fertilization. Many examples of double fertilization have been encountered in extensive work with known genetic hybrids in insects; and several examples requiring, or at least compatible with, double fertilization within a single egg are known in mammals and man. In mice F. N. Woodiel and L. B. Russell have reported a mosaic yellow and black female which had received and transmitted two chromosomes of the same pair from her mother as well as one homologue from her father. The three chromosomes of concern had three different agouti alleles, a, a^x, and A^y, and each chromosome was additionally marked by one or two other recessives in coupling linkage. The visibly mosaic mouse transmitted her sire's $a\ kr$ chromosome to 16 of her offspring, gave one of her mother's chromosomes, $a^x\ kr$, to 3 more offspring and her mother's other chromosome, $A^y\ un\ we$, to 15 more mice. Because these ratios differ from those from a trisomic both in number and in kind, the hypothesis that the mosaically colored mother had two kinds of cells, $A^y a$ and $a^x a$, derived from double fertilization is very plausible.

A human hermaphroditic girl probably from double fertilization showed at least three genetic differences traceable to her father's heterozygosity in different pairs of chromosomes. Her possession of one brown eye like his is perhaps a good fourth difference. Her mother had recessive hazel eyes and contributed the alleles A_1, MS^u and R^1 from heterozygous pairs to both kinds of tissues of this child. Her father gave MS and R^2 to one population of cells, but he handed on Ns and r to the other kind of blood cells. In separate tests XX cells and XY cells were found from both sides of the abdomen, other blood cells, and from two places in an ovotestis and elsewhere. Most probably all of these differences came from the entrance of two different kinds of sperm which fertilized the same kind of maternal nuclei.

A very obvious double mosaic has been observed by Bostian. The man had one brown eye and one blue eye, and, furthermore, one earlobe was free and the other was attached (Figure 24-3). The recessive attached lobe and the recessive blue eye were on opposite sides of the head, a fact which suggests a possible origin from somatic crossing over in a certain pair of chromosomes, but which is also compatible with origin by double fertilization. Additional information from blood testing and karyotyping might favor one of these possibilities over the other.

LYON HYPOTHESIS: REGULATORY MOSAICISM

One of the unsolved mysteries of animal genetics is the generally similar expression of sex-linked phenotypes in X and in XX individuals. Two doses of a weakly acting gene usually produce no more and no less of a phenotypic difference from the standard type than does one dose. Of course, there are hundreds of other genes linked in coupling phase in each of the X-chromosomes of the observed individuals, and the whole complex of compensating and noncompensating gene pairs has long been subject to the weeding out influences of natural selection. The manner of *dosage compensation* has long been considered, and one possibility is that each X-chromosome has accumulated so many plus and minus modifiers that the net effect of past selection has been a balanced level of expression which is usually at the same phenotypic level in the two sexes. Opportunities to establish a balance are better for X-linked genes than for autosomal genes because one-third of the X-chromosomes are subject to severe selection in hemizygous males in each generation (Chapter 12).

The contrast observable between the XX female and the XXX metafemale is not as great as that between the normal diploid with two chromosomes 21 and the Down's type with three of this tiny chromosome. These increases of 50 percent in the trisomics produce more change than the 100 percent increase in genes from the one X of a male to the XX of a female. For instance, hemophilia in female dogs is no worse than it is in male dogs. Also the intermediate alleles protanomaly and deuteranomaly seem to produce the same phenotypes whether in single dose in men or in double dose in women. When many suitable examples are compared, most of them show gene dosage compensation while a few, like the eosin allele of white in *Drosophila*, show a darker eye color in the two-X females than in the one-X male.

The *inactive X hypothesis*, formulated in respect to mice in 1961 and widely known as the Lyon hypothesis after Dr. Mary Lyon of Harwell, England, states that only one of the two X-chromosomes in the homogametic sex is functional while the other condenses to form the Barr body. The X inactivated in some cells would be that from the father, in other cells it would be that from the mother. Hence any tissue in the body of a woman would be a mosaic of cells which would show dominance of all genes having diffusable products but would remain a fine-grained mosaic for other intracellular differences. Such a mosaic of cells might be difficult to demonstrate, particularly among rigid tissues, although cells which can be separated and cloned might show antigenic differences. This hypothesis has stimulated many new investigations, some of which are currently being completed.

In sibships segregating for Duchenne muscle dystrophy, Pearson and co-workers have found microscopically visible mosaicism in the muscle tissue of half of the sisters of affected males. The same kinds of muscle change were found in some of the boys too young to have developed overt muscle weakness. Among the heterozygous women there was more abnormal tissue found among the younger women, as if this were partly replaced by normal muscle fibers in older heterozygotes. Both ages had elevated creatine phosphokinase activity and basophilia around the abnormal muscle fiber nests.

Cells of Caucasians and Negroes of four constitutions in respect to g-6-P-d were successfully separated and grown into clones of cells by Davidson and colleagues and then found to be pure in type in spite of having come from heterozygous sources. From each of two carrier women one clone showing enzyme deficiency and three lines showing full enzyme activity were isolated. The low enzyme clones from the heterozygotes had as little activity as did the cells of homozygous enzyme-deficient women or as did the cells of hemizygous male relatives. Simultaneously, the high line clones of the same heterozygotes had as much enzyme activity as did cells from normal hemizygous men or homozygous women in respect to glucose-6-phosphate-dehydrogenase. The same workers used the qualitative difference in fast and slow mobility in the electrophoresis of the g-6-P-d enzyme to test the phenotypes of cells grown in vitro from six known heterozygous Negro women. Each person provided several clones, from a minimum of 5 to a maximum of 14 growing sublines. That last person gave 7 fast clones and 7 slow clones. Other women's cells and clones were in the rather extreme ratios of 8 : 2, 1 : 8, both 0 : 8 and 8 : 0, and finally 0 : 5. Evidently, the cells provided by the last three heterozygotes had already become differentiated as to which was their inactive allele at the g-6-P-d locus.

The tortoise-shell cat is now recognized to be an example of early formation of a mosaic of yellow cells and black cells. For many years it was widely known that mottled yellow-and-black cats (or calico cats) are usually female and that their male ancestor and descendants were individually all yellow or all black (Figure 24-4). The rare male exceptions, which

Mosaicism for X-linked alleles

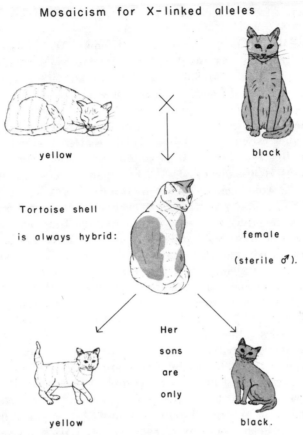

yellow

×

black

Tortoise shell

is always hybrid:

female

(sterile ♂).

Her

sons

are

only

yellow

black.

FIGURE 24-4 A common example of mosaicism. The tortoise shell cat is usually a hybrid XX female or rarely an XXY sterile male. Courtesy of Judy McNease James.

were mottled yellow-and-black, have often proven to be sterile males. Since the advent of the Lyon hypothesis, it has been shown that a high percentage of the exceptional tortoise-shell males are XXY in constitution; thus they can be heterozygous like their sisters. The fact that the yellow patches are large and adjacent to black patches, which are also rather large, indicates that the differentiation of the heterozygous cells into producers of yellow pigment or of black pigment takes place early and remains fixed. A long and sharp color boundary often coincides with the center of the face or belly, to which pigment cells from the left and right side have migrated and met. There is considerable variability in the total color balance; some tortoise-shell cats are largely yellow; others are largely black.

The possibility of greater variability of female MZ twins as compared with male MZ twins was raised and investigated by Vandenberg and the McKusicks. From the Michigan Hereditary Abilities Study there were available 21 female MZ pairs and 23 male MZ pairs on which a great number of physiological and psychological measurements had been made. If the genes concerned with the measured quantitative characters were numerous, they would probably be widely scattered among all chromosomes, including the X pair. If so, greater variability would be expected among females than among male MZ twin pairs, due to the alternative X constitution of women as contrasted with the uniform X genotype of male MZ twins. The first report seemed clearly to support the hypothesis, but errors in the study were soon discovered and those authors promptly and properly withdrew their earlier conclusion. An effect of X-inactivation upon a quantitative character is undoubtedly more difficult to demonstrate than is an effect of a single gene pair known to be sex-linked.

Cytological evidence identifying the Barr body with the inactivated X (or modified X) chromosome has been sought with rewarding results. One line of evidence indicates that a Barr body continues to give rise to other Barr bodies rather than reverting to active status. In a study of newly mutant polyploid cell lines DeMars has found that tetraploid cultures have the sex chromatin bodies appearing in loose pairs at the periphery of resting cell nuclei, that octoploid lines have Barr bodies in groups of four, and that higher polyploid clones have even larger numbers of Barr bodies in separate groups (Figure 24-5). These numbers are summarized for even ploidy by *Harnden's rule*, $\#BB = \#X - (\text{ploidy}/2)$, that the total number of X chromosomes minus half the degree of ploidy equals the number of observed Barr bodies. Thus for the diploid cell the Barr bodies are one less than the total X chromosomes.

Random inactivation of either the maternal X or the paternal X chromosome seems to be the rule, and the relegation of one of them to the Barr body and the continued typical functioning of the other chromosome seems to take place early in development (Figure 24-6). A possible exception to random choice is the observation, usually long after birth, that a structurally large or small X travels in cell lines with larger or smaller Barr bodies. Clones with a large X-chromosome (iso-long-arm) have large Barr bodies; clones with a short X (deficiency) have smaller Barr bodies. Selection during embryonic growth may have favored those cells which retained the normal X on active status and thus show a derived uniformity of abnormal Barr bodies. However, the early decision apparently is final, otherwise

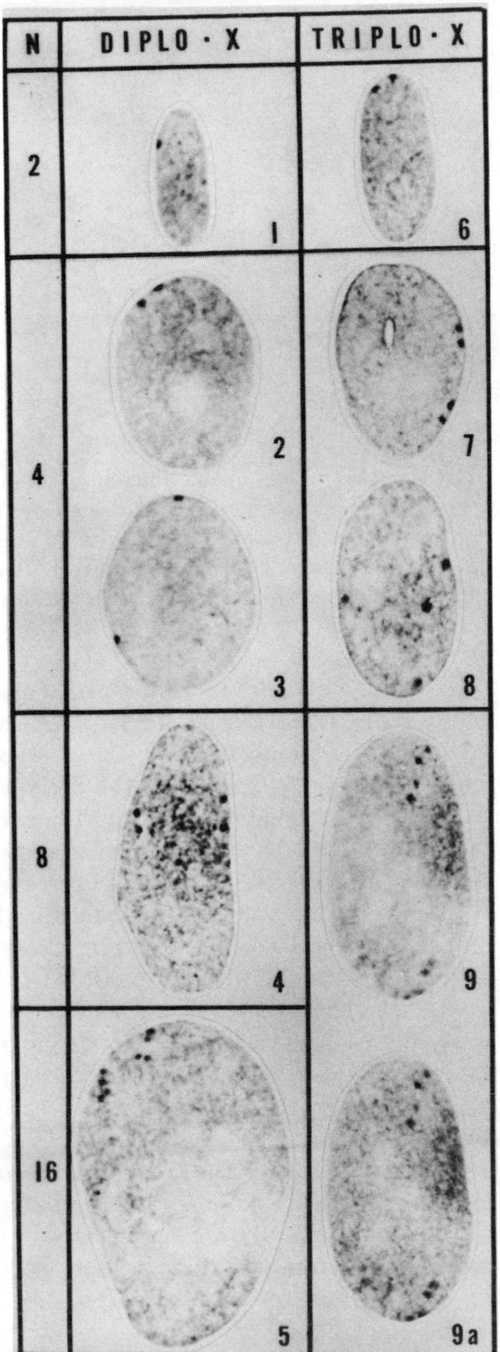

FIGURE 24-5 Number of Barr bodies in the nuclei of cells cultured from originally 46-chromosome strains (left) and from 47-chromosome strains (right). The sex chromatin spots tend to double with each increase in polyploidy (top to bottom). From DeMars, Science, **141:** 650 (1963).

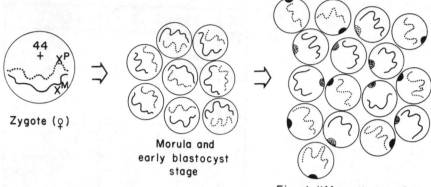

Zygote (♀)

Morula and
early blastocyst
stage

Fixed differentiation of X
chromosomes begins in late
blastocyst stage

FIGURE 24-6   The random differentiation of the maternal X or the paternal X chromosome and the appearance of a heteropycnotic sex chromatin spot (Barr body) in an early female embryo. Clones of X^P cells and clones of X^M cells become intermingled in mosaic fashion. From M. Barr, *Proceedings of the Second International Conference on Congenital Malformations.* New York, International Medical Congress, 1964.

both small and large Barr bodies would appear in the resting nuclei of cells known to be heterozygous for structurally unequal X-chromosomes.

Other correlations between the metaphase X-chromosomes and the interphase Barr body indicate the derivation of the latter from only one of the former. Radioactive thymidine containing tritium can be fed briefly (in pulse labeling) to growing cultures of leucocytes, which may be harvested after desired intervals of time, stained, covered with photographic emulsion and later studied both cytologically and autoradiographically. In general, the chromosomes become radioactively labeled at various times during the synthetic period (Figure 25-1) between cell divisions. It is of particular interest that some chromosomes are late in labeling, among them an X-chromosome of females. In this manner, Morishima and colleagues have studied many clones taken from leucocytes of a woman who was a triple mosaic for the total numbers of chromosomes in her cells, and they have compared the labeling of her cells with that of clones from normal persons of both sexes. They found that a late-labeling X was usually absent from the XY cells of normal males and also from the clone showing only 45 chromosomes. The latter were XO at metaphase and showed no Barr bodies at interphase. In comparison, normal females and the clone with 46 chromosomes from the genotypically triple mosaic usually had one late-labeling X and one Barr body. From the 47-chromosome clones, which also usually showed two Barr bodies, either one or two late-replicating X-chromosomes were found. Those authors also noted that the late-replicating sex chromosome was nearer the periphery of the dividing nucleus more often than expected. This is an interesting coincidence in that the regular position of the Barr body is also at the periphery of the interphase nucleus. This and other data are consistent with identifying second and third X-chromosomes of diploids with the first and second intermitotic Barr bodies. However, L. B. Russell suggests that perhaps only a part of the additional X rather than the whole paternal or whole maternal X contracts to become the deeply staining mass of nuclear sex chromatin of normal females, of Klinefelter males and of other X polysomics.

THE MOSAIC THEORY OF CANCER

Leukemia is one variety of cancer sometimes of spontaneous origin and sometimes induced by therapeutic radiation or by fallout (see next chapter). The mosaic origin theory holds that a somatic mutation, either genic or chromosomal, removes the effect of some regulatory gene or section of chromosome so that the cell multiplies more rapidly than is desirable for the organization of the individual. A somatic gene mutation would not show cytologically, neither would the products of somatic crossing over, nor the results of small deficiencies nor of inversions within a chromosome arm. Cytological detection of all translocations except exhanges of equal lengths of chromosomes is possible but tedious and difficult. Detection of inversions across the centromere is possible but under the same difficulties as translocations; in fact they could be considered as translocations of unequal amounts of different arms of one chromosome. Aneuploids and polyploids could be readily detected but might be coincidental rather than causative. Many studies of the origin of leukemia have been made, but a clear explanation of wide application is not available at this writing.

Other kinds of cancer similarly might involve somatic mutation of genic or chromosomal extent, but alternative possibilities involve normal aging processes and the reaching of a threshold for the formation of a cancer. Whatever the cause, the neoplastic cells comprise a clone at least from the physiological aspect and perhaps also from the genotypic viewpoint.

MOSAICISM THROUGH VIRAL INFECTION

The study of human cells in tissue cultures has shown many parallels to the transformation and transduction of the capabilities of bacterial cells which have been infected by viruses. Mosaicism of mammal cells is particularly important in that one or two of the several causes of cancer involve the effect of viruses upon the surface of the cell, or on the regulatory activity of the cell nucleus or even on the composition of the chromosomes of the host cell. Thus some cells and their descendant tissues will be genetically changed and will form a clone of cancerous cells whereas others will not be changed.

Virus infection is only one of the agencies which may stimulate some small fraction of cells to become cancerous. Other agents include ionizing radiation and various chemicals (next chapter), hormones and the mere separation of some cells from their normally adjacent neighbors. The action of viruses on other cells was first studied extensively with bacteria and bacteriophage viruses. More recently the studies have broadened to include the viruses of chickens, of rodents and of cultured human cells among other suitable experimental material; and much is now known about the size, number, structure and chemical composition of various kinds of infective viruses.

The viruses which infect and occasionally transform cells are of two chemical categories, the RNA viruses and the DNA viruses. The length of the molecule of RNA which infects chickens and causes an increase in leukosis among blood cells has been estimated as a length including about 50 genes. Other RNA viruses of this size have been demonstrated as causing tumors in the solid tissues of rodents. The DNA viruses of similar rodents and the kinds found in the warts of humans are almost that large in terms of the numbers of viral genes which enter host cells and transform a small fraction, like 10^{-5} of invaded cells.

The action of *transformation* in mammals results in changing the phenotype of a cell and of its descendant cells. The transformation requires two or more steps in what is called a progression from normal control of the cell in step with the body metabolism to uncontrolled cancerous growth. The host cell must first be infected, and many chemical changes doubtless follow this invasion of foreign DNA. An important subsequent change is the breakage of chromosomes, which can give rise to the variety of mutant changes already described in the previous chapter. Following breakage a final step in the progression of transformation is the incorporation of a length of the foreign DNA into a chromosome of the host cell. Obviously, a host cell transformed to this extent will, if it continues to live and divide, produce daughter cells, and eventually a clone, of genetical constitution different from the surrounding tissues, which it might invade and even replace.

Evidence for the genotypic change comes from the response of one type of cell, in the pigmented iris of the eye, to two different kinds of virus. Both viruses agree in causing dedifferentiation of the pigment cells to a more embryonic form, but one kind of virus results in spindle-shaped cells whereas another kind of virus transforms the invaded cells to round embryonic cells. Still other viruses cause changes in the opposite direction in that they speed the differentiation of certain embryonic tissues. It should not be surprising that the responses can be so definitely directional if the length of the invading virus contains dozens of genes, as has been estimated jointly from physical and genetic measurements in a wide variety of biological material including insects, bacteria and other organisms.

SUMMARY

An initial and widespread assumption in the study of inheritance is that all the cells of an individual are genetically identical, thanks to the precise nature of mitosis, of DNA replication and of fertilization; however, exceptions are possible. The nonuniform individuals are called chimeras or mosaic mixtures of genetically different tissues. Some mosaic people, mice and insects have started from an initial mixture of nuclei derived from two sperm fertilizing and multiplying in one egg. Other people and cattle are mosaic because of a mixture of blood-forming cells via a small break in the placenta during pregnancy. Still other individuals are mosaic because of nondisjunction during some early or late mitotic cell division, and many examples of persons mosaic in the number of their X-Y chromosome constitution are known. Rarely also the chromosomes may break and give rise to tissue with structurally mutant chromosomes; and genic mutation could produce phenotypes not verifiably distinguishable from some of the chromosomal mutants. Mutation affecting the regulatory genes of the cell may allow the cell to produce a runaway clone of cancerous tissue. Although all of the above are rare exceptions to normal growth and development, a possibly common type of mosaicism concerns the sex-linked genes of women and perhaps female mammals generally.

The inactive-X hypothesis of Mary Lyon and others in 1961 suggests that only one X-chromosome remains functional per cell of diploid individuals, and that every woman is a mosaic of two kinds of cells, those with the paternal X-chromosome still acting and other cells with only the maternal X still acting. This may be the mammalian answer to the problem of dosage compensation between male and female phenotypes. This is one of the exciting new ideas in current research in genetics.

SUGGESTED READING

On Mosaicism

Atwood, K. C., and F. J. Pepper. Erythrocyte automosaicism in some persons of known genotype. Science **134:** 2100–2102 (1961). An attempt to measure mutation rates in large natural populations of human cells.

Gartler, S. M., S. H. Waxman, and Eloise Giblett, An XX/XY human hermaphrodite resulting from double fertilization. Proc. Nat. Acad. Sci. U.S.A. **48:** 332–335, (1962). The case described in text.

Hannah-Alava, Aloha, Genetic mosaics. Sci. Amer. **202** (No. 5): 118–130 (May, 1960). Mosaic mammals, birds, plants, insects.

Mikkelsen, M., A. Frøland, J. Ellebjerg, XO/XX mosaicism in a pair of presumably MZ twins with different phenotypes. Cytogenetics **2:** 86–98 (1963). Includes references to 12 mosaic one-egg twins.

Schneiderman, L. J., C. A. B. Smith, Non-random distribution of certain homologous pairs of normal human chromosomes in metaphase. Nature **195:** 1229–1230 (1962). Observations which relate to the preconditions for somatic crossing over and twin spot mosaicism.

On The Inactive-X Hypothesis and Barr Bodies

Editorial, Lyonization of the X-chromosome. Lancet No. 7311: 769–770 (1963). Contains a short history of the hypothesis and evidence that decision between the maternal and paternal X-chromosomes comes on the 12th day.

Davidson, R. G., H. M. Nitowsky, and Barton Childs, Demonstration of two populations of cells in the human female heterozygous for g-6-P-d variants. Proc. Nat. Acad. Sci. U.S.A. **50:** 481–485 (1963). Further details on cases summarized in text.

DeMars, Robert, Sex chromatin patterns and the Lyon hypothesis. Science **141:** 649–650 (1963). Describes techniques for recognizing recently formed tetraploid and octoploid cells, whose sex chromatin masses appear grouped in twos and fours.

Harris, H., D. A. Hopkinson, N. Spencer, W. M. Court-Brown and D. Mantle, Red cell g-6-P-d activity in individuals with abnormal numbers of X chromosomes. Ann. Hum. Genet. **27:** 59–66 (1963). History and recent contradictory evidence.

Lyon, Mary F., Gene action in the X-chromosome of the mouse (*Mus musculus L.*). Nature **190:** 372–373 (1961). Early statement of the inactive-X hypothesis.

Morishima, A., M. M. Grumbach and J. H. Taylor, Asynchronous duplication of human chromosomes and the origin of sex chromatin. Proc. Nat. Acad. Sci. U.S.A. **48:** 756–763 (1962). In leukocyte cultures from clones of 45, 46, or 47 chromosomes labeling with tritiated thymidine reveals the late replication of the second and third X-chromosomes.

Pearson, Carl M., W. M. Fowler and S. W. Wright, X-chromosome mosaicism in females with muscular dystrophy. Proc. Nat. Acad. Sci. U.S.A. **50**: 24–31 (1963). Consistent with the theory of sex-linked recessive determination, one-half of the sisters of affected boys have abnormal, degenerating fiber nests within their muscles.

Rashad, M. N., Lyonization of the X-chromosome. Lancet No. 7313: 885–886 (1963). A concise summary with many references.

Russell, L. B., Genetics of mammalian sex chromosomes. Science **133**: 1795-1803 (1961). A pioneer formulation of the inactive-X hypothesis.

Russell, L. B., Mammalian X-chromosome action: inactivation limited in region of origin. Science **140**: 976–978 (1963).

Stern, C., The fifth Huskins Memorial lecture: Dosage compensation — development of a concept and new facts. Canad. J. Genet. Cytol. **2**: 105–118 (1960). On the classical problem of controlled expression of sex-linked genes shortly before the formulation of the inactive-X hypothesis by Lyon and by Russell.

Wald, N., A. C. Upton, V. K. Jenkins and W. H. Borges, Radiation-induced mouse leukemia: consistent occurrence of an extra and a marker chromosome. Science **143**: 810–812 (1964).

PROBLEMS

24–1 Would it be easier to look for somatic mutant A cells and B cells in an O person, or for O cells in an AB person? Why?

24–2 Why would female MZ twins show greater dissimilarity for some characteristics than would male MZ twins?

24–3 (a) If after each and every mitotic division it were a matter of chance which X-chromosome formed a Barr body, how would the sizes of Barr bodies compare in adjacent cells of a heterozygous X/large-X female?
(b) What should be the interpretation of finding large masses of parallel degenerating muscle fibers in a heterozygote for the X-linked Duchenne muscle dystrophy?

24–4 How do the cells of a genetic mosaic differ from the cells of a (black and white) Himalayan rabbit?

24–5 Explain how the finding of a brown sector in a blue eye (assumed recessive) might be less frequent than the converse finding.

24–6 Briefly define

somatic segregation
somatic mutation
double fertilization
inactive X
clone

chapter 25

Induced Mutations

Until the year 1927 all mutations, whether genic or chromosomal, were supposed to have been of spontaneous origin. In that year Dr. H. J. Muller demonstrated that X-rays produce mutations in the sperm cells of irradiated *Drosophila* flies, and Dr. L. J. Stadler showed that X-rays were also mutagenic in a plant, namely, maize. The phenomena have been intensively studied ever since. The demonstrations were made possible by the fact that these two organisms, corn and the fruit fly, were at that time by far the genetically best known living things. Since then it has become possible to demonstrate the mutagenic agents in other plants and animals including human tissues. Furthermore, the list of mutagens now includes other physical agents such as temperature extremes and ultraviolet radiation. Since 1946 it has been known that chemicals also can be mutagenic, and it has been demonstrated that ionizing radiation causes mutations by chemical action in the vicinity of chromosomes. Presently viruses are known to transform several aspects of the genotype of the host cell in a permanent hereditary manner.

Both point mutations and chromosomal mutations may be produced by the inducing agents. In point mutations there is no demonstrable Deficiency, Duplication or Rearrangement of the chromosomal material, whereas in the production of Aberrations there is some such large structural alteration. The induced chromosomal Aberrations which involve breakage of the whole chromosome or of one of its replicated halves will be considered first. Studies of both human and other mammalian material will be described.

INDUCED BREAKAGE IN HUMAN TISSUE

Because various kinds of human cells can be grown in tissue culture, it is now possible to experiment directly with human chromosomes. Cells can be grown in flat layers and irradiated in place, or they can be washed

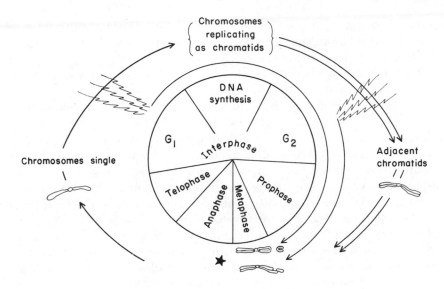

★ Two kinds of breaks detected in colchicine arrested metaphases

FIGURE 25-1 The origin of chromosome breaks contrasted with chromatid breaks. Irradiation in the G_1 period, early in the cycle of cell division, produces chromosome breakage and some dicentric bridges (one tie shown). Irradiation in the G_1 period, after DNA replication, usually breaks only one of two adjacent chromatids.

free into a suspension and treated by irradiation or by chemical mutagens. During the next cell division, the visible chromosomal types of mutants can be accurately scored and counted.   The character of the observed result changes regularly with the kind of activity of the cell at the time of treatment.

Cells in a growing tissue culture go through a regular cycle of growth and reproduction by mitotic cell division. In most tissues a majority of the cells at any one time are in interphase, while a small percentage are showing some stage of mitosis between prophase and telophase. The fraction of nuclei passing through active mitosis is known as the *mitotic index*. Preparations for mitosis are going on during a certain middle part of interphase known as the *synthetic period*. At that time practically all of the DNA is formed for the new chromosome (or for the new parts of the two chromatids); little or no synthesis of DNA occurs at the time when doubleness of a chromosome becomes visible in prophase or metaphase. The growth period within interphase before the synthesis begins is known as the G_2 *period*, and the period after synthesis and up until prophase is the G_1

period of interphase (Figure 25-1). Irradiation in G_1 yields results different from those following irradiation in G_2 depending on the singleness or doubleness of the chromosome at the time.

A strand broken when the chromosome is single is called a *chromosome break*, whereas a strand broken after replication is soon recognized as a *chromatid break*. Cells moving into mitosis soon after irradiation contain chromosomes which were replicated before the time of treatment, and these show a percentage of *isochromatid breaks* having both chromatids broken at exactly corresponding points. With intense doses of many roentgens of ionization there may be more than one broken strand per cell, so that some of the strands may reunite in a new way as chromatid exchanges. As time passes after irradiation, fewer of the chromatid types of aberrations are found in the irradiated tissue. For instance, 30 hours after irradiating fibroblast cells in tissue culture with doses of 25, 50 or 100 r (given during one minute) Chu, Giles and Passano found that chromatid aberrations had dropped from .02 to less than .01 per cell per roentgen; and chromatid types decreased to zero by 60 hours (Figure 25-2).

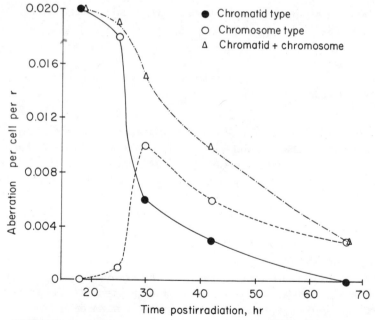

FIGURE 25-2 Radiosensitivity as measured by breakage per roentgen of dose at various times during the mitotic cycle of cultured human cells. From E. Chu, N. Giles and K. Passano, Proc. Nat. Acad. Sci. U.S.A., **47:** 830 (1961).

It may be noted in the same figure that chromosomal aberrations rose from zero to a peak of .01 per roentgen at 30 hours postirradiation and then decreased while the cells which were in the earlier part of the G_1 period moved into mitosis where they could be stained and studied. This type of sequence with time after treatment had been observed by Sax and many others on plant and animal material. The time relationships are important in any attempt to study the effect of increasing dosage of ionizing irradiation on living cells, because all stages of the cell cycle are not equally sensitive to the action of environmental agents.

Chromatid aberrations of several kinds may be profitably studied at 25 hours after irradiating human tissue cultures (Figure 25-3). Terminal Deletions show a simple linear relation to the total dose; thus, after a 100 r

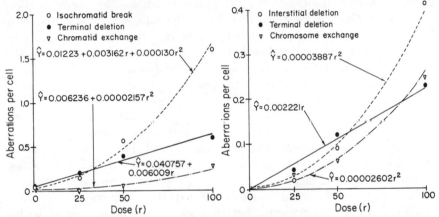

FIGURE 25-3   Aberrations: after 1 minute of exposure to X-rays of three different doses (left) in chromatids as detected 25 hours after irradiation and (right) in chromosomes as detected 42 hours after irradiating human cell lines. The single break aberrations (terminal deletions) follow a straight line relation to total dose. The two-break aberrations (exchanges, deletions and isochromatid breaks) have an exponential relation to dose. From E. Chu, N. Giles and K. Passano, Proc. Nat. Acad. Sci. U.S.A., **47**: 830 (1961).

dose, twice as many losses of an end of a chromatid were observed as after a 50 r dose; and after the latter dose twice as many terminal Deletions were found per cell as were found in similar tissue given a 25 r dose. This *linear relation* of dose to effect is readily explicable in terms of one break being enough to remove a small or large terminal segment of a chromosome from its centromere. Other aberrations which require the presence of two breaks to be open in the same cell behave differently. Exchanges between chromatids are of lower frequency than the above at these low dosages, and their distribution whether along a line or along a power curve is not yet distinguishable. However, the occurrence of isochromatid breaks increased much more rapidly than did the dose between 25 and 50 and 100 r. Similarly, studies in the plant *Tradescantia* have shown that many of these isochromatid Deletions are due to two usually independent breaks occurring in the same cell. Other exchanges between two broken chromatids or chromosomes follow similar power curves, to be described shortly.

Chromosomal aberrations studied 42 hours after receiving 1 minute of irradiation at one of these three doses likewise distinguish mutants resulting from one break and those resulting from two. The terminal Deletions of chromosomes here again increase linearly with total dose, from zero in the untreated control cultures to 0.2 per cell this late after a 100 r dose (Figure 25-3). However, the two-break interstitial Deletions increase from being the least frequent of the three observable aberrations after a 25 r dose to being the most frequent after 100 r. More importantly, their rate of increase is steeper as the total dose (briefly administered) is also increased and hence their frequency has an *exponential relation* to dose. Other recognizable two-break aberrations, namely, (a) ring chromosomes from the union of the proximal sides of breaks in opposite arms of the chromosome and (b) dicentric chromosomes resulting from the union proximally of breaks in two different chromosomes, follow an exponential curve of increase as the total short dose increases (same Figure). It is important that the aberrations be observed at the mitotic cell division which immediately follows irradiation, because these aberrant products, as the name implies, may be poorly viable and may be rapidly lost in one or a few more cell divisions. In other words, there is a selection process going on within the tissue. This result of chromosome breakage is the reason for the therapeutic use of X-rays in the arresting and control of many cancers without surgical removal of that abnormal somatic tissue. Cells with unstable aberrations like ring chromosomes and dicentrics do not readily reproduce themselves, although there are corresponding stable aberrations, particularly reciprocal Translocations, which may be found in constant proportions for years. Buckton and co-workers found Translocations in patients more than 12 years after there had been X-ray therapy for ankylosing spondylitis. Presumably some genic mutants which are not immediately damaging may also persist that long in the body.

INDUCED HETEROSOMY IN MAMMALS

In the culture of human tissue and that of other organisms the chromosome number is not always uniform throughout the culture nor constant during succeeding generations. The first kind of variability may be considered to be due to technical difficulties of scoring particularly where there is a definite modal number of chromosomes and not many cells recorded as having less than or more than the modal number for the preparation. However, when a new modal number continues to be recorded in several subcultures, it may be correctly inferred that a genetic change in chromosome number has taken place in an ancestral cell. If such mutants are found in tissue culture, it cannot always be assumed that the aberration was spontaneous rather than being due to some unidentified agent involved in tissue culturing, but if an additional strong mutagen is applied to some of the material and later there is a significant increase in mutant cells, we may speak of the excess above comparable controls as due to the known inducing agent. Chromosomes are sometimes lost following irradiation, and sometimes when a mitotic cell division is not completed, a polyploid cell with double the previous number of chromosomes will result.

Some changes in the frequency of chromosomal aberrations in the leukocyte cells of monozygotic twins have been detected by Lindgren and Norryd shortly after one twin had received extensive therapeutic irradiation of the vertebral column. One of these five year old twins had surgery for a brain ventricle tumor which was not entirely removable, and hence X-radiation to damage and kill metastasizing cells was indicated. Over 100 r of ionizing radiation were received in a 14-day period by this twin. Among 900 of his dividing leukocyte cells there was observed 5.3 percent of polyploid nuclei as compared with only 0.6 percent of 1000 analyzed cells from his untreated MZ twin. In a separate examination of 113 cells 16 percent of the irradiated twin's cells showed an aneuploid number of chromosomes, and 29 percent of the same chromosomes included in that total showed structural changes, chiefly as dicentric chromosomes and acentric fragments.

Chromosome loss has also been demonstrated in mice. Russell and Saylors have found a significant increase in XO exceptional daughters which showed the Tabby character of their mothers without any wild allele of this obtained from the father. The males had been X-rayed with 600 r on the posterior one-third of the body a few days before mating, so the tested chromosomes were in mature sperm at the time of treatment. The same authors found that irradiation of the female mice a few hours post-copulation, when it was estimated that nuclear fusion of sperm and egg had not yet occurred, produced a greater frequency of loss of either X-chromosome, paternal or maternal. A mere 100 r dose produced over 5 percent of daughters having lost one of their X-chromosomes. Among mice the XO individuals are both female and fertile, so genetic tests were possible; and the indicated stage of high sensitivity was the pronuclear stage, between sperm entrance and the formation of the diploid nucleus of the zygote. Loss of other chromosomes would not have been as readily detectable because of the drastic loss of balance in going from two autosomes to one autosome as compared with passing from the XX to the X conditions so typical of normal females and males, respectively.

INDUCED GENE MUTATION FREQUENCIES

Although irradiation which affects only a small fraction of the cells of the adult may produce no harmful systemic effects, it may damage an entire offspring and its later descendants. If a germ cell of the ovary or of the testis is caused to mutate, the offspring from that germ cell and subsequent descendants receiving the mutated gene may be slightly or severely handicapped. Very rarely would the descendant be improved by a random mutational change away from the established norm of the species. Such conclusions are solidly based in numerous studies of irradiated insects, plants and bacteria, and the dosage relationships of one-hit and of two-hit aberrations are similar to what has been said above about somatic cells of humans. However, until W. L. Russell undertook his program of measuring the relation of point mutations to dose in mice beginning in 1947, no dose-effect studies were available for any mammal, let alone man. Mice were sufficiently well known genetically to provide the background of information necessary for such a large-scale study of induced mutation. It began and continues at the Biology Division of the Oak Ridge National Laboratory.

Russell's research aimed successfully at the study of mutation from the normal Dominant to any recessive allele of certain gene loci. Seven recessive coat color mutants were selected for scoring because their expression was clearly different from the wild coat color combination. Wild type mice were irradiated, and at various times afterward they were mated to animals showing the multiple recessives. In the absence of new mutation at these loci, all offspring would be expected to show the Dominant wild phenotype, as most of them did. In a pilot experiment Russell found one F_1 mouse showing the coat color sepia representing a change in the Se locus of the irradiated parent; four other animals showed a distinct amount of spotting, evidently related to mutation at the S locus to recessive spotting; still two other mice were wild type in all of the other loci under direct test except that they were of the recessive pink-eye phenotype; another mouse showed a mutation to an albino allele at the C locus; and another revealed that there had been a change from intense pigmentation to the recessive dilute at the D locus of the mouse. In each of the above instances a recessive phenotype showed up in animals which otherwise would remain in the dominant class except after a mutation of the Dominant allele to a recessive form, or rarely after the loss of the Dominant allele by Deletion. Several variations of this pilot experiment were performed.

Mutation in Irradiated Male Mice. In the earliest of Russell's experiments a 600 r dose of X-rays was given quickly to normal wild type males, and then after several weeks they were mated to multiple recessive females. In this way offspring were obtained each carrying a paternal chromosome set which was in a spermatogonial cell of the sire during the several minutes of acute irradiation. Control matings were made at the same time between similar normal males and recessive females to give approximately the same number of offspring as in the irradiated series. Among some 48,000 mice from irradiated sires there was a wide range of response at the seven loci. For instance, 25 mutants to white-spotting occurred before any recessive mutants showing either agouti or sepia were found. Later studies showed that the range from the lowest to the highest mutation frequencies among these loci was a 30-fold increase. Yet such a range had been exceeded in studies by Stadler on the spontaneous mutation rate of certain loci in corn. Russell's studies revealed that the average induced mutation rate in the first mammalian species to be tested was a whole order of magnitude greater, perhaps 15 times the average rate per locus per roentgen as had been reported by Mary Alexander for 2 different species of *Drosophila*. This resulted in a downward revision of the irradiation considered permissible for persons handling strongly radioactive materials.

Russell's experiments concentrated first on the effects of exposing male mice to *acute* dosage of X-rays, because comparisons could be made with a large body of *Drosophila* data on the same sex. However, the *Drosophila* experiments had concentrated on studies of irradiated sperm and spermatid stages, where the mutation rate is highest, although the risk from the exposure of men is predominantly the formation of mutants in earlier cell stages, in the spermatogonial cells. Irradiation and testing of mouse spermatogonia revealed something not found in the *Drosophila* sperm, an effect of the rate of administration of the ionizing radiation in the production of apparent gene mutations when acute and *chronic* exposures were compared. For the production of chromosomal Aberrations in plants and animals the same total dose is much more effective if given quickly than if spread out over a long interval of time. Studies of mutations in mice by the specific locus method also showed an influence of the irradiation intensity.

When intensities of irradiation as diverse as 9 and .009 r per minute were found to give different mutation rates for the same total dose, even more extreme rates were tested at uniform totals. X-radiation at the rate of 90 r per minute was given to male mice until either 300 or 600 r had been accumulated in the acute dose-rate series. Animals exposed at a low dose rate from a cesium-137 source received irradiation at as little as .001 r per minute. The mutation rate after the acute dosage was more than three times the gene mutation rate at the chronic dose rate at the time of a progress report in 1963.

The investigation of the effect of prolonging the irradiation was also performed in *dose fractionation* studies. A total dose of 1000 r was administered at the acute rate continuously, or in two equal fractions or in five equal fractions, and the mutation rates were compared. A surprising result was the discovery that in mice an interval of one day between receiving the two halves of the dose was much more mutagenic than was the shorter interval of merely two hours. This suggests that gene mutation, like chromosome breakage and reunion, is a two-step affair involving a premutational change followed by a completion of the mutation. The existence of a dose rate effect in the male mouse raised the question of whether the effect occurred within the spermatogonial cells or whether the observed mutant offspring were the result of differential growth and selection between damaged and undamaged cells. Experiments with irradiated female mice shed light on this point.

Mutation in Irradiated Female Mice. The germ cells present in juvenile and mature female mice, and in girls and women also (Chapter 2), are much more uniform in stage than is the sequence of mitotic stages which are present simultaneously in an adult male. From birth onward primary oocytes are present in an arrested or *dictyate* stage of prophase, whereas the oogonial stages which preceded them are no longer found. Thus a direct comparison of the irradiation of gonial stages of mammals in the two sexes cannot be made (except by irradiation of fetuses and dams), but the results of irradiating mice with all potential eggs in the oocyte stage indicate in some measure the risk from the exposure of young girls and women to ionizing irradiation. Experiments to measure the mutagenic risks in female mice have been conducted on a very large scale, again at the Oak Ridge National Laboratory and also at Harwell in England.

Among female mice the difference in mutation rate after irradiation at 90 r per minute seems to be even higher above that in the other sex, and the rate following the .001 r per minute dose appears to be lower than that previously measured in males. The significance of this comparison is that the dose rate effect in females is most surely an effect within the cell uncomplicated by later losses of some cells. Because the oocytes irradiated in either immature or mature female mammals do not undergo mitotic cell division, there is no chance for preferential multiplication of the un-injured cells. However, in the testis there is much mitotic multiplication of spermatogonial cells throughout life, and selection among damaged and undamaged cells in males would be possible, but a dosage effect continues to be found even with small and therefore less harmful total doses. It thus appears that the mutation process might be arrested and repaired somewhere during or after exposure. Russell estimates that some two-thirds of the spermatogonial mutations and practically all of the oocytial mutations would be reparable if intracellular secrets were better known.

MINOR SEX-RATIO CHANGES IN HUMANS

Similar multiple testcrosses in mankind are unknown but observations may be made on ordinary sex-linkage. Because males have only one X-chromosome, any recessive gene in that X will usually show in his pheno-type (barring epistasis). This X-chromosome of the male comes from his mother and will thus reveal one allele of each locus on the maternal sex chromosomes; conversely as a parent his X-chromosome, now called paternal, will pass to his daughters who will show any Dominant genes, including new Dominant mutants, of their father. Thus the daughters of irradiated fathers might be observed for a possibly elevated frequency of new Dominant mutants, and the sons of irradiated mothers might be studied for new recessive alleles. The problem is knowing what phenotypes to look for and how to look for them uniformly over time and distance. This problem was solved in 1927 by Muller in *Drosophila* in the study of sex-linked lethal alleles, which may be formed at any of hundreds of loci along the X-chromosome. A dominant Lethal arising in the single X of some germ cell of a male would not kill him but would kill one of his potential daughters after fertilization of an ovum. Conversely, any recessive lethal gene in the X passed on from a mother to an XY zygote would be effective in such an hemizygous male and would kill off that potential offspring. Comparisons are therefore made of the sex ratios issuing from two paired groups of parents, treated and control fathers for a possible decrease of live daughters and exposed versus nonexposed mothers for a possible decrease in the ratio of live sons. Such comparisons have been made of the numbers of sons and daughters of four kinds of parents, namely, male radiologists, women having had irradiation because of apparent sterility, men or women who have had irradiation in the vicinity of the gonads for sciatic neuralgia or other complaints and finally Japanese who became parents after exposure to the bomb irradiation in Hiroshima and Nagasaki. These studies were reviewed together by Schull and Neel in 1957 and some confirmation of sex-linked recessive lethal effects in humans was found even at the low doses of exposure.

Whatever genetic damage may be measured by any studies of sex-linked lethals will be only a small fraction of the total genetic damage. Other chromosomes not as readily testable will also harbor new lethals to act in later generations in homozygotes, and even the sex-linked recessives will pass undetected to daughters one-half of the time. An indication of the distribution of recessive genetic damage through many generations after starting with an irradiated male is given in Figure 25-4. The time is just arriving when grandchildren of the Japanese who were irradiated in 1945

Sex ratio changes following one exposure

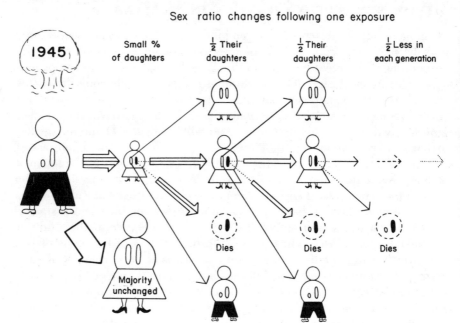

FIGURE 25-4 Effects of one new sex-linked recessive lethal allele anywhere in the length of an X chromosome (darkened) from an irradiated male (left) or control male. The 1 : 2 sex ratio in such families is diluted in each generation, but the lethal gene is only slowly eliminated. An irradiated woman would similarly transmit through some daughters to some grandchildren.

will begin to appear. However, the measurable effects on the sex ratio in this generation may be on the borderline of significance in mass data. Because of the small sizes of human families it will probably prove impossible also to distinguish many of the lethal heterozygotes from their normal sisters. Yet comparison with the effects of higher doses of irradiation in mice and fruit flies indicates that induced genetic damage in humans is real even though concealed by the numbers problem.

IRRADIATION-INDUCED LEUKEMIA

Even if induced mutations are hard to measure accurately in species other than mice, induction of leukemia in somatic tissues is a conspicuous result of irradiation in any mammal. Leukemic cells grow rapidly, as many other cancerous cells do, but there are more possible starting points. It has been estimated that the number of leukocytes and lymphocytes in the human body is in the millions of millions. Even if only a small fraction of these were subject to the risk of mutation, and even if the mutation frequency were very low, an appreciable number of persons would be victims of leukemia. Any agent, ionizing irradiation or other, which increases the mutation in this vast population of cells would correspondingly increase the deaths among persons exposed. Each person is, in effect, a giant culture plate for the detection of any mutation from a normal leukemoblast to a cell founding a leukemic clone at any time during the proverbial three score years and ten.

The incidence of leukemia has been intensively studied in the population of whole countries, of large cities and of special categories of individuals some with higher exposures to radiation than others. It has been demonstrated that the incidence of leukemia has increased in the white population of the United States from 42 to 68 per million per year in the interval from 1940 to 1954, and these cases are assumed to be spontaneous leukemias. Among some 1800 persons exposed in Hiroshima and Nagasaki within 1000 meters of ground zero, there were 18 cases of death from leukemia making a 1/100 frequency over a carefully studied span of 7.8 years. Hardly one of these could be considered a spontaneous case. Similarly, high frequencies of leukemia have been found among men who had received heavy irradiation in the vertebral column as a treatment to arrest the progress of ankylosing spondylitis. Crude rates of from 220 to over 1000 cases per million men per year according to total dose, have been reported among patients treated for this particular rheumatoid arthritis of the spine.

Relation of Disease to Dose. Two questions may be elucidated by careful studies of dose-effect curves, one relating to cause and the other relating to safety. A linear relation could indicate either gene mutation or chromosomal aberration resulting from a single break in a chromosome, whereas an exponential relation could indicate that two simultaneous breaks would need to be present and open at the same time in order for the deleterious change to leukemogenesis to occur. If either of these curves dropped off suddenly to the control value at lower dosages, it might be possible to name a threshold for the beginning of the mutational increase and a safe dose below it.

In several independent studies a linear relationship was found between leukemia incidence and total dose of ionizing radiation. This was clearly so at the higher doses, and from them a rate per roentgen could be computed after taking into account the amount of the body exposed. For spondylitics the exposure was to the vertebral column, to some children with enlarged thymus glands it was the chest only which was X-rayed. To radiologists and to the survivors of the atomic bomb the exposure tended to be on the whole body, a scope of exposure which is known, in rats, to be much more damaging to the individual than is irradiation of a half of the body. Whole body exposure to natural background sources of radiation was also assumed in a study on the residents of Brooklyn, New York. The effect in these several studies was computed for the dose expressed in *rads* (radiation dose absorbed in tissue) instead of in roentgens. The estimates from the five kinds of study fell within similar and widely overlapping ranges within which the best estimate was one or two cases of induced leukemia per rad per 100,000 individuals per year of life.

The Threshold Dose Problem. The possibility of using a safe dose of irradiation without any leukemia being induced should be explored. Such would resemble the proper dose of a medicine which slowly disappears through the kidneys, but because the chromosomes are so firmly incorporated into the cell a harmless dose may be harder to find. More likely a tolerable dose might be specified, one which causes some cell damage, some cell death but not the death of too many cells of the body. Adequate replacement is possible after some burning or cutting of skin cells, and a moderate fraction of the circulating blood cells can be replaced after severe bleeding or after a deliberate blood donation, but the question of induced leukemia is not like those forms of damage. It is a matter of whether one metastasizing cell or none is produced, and the human body is all too good an indicator of whether this has occurred.

For ordinary statistical reasons the question of a threshold dose is much harder to answer than to ask. It is interesting to note first that two opposite interpretations were put on the same data from the Hiroshima study. A linear relation down through three different geographical zones to a control level in the fourth zone was reported, only to be challenged shortly by an additional observation. It was pointed out that in the farthest zone to show an increase, the ring 1500 to 1999 meters from the hypocenter, all of its cases were in the inner half of the distance, as if a threshold had not been reached in the exposures received by persons beyond, say, 1750 meters distance. The problem is a typical one of small numbers; only eight cases of leukemia had occurred during eight years before late 1955 among 20,113 persons being observed from this area of exposure. The fact that the subdivision between inner and outer halves of the radial distance made an 8 : 0 instead of 4 : 4 distribution could have been merely fortuitous. Solution to the question awaits further evidence from other lines of inquiry.

The magnitude of the problem of demonstrating a threshold dose for leukemia has been pointed out by Carol Buck. If one asks whether 5 r accumulated from birth to age 34 was or was not leukemogenic, one would have to observe uniformly 6,000,000 such exposed persons over the next ten year period of their lives. If an accumulated dose of 20 r were to be assessed, it would take a group of 500,000 persons under the same conditions of study. If a threshold were more than ten times that high, a ten year study would require 10,000 persons with an accumulated dose of 200 r to demonstrate or to deny that possibility. For lack of any evidence of a threshold below which radiation might not add to the normal incidence of leukemia it would be prudent to assume that the relation is linear with dose down to the smallest exposure. Dr. Buck further points out that fetuses seem to be about eight times as susceptible to the induction of leukemia as are adults, according to a review of 792 leukemic deaths during a three year period among 6,000,000 children in England and Wales under ten years of age. Thus only the danger has been shown; safety has not yet been demonstrated. Hence irradiation dangers must be weighed against the other hazards to life. Here, for instance, it may be pointed out that the leukemic patient himself can be treated and sometimes saved by heavy irradiation to kill the rapidly dividing cells.

Possible Mechanisms of Leukemogenesis. Several modes of origin have been considered for the several kinds of leukemias. Metabolic upsets, hormonal changes, chromosomal Deletion and viral action are among the suggested precipitating causes, and two of these will be discussed here. The chronic myelocytic kind of leukemia seems to be associated rather regularly with a shortened chromosome of pair 21 known as the Philadelphia chromosome, Ph[1], named from its location of discovery. This visibly different Deletion chromosome is more often seen in freshly drawn blood than in cultured leukocytes from the same persons, as if conditions outside the body favored the growth of cells different from those gaining in relative abundance inside the blood stream. Not all kinds of leukemias have the Ph[1] deletion chromosome; other kinds may be due to genic change or to smaller aberrations not distinguishable from gene mutation by cytological study. The recent discovery of at least one high correlation between a chromosomal change and a particular leukemia is a long delayed realization of a prediction by the great biologist T. Boveri in 1912 that abnormal chromosomes may initiate neoplasmic growth.

Viruses of the RNA variety are associated with leukemogenesis in rodents and in birds. Viruses in general may infect and kill the cells which they invade, or they may merely infect and remain somewhat latent. There is much multiplication of the virus particles particularly in the cells killed, and when viral concentrations are large, a very small fraction of infected cells are transduced genetically. Where transduction has been studied in culture the transduced cells are only 1/100,000 as numerous as the viral particles in the culture. In studies on leukemogenesis in mice the use of irradiation will increase the incidence of leukemia, as it does in man. Yet the mechanism could be by various pathways. The radiation could weaken the host cells to the activities of virus already harbored or to the invasion of new virus particles. Alternatively, or perhaps additionally, the radiation could affect the concentration of the virus or engender a mutant form of the virus. In any event an increased occurrence of cancerous growths such as leukemia is a clearly observable result.

Viruses of the DNA variety cause tumors in cells not as specialized as the blood-forming cells discussed above, and for them chromatid breaks may have great significance. Cells recently infected with DNA viruses begin to grow and to show an elevated incidence of chromatid breaks but are not yet cancerous. Transduction is not completed until after several generations and then in only a small fraction of cells, among which altered chromosomes are often found. The suggestion is clear from other studies in microbiology, that some of the virus particles (bacteriophage) which invade and usually destroy bacteria actually become a part of the bacterial genome. Thus the completed transduction is permanent like a mutational change.

CHEMICAL MUTAGENS

Investigations of chemical mutagenesis were begun secretly during World War II and published thereafter. Shortly it was found that ultraviolet irradiation of the culture medium could cause mutations in bacteria, so in at least that case irradiation was acting through chemical changes rather than directly breaking chromosomes or causing genic mutations. A vast variety of chemicals, some of them drugs, some carcinogens, some simple inorganic compounds, have been tested for their mutagenic power in the lower organisms. Some of the carcinogens are mutagenic, but all of them are not. Mutagenicity of a substance may be higher in one species than in another; and within a species some strains are more resistant to the induction of mutations than are others. Of special interest is the demonstration that 5-bromo uracil, similar to a normal component of RNA, can cause increased mutation in the DNA of other organisms by seeming to take the place of thymine temporarily. The result is an upsetting of the pairing relationship of the DNA and a shift from a T-A pair to a C-G pair according to one theory of action. Although the halogenated uracils are highly specific, they are very weak as mutagens. Very few of the chemicals are as mutagenic as is ionizing irradiation.

SUMMARY

Mutations are produced by ionizing irradiation not only in the lowest forms of life but also in mammals. Some chemicals also achieve the same result, but to a lesser degree. Induced changes in the germ line show in a later generation as mutant individuals; in the somatic cells the result is mutant cell lines called clones, and sometimes these clones are cancerous.

Cellular inherited changes may be genic or chromosomal. The frequency of genic changes increases linearly with dose, and no threshold irradiation dose has been demonstrated in any test organism. Recessive lethal mutants in the X-chromosome may change the sex ratio: fewer sons when the mother is irradiated (recessive sex-linked lethal action) or fewer daughters where a dominant Lethal is induced in the father's X-chromosome. This test ignores what is happening in the other 22 pairs. Chromosomal mutants involving but a single break follow the same dosage rule; but two-break Rearrangements increase exponentially with the total dose given intensely. Prenatally the gonial cells of both sexes are endangered. After birth a girl has only oocytes at risk. Cells vary in radiosensitivity.

Mutant somatic cells result from similar physical and chemical mutagens. Although genic changes are demonstrable less readily in the soma, cytological observations of somatic cells show fragments, bridges and chromosomes of altered total length or changed arm ratios. Chronic irradiation seems to result in shorter average length of life and in specific diseases such as leukemia.

SUGGESTED READING

Edwards, R. G., and A. G. Searle, Genetic radiosensitivity of specific postdictyate stages in mouse oocytes. Genet. Res. 4: 389–398 (1963). After inducing ovulation the origin of new dominant lethals was measured.

Neel, J. V., *Changing Perspectives on the Genetic Effects of Radiation*, Springfield, Ill., Thomas, 1963, 97 pp. A comprehensive and well-referenced account of studies on mutations in man, human tissue cultures, and experimental mammals.

Puck, T. T., Radiation and the human cell. Sci. Amer. **202** (No. 4): 142–153 (and reprint series, April 1960), San Francisco, Freeman, 1960. Considers chromosomal aberrations, giant cells and survival curves.

Russell, W. L., Genetic hazards of radiation. Proc. Amer. Phil. Soc. **107**: 11–17 (1963). Induced mutations in a mammal (mouse), a current summary.

Schull, W. J., and J. V. Neel, Radiation and the sex ratio in man. Science **128**: 343–348 (1958). Compares data from Hiroshima and Nagasaki with studies on children of radiologists, of persons receiving therapeutic X-rays of regions close to the gonads.

Sci. Amer. **201** (No. 3): 74–176, 219–232 (Sept., 1959) Eight articles on ionizing radiation.

Sobels, F. H., ed. *Repair from Genetic Radiation Damage and Differential Radiosensitivity in Germ Cells* New York, Macmillan, 1963, 454 pp. From a conference of research workers relating insect mutation studies to those in humans, plants and protozoa, with a summary by R. F. Kimball.

Wallace, Bruce, and T. Dobzhansky, *Radiation, Genes and Man*, New York, Holt, 1959, 205 pp. A very readable account.

PROBLEMS

25-1 How can a single chromosome, broken once in the G_1 period, form a chromatid tie at anaphase?

25-2 Which of the following types of aberrations are linearly related to dose: terminal deficiencies, translocations, long deletions, chromatid ties?

25-3 (a) Is an induced mutation rate of 3/100,000 for one locus significantly above zero for another locus in the same size and plan of experiment?
(b) Is 8/100,000 significantly above the parametric value of .00003?
(c) Is 10/100,000 significantly different from 5/100,000?

25-4 On Figure 25-3 (right side) what numbers of observations would be necessary after a 75 roentgen dose to establish that outcomes on the higher dashed line and on the solid line were significantly different from each other at the 95 percent confidence level?

25-5 Briefly define

> threshold dose
> exponential relation to dose
> dose fractionation
> one-hit curve
> G_1 period

chapter 26

Selection and Random Genetic Drift

The genetic composition of a population does not change without some cause or causes, and two of these causes will be examined in this chapter. As was pointed out in Chapter 6, the gene frequency for each allele tends to remain constant from generation to generation. Hardy and Weinberg independently pointed out that dominants remain at a level and do not automatically increase, as some persons had thought. Conversely, recessive alleles also remain at their respective frequencies under ideal conditions. Gene frequencies will change, however, by mutation, by natural selection and by random fluctuations which may even mean the complete loss of either allele from a small-sized population. Mutation will tend to restore rare alleles to a population, after which selection and genetic drift will come into play. Continued selection in a constant environment will tend to replace a disadvantageous allele by the better one, but genetic drift, being random, can either assist or oppose the changes favored by natural selection. Hence the actions of selection and of drift and even of mutation may be variously interwoven in life.

Selection may be slight or severe in amount and positive or negative in respect to an uncommon characteristic. A few individuals may be favored for reproductive purposes in positive selection for the trait which they show; or conversely, a few individuals of another type may be prevented from reproducing in a program, ill-advised or otherwise, of negative selection. Migration is also selective in both positive and negative aspects. Immigration brings in many alleles which are in greater or lesser frequency among the migrants than in the host population; and emigration may have removed an unrepresentative sample of alleles, or a valuable combination of alleles from the gene pool of the mother country.

MEANS OF DELIBERATE SELECTION

The manner of selecting an individual can be according to his own phenotype, according to his ancestry or according to the average of his progeny.

The first, *phenotypic selection,* is biologically the oldest and the most widely known method of changing a breed or a population. Almost all of natural selection and the beginning stages of many programs for the conscious improvement of plants and domesticated animals employ phenotypic selection. To the reader sophisticated in genetics several difficulties in the practice of phenotypic selection will come to mind such as the existence of phenocopies, hidden recessives and assortment of genes involved in quantitative inheritance. Contrasts between illustrious parents and some not-so-illustrious children, as well as exceptional children from humble beginnings, may also come to mind. Hence where humans have desired more reliable improvement two other kinds of selection have been invented and practiced.

Selection because of an outstanding ancestor (good or bad) among humans and selection on the basis of one or more past champions (or hemophilics) among dogs or among other show animals constitute examples of *pedigree selection.* Many fine children have been produced and some Dominant defects have been kept out of certain families by a due consideration of ancestors and of collateral relatives of an intended spouse. The principle of pedigree selection is also much used in the breeding of race horses and many other kinds of mammals and domestic fowl. The basis for selection according to ancestors is that persons whose family trees included several very desirable individuals in the past have a better chance of producing the same or a similar kind in the next generation than would marriage partners from family trees without such ancestors. Partially offsetting this general expectation is the continual occurrence of Mendelian segregation and assortment between each two generations. This difficulty has been successfully circumvented in experimental animals.

A type of selection which is effectively used in plant and animal improvement is *progeny selection.* Individuals are chosen for extensive breeding or are culled only after the average of many offspring has been determined for the desired trait or combination of traits. It frequently turns out that the highest average performance among sibships comes from parents slightly less than superb phenotypically, and sometimes the parents are individually mediocre. For instance, in certain poultry flocks egg production had been raised to a plateau and an apparent limit of improvement by the direct selection of good hens and the brothers or sires of other good hens; but with the institution of progeny testing before selection there emerged immediate improvement over the next several generations to a substantially higher plateau. To do this, the progeny testing must be generous for each prospective selectee, and many potential preferred parents must be tested to provide an adequate range of choice. Only after many records are filed and summarized is culling and selecting of the parental generation done. Then the members of the next generation are again progeny tested and the selection process is repeated. The method of progeny selection is excellent for a clearly defined quantitative character of great economic importance such as egg production in hens, but it requires a large investment in housing, feeding and in record keeping and computation. Human genetics does not stand at the threshold of such methods, nor is it ready to advocate the kinds of phenotypic eugenics which had some vogue early in the twentieth century when genetics was new both as a science and as an art.

SELECTION IN LARGE POPULATIONS

Natural selection is probably more adverse against lethal and unfavorable aspects of the phenotype than it is strongly positive in favor of some one type. Therefore in this section we shall consider complete adverse selection and also partial adverse selection against phenotypes with fairly simple genetic differentiation, monohybrid or dihybrid (digenic). In order to generalize as to the progress under selection, it is necessary to assume that large numbers of individuals are present in the population and even in the negatively selected class in order to avoid the influence of random fluctuations (to be treated later under genetic drift).

Complete Negative Selection. Against a Dominant characteristic phenotypic selection is completely effective in one generation regardless of the previous high or low frequency of that phenotype. This is the opposite side of the coin saying that "recessives breed true." In the choice of recessives as parents one is selecting completely against Dominant individuals whether they be many or few in the population. This is shown by the drop to zero gene frequency in one generation by the dashed line in Figure 26-1. All other phenotypes respond less dramatically and to differing amounts at different levels of prevalence. At intermediate frequencies the effect of selection is greatest (Table 26-1). Compare the drop in frequency of recessives from 25 to 11.11 percent between generations 1 and 2 with the drop from 1 to 0.83 percent between generations 9 and 10.

The reduction of phenotypic frequencies below the 1 percent level by complete adverse selection is graphed for three typical simple phenotypes in Figure 26-1. First, a simple recessive phenotype continues to appear in the population at the frequencies shown by the solid line although no recessive parent is ever used. By extrapolation from this graph one may conclude correctly that a simple recessive phenotype can never be eliminated from a large population merely by rejecting all recessives from each generation. Secondly, against a recessive-recessive phenotype (see duplicate dominant epistasis in Chapter 10) selection is even less effective. Ten generations of

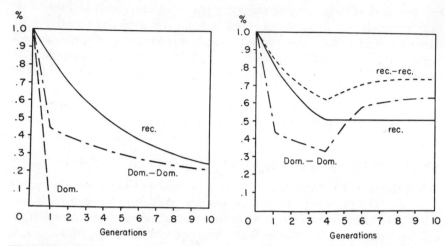

FIGURE 26-1 Frequencies of various phenotypes in a population after complete adverse selection in each of ten generations (left) against the type of parents specified, and after only four generations (right). Cessation of selection makes no further change for the one-locus phenotypes, but the digenic phenotypes rebound somewhat to equilibrium above the lowest frequency attained by selection. After Koller, Zeitschrift menschliche Vererbungs- Konstitutionslehre, **19**: 264–268 (1935/1936), Springer-Verlag, Berlin.

TABLE 26-1 Effects of complete selection against a recessive trait[a]

Generations	Gene frequency	Recessive homozygotes, %	Heterozygotes, %	Dominant homozygotes, %
1	0.500	25.00	50.00	25.00
2	0.333	11.11	44.44	44.44
3	0.250	6.25	37.50	56.25
4	0.200	4.00	32.00	64.00
5	0.167	2.78	27.78	69.44
9	0.100	1.00	18.00	81.00
10	0.091	0.83	16.53	82.64
20	0.048	0.23	9.07	90.70
30	0.032	0.10	6.24	93.65
40	0.024	0.06	4.76	95.18
50	0.020	0.04	3.84	96.12
100	0.010	0.01	1.96	98.03

[a]From *Principles of Genetics*, 5th edition, by Sinnott, Dunn, and Dobzhansky. Copyright 1958. McGraw-Hill Book Company. Used by permission.

discarding the undesired phenotype reduces the kind from 1 percent to approximately .5 percent, a small reward for perhaps a large screening effort. Many human phenotypes as yet unanalyzed will doubtless fall into this category. Thirdly, against a phenotype depending upon the simultaneous presence of two Dominant alleles in different independently assorting loci, the reduction in the first generation is great, but it is very slow thereafter. Other phenotypes respond to selection along still different curves, but the lesson is already evident: only the Dominant single factor phenotype can be eliminated, whereas digenic phenotypes and simple recessive phenotypes will reappear in each generation from parents of acceptable appearance.

The sudden relaxation of selection leads to different frequencies for the digenic phenotypes as contrasted with the single factor phenotypes. The prevalence of any single factor recessive remains constant at whatever level it had reached when selection was relaxed, and this is in accord with the Hardy-Weinberg equilibrium as described in the monohybrid section of this text. Although this principle of equilibrium may be extended at once to the chromosomes as monohybrid pairs, equilibrium for two factor phenotypes is attained only after several generations of no selection, and it is reached at a level of phenotypes above that to which adverse selection had driven it. This is particularly true of the phenotype resulting from the presence of two Dominants of different gene pairs. Reference is again made to Figure 26-1. The rate of rebound is based on the common assumption that the two loci are unlinked. Linkage would delay the response to selection and would also affect the rebound following cessation of selection.

Partial Negative Selection. The mild handicapping of a certain phenotype is a more common situation than is complete adverse selection. The odds against reproduction for a certain type may range from slight to severe, and the effect will vary correspondingly. For example, the effects of 1 percent selection (or of 10 percent or of 50 percent selection) against a simple recessive phenotype may be compared with the results of complete selection in Table 26-2. Here the starting frequency of recessives is taken to be at the 1 percent level of recessives, a level which may be found in Table 26-1 (generation 9) and also in Figures 26-1 and 26-2. In the figures the changes in occurrence of other phenotypes may be compared. For instance, the frequency of simple Dominant phenotypes decreases dramatically in the first one or two generations of 50 percent adverse selection, but it makes an asymptotic approach to zero frequency during many subsequent generations. This contrasts sharply with immediate elimination of Dominants by complete selection. In addition, note the even slower reduction in the frequency of recessive and double recessive phenotypes by partial selection. For an instance of 50 percent selection in nature, it may be recalled that

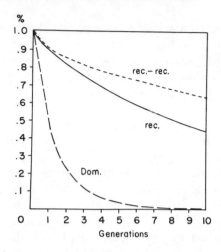

FIGURE 26-2 Some phenotypic frequencies after 50 percent adverse selection against certain phenotypes. Equilibrium or extinction is approached more slowly than in Figure 26-1. After Koller, Zeitschrift menlischliche Vererbungs- Konstitutionslehre, **19**: 264–268 (1935/1936), Springer-Verlag, Berlin.

TABLE 26-2 Effects of complete selection ($s = 1.0$) and of partial selection ($s < 1.0$) against a recessive trait on the frequency in percent of individuals homozygous for the recessive gene[a]

Generation	$s = 1.0$	$s = 0.50$	$s = 0.10$	$s = 0.01$
1	1.00	1.00	1.00	1.00
10	0.25	0.46	0.84	0.98
20	0.11	0.26	0.71	0.97

[a]From *Principles of Genetics* by Sinnott, Dunn, and Dobzhansky. Copyright 1958. McGraw-Hill Book Company. Used by permission.

Reciprocal Translocation individuals involving long pieces of nonhomologous chromosomes are semisterile; half of their gametes from free assortment of centromeres are Duplication-Deficiencies of opposite types, both of which are usually lethal. Translocation mongoloids are an exception in that they may have three-fourths fertility if they mature.

Positive Selection. Stringent positive selection is often practiced by animal and plant breeders, but it is seldom used on any large scale in human populations. Perhaps the latter omission is a good one considering the present state of knowledge in just two fields, genetics and politics. A positive selection program in man is far from appropriate until there is better understanding of technical methods and human goals. As a limited example of selection in man we may cite the Sumo wrestlers of Japan. These were men of enormous proportions who resulted from generations of selective inbreeding of successful wrestlers and the daughters of wrestlers. No one gene seems to be responsible for an overly large phenotype either here or in the giant breeds of rabbits or other rodents; instead many factor pairs

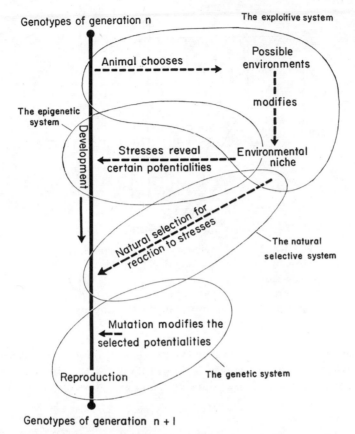

Genotypes of generation n

The exploitive system

Animal chooses

Possible environments

modifies

The epigenetic system

Development

Stresses reveal certain potentialities

Environmental niche

Natural selection for reaction to stresses

The natural selective system

Mutation modifies the selected potentialities

Reproduction

The genetic system

Genotypes of generation n + l

FIGURE 26-3 Between one generation and the next the genotype reacts with the environment before the selective effects of the environment are completed. Thus adaptability to a certain kind of stress may be favored. From Waddington, Nature, **183:** 1636 (1959).

seem to contribute to the differentiation from individuals of size normal for the species.

A type of positive selection less direct than usual is selection for adaptability. This can take many forms, all of which are harder to test than is direct selection of a phenotype. A particular program which is of special interest to geneticists is the selection for a phenocopy produced in a normal organism by some environmental challenge. Waddington has examined this thoroughly in insect material and has described the steps by which there may be an evolutionary assimilation of an acquired character. Figure 26-3

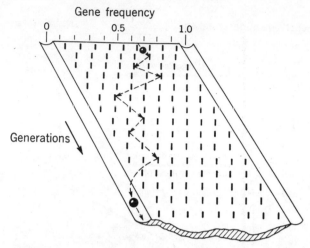

FIGURE 26-4 Model for random changes in gene frequency, which may be wide fluctuations in small populations. Scale represents five parents per generation. From Ehrlich and Holm, *The Process of Evolution*, Copyright 1963, McGraw-Hill Book Company. Used by permission.

shows the areas of reaction of genotype with environment and conversely, during one life cycle. Incidentally, it will be noted that heredity and environment have no mutually exclusive boundary; they are well interlaced in all investigations.

ALLELES IN SMALL POPULATIONS

Before mild selection can get to work the vagaries of random sampling may lose one allele or lose another from a small population. This is best described in an extreme case where only two parents become the parents of the next generation, a Noah's ark effect. The pairs of animals coming on board would have only a total of four genes at each locus. With such a small sample size any allele which was reasonably rare in the population might be absent on the ark, and a common allele at another locus might be underrepresented or overrepresented. If subsequently only two of the offspring become the parents of still another generation, the danger of absence or of exclusive transmission of an allele is again incurred. If a smaller statistical fluctuation happens to deviate in the same direction for two or three successive generations, one allele frequency may drift to zero and its opposite allele will be fixed at 100 percent. Figure 26-4 suggests the outcome of several wide fluctuations. Wide fluctuation or loss of an allele for reason of small sample size is called *genetic drift*. In instances it can carry a gene frequency to zero or to one in just one generation of inbreeding, simply as a matter of random sampling in a very small population. Genetic drift is inevitable in any population even if all individuals breed and breed equally because the gametes merely sample the genotype, but the magnitude of the effect varies inversely with population size.

Random genetic drift in small populations is also known as the *Sewall Wright effect* named for the geneticist who showed its implications and who made many other contributions to population genetics generally and to mouse and mammalian genetics particularly. He pointed out, for instance, that a new mutant may be lost by random drift to zero frequency before it may be favored for slow increase by positive natural selection. Conversely, alleles which may now be favored by natural selection may have survived initially by luck. Dr. Wright has computed the chances of a single new mutant surviving for many generations (a small chance) and of both surviving and of increasing (an even smaller chance). From a consideration of these small probabilities the concept of *mutation pressure* arises; repeated mutations eventually can place a neutral allele or a slightly advantageous allele in the population even though most new mutations die out after a few generations for numerical reasons.

Random drift can be readily demonstrated in small populations of insects, and signs of drift may be sought apart from natural selection even in human population isolates. Bentley Glass and co-workers have made an intensive study of a community of Dunkers living in Franklin County, Pennsylvania, for the purpose of comparing their gene frequencies with the frequencies of those same alleles in two larger populations, namely, in the surrounding but separate American mixture and in the parts of Germany from which 27 families of the Dunker sect emigrated two centuries ago. In one of six respects all populations agreed; their rhesus alleles were not dissimilar. The present populations of Americans and of West Germans had many gene frequency agreements with each other whereas the Dunker community differed from the two large populations in the frequencies of blood group alleles i^A and i^B and also M and N of the Landsteiner locus. The distinctive frequencies in the smaller population were judged not to be due to selective advantage, or else both of the Pennsylvanian populations would have shown changes in the same direction from that of the European source. When the possible effects of selection and of migration had been evaluated, a large residual difference in some allele frequencies remained and seemed to be genuinely attributable to random genetic drift in the small Dunker community.

The data on the Dunker individuals was then reassembled into three age groups to see whether there was currently any marked change in respect to each of the blood loci tested. In addition, data on earlobe, handedness, mid-digital hair, hyperextensibility of the thumb (Figure 26-5) and two other physical features were compared by age groups. Because the average

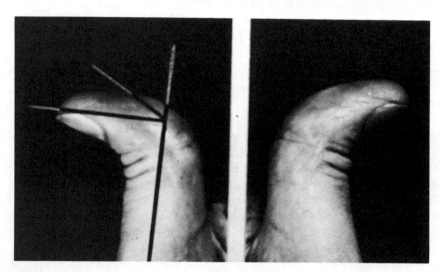

FIGURE 26-5 Thumb showing hyperextensibility compared with a normal thumb. The difference is genetically determined. Courtesy of Bentley Glass.

age at birth of the first child in this community was 27 years, the middle generation was defined to include all persons of ages 28 to 55 (mainly parents), generation 1 consisted of all persons of age 56 or above (mainly grandparents) and generation 3 consisted of all tested individuals of age 27 or less. These three generations did not show changes significant by Chi-square tests in respect to allele frequencies or phenotype frequencies in six of nine comparisons, and in two of these last (right handedness and fifth digit not reaching the last joint of the adjacent finger) a change significant at the 5 percent level was found only between generation 3 and the two older generations combined. These could be simple examples of drift. Of particular interest were the successive changes in the same direction between generations in respect to one of the three blood antigenic loci. Although the M frequency drifted upward by a moderate amount between generations 1 and 2 and again between generations 2 and 3, the change accumulated in just two generations was significant at the .01 probability level. (Study Table 26-3.) Thus one gene frequency has been caught in the act of drifting in a population where other gene frequencies remained stable. These other loci indicated that immigration or gene flow had not brought in an excess of the M allele but that it had merely changed by sampling error while most other loci retained their previous allele frequencies.

TABLE 26-3   Franklin County (Pa.) Dunkers — Age-group analysis of MN blood group phenotypes[a]

	M		MN		N		
Generation	No.	%	No.	%	No.	%	Total
1	12	28.6	22	52.4	8	19.0	42
2	34	44.8	32	42.1	10	13.1	76
3	48	55.8	30	34.9	8	9.3	86

$$X^2 \text{ Gen. 1 and 2} = 2.98 \qquad .30 > P > .20$$
$$X^2 \text{ Gen. 2 and 3} = 2.00 \qquad .50 > P > .30$$
$$X^2 \text{ Gen. 1 and 3} = 9.50 \qquad .01 > P > .005$$

[a]Bentley Glass. On the evidence of random genetic drift in human populations, Amer. J. Phys. Anthrop., **14**: 545 (1956).

Among 75 villages in the valley above Parma, Italy, heterogeneity in the distribution of the major blood types was found in a large study by Cavalli-Sforza. He compared three MN types, six ABO types and eight rhesus types separately and in various combinations. Among the villages in the mountain and foothill area there was a great diversity which was attributed to genetic drift. In the more heavily populated plains there was less variability of the blood type distributions. To make the various comparisons Cavalli-Sforza used an approximate measure of drift based on excess values of X^2 compared to the number of degrees of freedom associated with the calculation. The result of this formulation of "drift" plotted against population density in each of nine administrative subareas which contained the villages is presented as Figure 26-6. The more sparsely settled areas showed excessive variability, and the more populous areas did not reveal genetic drift by this test.

FAVORABLE MUTANTS IN POPULATIONS

Both natural selection and statistical variation are involved in the reproduction of any Mendelian (panmictic) population. One aspect of their interaction may be illustrated by considering the fate of a new mutant allele arising once in a generation or else many times in larger totals or more generations. Let us consider what would happen in 100 small populations

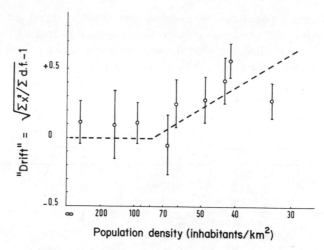

FIGURE 26-6 The correlation between a measurement for "drift" for blood groups in nine districts of the long-inhabited Parma Valley and their present population density. From Cavalli-Sforza in E. Goldschmidt, ed., *The Genetics of Migrant and Isolate Populations*, New York, Association for the Aid of Crippled Children, 1963.

(perhaps on separate islands without intermigration) and in one large population of a size equal to the sum of the small isolates.

If only one mutation to an advantageous allele occurred in the large population and also in one of the small groups, history could be made in several ways. The new gene could be lost from either population in the very next generation simply because of meiotic segregation in spite of the advantages the mutant may have conferred to the heterozygote. Alternatively, it might maintain its frequency of $1/n$ in the next generation or with a little luck increase to $2/n$, or even more, at the time of fertilization of the zygotes for the new generation. Its advantage over the prevailing homozygous genotype would not change this frequency appreciably in either size of population during the growth and reproduction of merely one generation, although if we take for granted that the new allele will survive through many generations its assumed advantage will eventually have an effect. Before this can happen, however, random drift has important roles to play. At the beginning of each generation the numerical representation of the favorable allele (3, 2 or 1) can be reduced dramatically or even decisively, to zero, in either size of population. Correspondingly, it can just as readily increase by 1, 2 or 3 in number; but proportionally any increase is greater (though perhaps temporary) in the small population than in a much larger population. Where this chance increase is proportionally great, genetic drift has done quickly in the small population what natural selection may do very slowly in the large population. Thus the new advantageous allele arising but once would probably not remain in either large or small population after a few generations, although if it should survive the hurdles of meiosis, the smaller population could have it at a higher frequency than the larger group. This is the picture of the fate of a nonrecurrent mutation.

With a larger number of small populations and a correspondingly larger large population additional mutations of the same kind would change the picture. *Recurrent mutation* to the same advantageous allele would insure that the large population would contain the new gene at a low level which would eventually increase through natural selection to a level safe against loss. Among the small populations recurrent mutations would arise randomly and again would survive into subsequent generations randomly. After several generations most of the small populations would not include any example of the new gene either because they never had a mutation of this kind or because those populations having a favorable mutant ancestor lost the allele by genetic drift in spite of its average advantage. The minority of the isolates which did retain the allele would have it at various gene frequencies many of which would be higher than that arrived at in the one large population. Thus small populations can have gene frequencies which fluctuate with time or, as an historical consequence, which are widely varying among small populations. The larger populations show less of this effect of genetic drift and more of the effect of favorable selective advantage.

If the populations are not complete isolates but some migration occurs, migration partakes of the attributes of selection, of small sample drift and of mutation. Immigration may bring in one example of an allele new to the host population and may act like a new mutation in regard to that locus. Actually, it is introducing whole chromosome sets which may contain many new genomes and many chromosomes with coupling linkage differences. If the immigrants bring in several examples of a mutant new to the population, preservation over many generations would be more likely; and under the assumption of survival further gene frequency changes would depend more upon selective advantage in a smaller population. The size of the migrant group will also be subject to the inevitable play of random sampling effect. A larger group of emigrants will sample more representatively than will a smaller group, which may exhibit any one of many widely divergent samples from the source population or one of its social strata. The migrants might be temperamentally different from the remaining individuals although persons coming to the United States over the past several centuries seem to have sampled representatively the blood group alleles of the communities from which they came. Large scale emigrations doubtless are one form of negative selection within the homeland.

SUMMARY

Genetic drift due to random sampling variations operates conspicuously in smaller populations and less noticeably where larger numbers of parents transmit genes to the next generation. By the action of drift either allele at a locus may be increased or decreased in frequency or lost entirely without the necessary intervention of selection. By selection at any particular degree of severity and in one kind of environment, the allele frequencies change in one direction rapidly for intermediate frequencies and more slowly for rarer phenotypes. Elimination from a large population is possible only against a phenotype due to a single Dominant gene and then only by complete adverse selection; all other phenotypes and degrees of selection involve merely reduction in frequency, not elimination. Relaxation of selection against simple homozygous recessives results in a maintenance of the phenotype at the level reached by selection, but relaxation of selection against a digenic phenotype is followed by a partial rebound. In smaller populations the above generalizations about selection may be severely upset by random drift in one or more generations. In certain environments, perhaps in many, selection for the heterozygote may take effect.

In addition to the natural or artificial selection of phenotypes above, humans often practice pedigree selection of their spouses or of their horses or dogs, but among chickens and other animals of economic importance the method of progeny selection is the most productive of all.

Selection for adaptabiilty is ultimately important in all species which will continue. Selection for the ability of the growing individuals to make a phenocopy of some other type may in several generations result in greater genetic ability to produce that type with or without further environmental challenges. This is called genetic assimilation of an acquired character.

SUGGESTED READING

Glass, B., M. S. Sacks, E. F. Jahn and C. Hess, Genetic drift in a religious isolate. Amer. Natur. **86:** 145–159 (1952). A concise description of population size in respect to mutation, migration and selection, of the history of the Dunkers and their 55 North American communities and of details of the several genetic comparisons reexamined in the next paper.

Glass. B., On the evidence of random genetic drift in human populations. Amer. J. Phys. Anthrop. 14 N.S.: 541–555 (1956). Continues the above by age-group analysis and includes a broad discussion of past evolution and future adaptability.

Mather, Wharton B., *Principles of Quantitative Genetics*, Minneapolis, Burgess, 1964, 152 pp. Gives a mathematical treatment of mutation and selection in four chapters which with four more comprise a unified treatment of population genetics.

Sutter, J., "The relationship between human population genetics and demography," pp. 160–167 in E. Goldschmidt, ed., *The Genetics of Migrant and Isolate Populations*, New York, Association for the Aid of Crippled Children, Wilkins, 1963.

Snyder, L. H., and Paul R. David, Chapter 16, "Selection and methods of breeding," pp. 222–245, and Chapter 29, "Eugenics," pp. 458–495 in *The Principles of Heredity*, 5th ed., Boston, Heath, 1957, 507 pp.

PROBLEMS

26–1   How many generations of complete adverse selection against a recessive trait would be required to reduce it to $\frac{1}{4}$ of each of the following phenotypic frequencies (use Table 26-1): 25, 4, 1, .23, and .04 percent?

26–2   Compute the sampling error by the formula for SE_r in Chapter 14 for an allele frequency of .1 in a gene pool
(a) Of 10 genes
(b) Of 50 genes
(c) Of 200 genes
(d) Of 1000 genes

26–3   If an allele frequency does change, what are the chances that it will change in the same direction
(a) In both of two new generations?
(b) In each of three new generations?

26–4   If the same slightly advantageous mutation occurred just once on 15 of 30 islands having populations of 100,000 each and also 15 times within a mainland population of 3,000,000, where would you expect to find the highest and the lowest frequencies of descendants of this same mutant after 10 generations or more (neglecting all the more recent mutants)?

26–5   Consider a population of minimum size, one male and one female in each generation.
(a) Starting from two heterozygous parents, *Hh*, write out all of the possible kinds of parent pairs and their frequencies in the next generation.
(b) Continue the process into the following generation.

chapter 27

Present Racial Differences

Races comprise a convenient level of subdivision of a species; and a race is a population of interbreeding individuals. A smaller or larger grouping is described by the term "kinship," "tribe," "variety" or "subspecies," among others. The satisfactory use of any or all of these terms among humans, other animals or plants depends upon custom and upon the authority of scholarly specialists on each particular group of organisms. It may come as a surprise to learn that there is no rigid and widely applicable biological definition of the limits of a *species* of animals or of plants. Biologists tend to accept most of the examples of species as described by previous scholars, and only a small fraction of described species are redefined by lumping two or more species together or by splitting one species into two or more. Where experiments in hybridizing can be performed to supplement the enumeration of structural similarities and differences seen in closely related organisms, interfertility is a good sign that the parents belong to the same species and, conversely, sterility in an outcross is a good sign that different species are present. Since all varieties of humans from all parts of the earth seem to be interfertile when they meet extensively, humans are considered by most biologists to be one species, *Homo sapiens*, although one author, R. R. Gates, proposed dividing the one species several ways. After recognizing this fundamental difficulty in defining the larger taxonomic unit, the species, we may proceed with caution and with understanding to point out that races are better defined by example than by boundaries.

The major races of man have been described by skin color as red, white, yellow and black, but this omits small yet important races in Australia and around the Bay of Biscayne in southwestern France and adjacent Spain. Because black skins appear in the peoples of Africa, India and the South Pacific, some names for races not entirely based on color are preferable. The anthropologists have adequately defined the most obvious subdivisions of the human species as being *major races*. According to Boyd (1950) these

are (1) the Basques near the Spanish peninsula, (2) the Caucasoids, originating in western Europe but extending also into North Africa, the Middle
East and into India, (3) the Africans, largely below the Sahara Desert, (4)
the Mongoloids, typically of central Asia and southeastward, (5) the
Australoids, aboriginal inhabitants of Australia and (6) the Amerinds of
North and South America. Garn (1961) listed 9 geographical races and 32
populations. Further subdivision into smaller races such as the Japanese
and the Canton Chinese, the Aztecs and the Incas, the Poles and the
Hungarians, the Scotch and the Irish, are familiar and useful designations.
The various groups have received names because of their differences much
as two individuals receive different names, so the problem of races is not
the existence of differences but the interpretation and evaluation of those
differences and of the remaining similarities. In discussing races the geneticist prefers to begin with the known genes rather than with the more
difficult though eventually more important polygenic phenotypes. Skin
color differences are apparently polygenic rather than simple (Chapter 10).

GENE FREQUENCIES OF HUMAN RACES

Whatever genes are responsible for producing five fingers and five toes
and a diminutive coating of body hair are probably uniform among men; at
least we have no conspicuous evidence to the contrary. However, the
common blood type differences which we have found within many families
are not evenly distributed around the world. Sibs may be *polymorphic* in
regard to one or more of the blood group systems unless they happen to be
identical twins, and any one phenotype may be more prevalent among
natives of certain areas than of other areas. The various types of men found
in Europe or Asia give rise to the term that humans are a *polytypic* species,
some are very tall, some are black-haired, some are round-headed, some are
yellow-skinned and some have the blood group B allele more often than
others; and these occur in various combinations or types.

A comparison of the clearly known genetic similarities and differences
between the two major races in North America will be illustrative for all
races. In Table 27-1 Negroes and whites are compared against the known
extremes of gene frequency specified for eight genetically independent loci
and for several members of a multiple allelic series. The list shows a few
alleles which are present in the North American Negro but absent in the
neighboring white population (Sickle cell, Duffy negative and Sutter
antigens). Most of the alleles are present in both races but in different
amounts. The peoples living in the far edges of the land mass of Eurasia,
such as the American Indians and the Chinese, lack certain alleles (rhesus

TABLE 27-1   Some allele frequencies within races[a]

Gene	Phenotype	NORTH AMERICAN		Highest and lowest known frequencies	
		Negro	White		
T	Taster of PTC	.91	.70	.96	Chinese, Amerinds
				.63	Arabs
Fy	Duffy negative	.68	.0	.90	West African Negroes
L^{Ms}	Landsteiner Ms	.40	.30	.60	Eskimos
				.26	Australoids
Rh^o	Rhesus D positive	.55	.05	.0	Asians, Amerinds
rh, cde	rhesus negative	.28	.38	.53	Basques (early Europeans)
				.0	Chinese
i	corpuscle donor	.74	.67	.98	Amerinds
				.52	Egyptians, Armenians
i^A	antigen A	.12	.26	.52	Blackfeet (.38 Polynesians)
				.01	other Amerinds
i^B	antigen B	.14	.07	.27	Irkutsk Siberians
				.0	Amerinds, Australoids, Basques
Si	Sickle cells	≤.28	.0	.0	other Caucasians
V	anti-V in rh or Rh^o	.14	.003	.22	West African Negroes
Js^a	Sutter antigen	.10	.0	.0	Asians, Eskimos

[a]Data from *Genetics and the Races of Man* by William C. Boyd. Boston, Little, Brown and Company, 1950; *Principles of Human Genetics*, 2nd edition, by Curt Stern. San Francisco: W. H. Freeman and Company, 1960; *Blood Groups in Man*, 4th edition, by R. R. Race and Ruth Sanger. Oxford, England, Blackwell Scientific Publications, 1962.

negative, antigen B), or else these remote people exhibit the high extreme of a gene frequency (Taster allele, blood group O). However, there are also instances of centrally located populations which show an extreme frequency for an allele (Taster allele lowest among Arabs, i allele lowest among Egyptians and Armenians, i^B highest in mid-Siberia).

The six major races may be typified by certain combinations of allele frequencies, although because of intergrades they cannot be delimited. The three eastern races are all high in the total of various rhesus positive alleles, and in addition the i^B gene has a world high of .27 in central Asia among the Mongols and remains high among the Ainu of Japan. By contrast the Amerinds and the Australoids have no B allele and are distinguishable by the Landsteiner locus. The Australoids have the lowest frequency of L^{Ms}, .26, while the Amerinds show .60 for this allele, the highest in the world. Thus certain combinations of extreme frequencies of rhesus, i^B and L^{Ms} differentiate typical Chinese, Australian aborigines and Amerinds from each other and from the other major races of mankind. The Basque peoples of France and Spain can also be typified by extremes. They too have no i^B

allele, but they have the lowest world frequency of all rhesus positive alleles, around .40; and about one-half of their anti-A reactions are due to the allele i^{A_2} (Chapter 8) which has a lower or zero frequency in all other races. Negroes and Caucasoids differ markedly at the Duffy locus and definitely at several other loci. African Negroes have a very high frequency, .90, for the Duffy allele $Fy(a-b-)$, whereas Caucasoids have other alleles giving positive reactions either with a, b or with both in the Duffy antigenic system. Negroes show higher allele frequencies than do Caucasians in regard to Duffy negative; also Negroes are higher in i^B, i^{A_2} among all A, rhesus positive alleles and the V antigen, which is possibly related to rhesus. Conversely, in respect to Negroes the Caucasoids are lower in rhesus positive, i^{A_2} among all A, blood type B, the Duffy negative allele and the new V allele. (Refer again to Table 27-1.)

The gene frequencies which have been typified above actually show gradations or *clines* over the face of the earth. From its high level in central Asia the B allele frequency decreases to the west and southeast and descends to zero before reaching Australia or America. The blood antigen A is also absent from most of the American Indians, but it has a steep gradation in the territories around the home of the Blackfeet tribe. In the cities and towns of the British isles one also finds clines. In Scotland one finds more O alleles and fewer A alleles than one finds in southern England. The differences tend to persist for many generations among the descendants who have emigrated from distant parts of a cline to a new country. Several clines appear in the data of Table 27-2.

TABLE 27-2   ABO Blood group distributions and finger pattern indices among three populations[a]

	Number of persons	BLOOD GROUPS, %				Number of persons	Pattern indices
		O	A	B	AB		
Egyptians	10,045	32.6	35.4	24.3	7.4	1,271	14.25
Northern Sudanese	4,370	45.4	27.8	22.2	4.5	100	14.22
Southern Sudanese	312	52.5	25.6	18.2	4.1	420	12.17

[a]From David C. Rife, *Heredity and Human Nature*, New York, Vantage Press, 1959, p. 151. By permission of author and publisher.

GENETIC DIFFERENCES IN SMALLER ISOLATES

The Blackfeet Indians of western United States and Canada are exceptions to the rule that the Amerinds are blood type O. The i^A allele is found in this tribe at frequencies around .52; and the next highest frequencies for it are in the high thirties among the Scandinavians, Hawaiians, Portuguese and Armenians. Populations neighboring on these have somewhat lower frequencies of allele A.

The Negroes around Charleston, South Carolina, are so numerous and are so seldom in contact with other peoples that they have their own speech dialect (Gullah). They have been compared with Negroes of New York, with Negroes of West Africa and with British white in respect to serological groups and blood hemoglobins by Pollitzer, who found a closer resemblance between Gullah Negroes and West African Negroes than between either of these groups and the Negro residents of New York City. Conversely, the white population differed considerably from the New York Negroes, differed a little more from the Charleston Negroes and even more from the West Africans on a serological basis. The general pattern of these blood differences agreed well with the pattern of similarities and differences described by earlier anthropologists on the basis of larger physical characteristics.

Subgroups of Caucasians living in the same city or state may nevertheless remain partially isolated and therefore show distinctions in genetic traits. The example of the Dunkers in Pennsylvania has already been described in Chapter 26. In a study by Rife at a large state university significant differences in handedness were found among two subdivisions of the student body according to religious background. Right-handed persons comprised 90 percent of the Protestant population and 84 percent of the Jewish population (Table 27-3). This difference is statistically significant, and it doubtless has some genetic foundation in spite of attempts during earlier school years to modify some persons to right-handedness.

TABLE 27-3   Protestant and Jewish students at the Ohio State University classified according to handedness[a]

Population	Number persons	Right-handed, %	Left-handed, %
Protestant	1,700	90.01	9.99
Jewish	535	84.12	15.88

[a]From David C. Rife, *Heredity and Human Nature*, New York, Vantage Press, 1959, p. 144. By permission of author and publisher.

A study of stature at the same university revealed significant differences among three ancestral groups. The data, given separately for males and for females in Table 27-4, show that the mean height of the large group of British Protestants was intermediate between those of the other two student groups. The part that nutritional differences may have contributed to the direction and amount of these differences is assumed to be negligible.

However, babies and children who were under starvation conditions in Germany between 1914 and 1918 showed reduced average height as military recruits 20 years later.

TABLE 27-4 Comparisons of average stature of students at the Ohio State University classified according to sex and religion[a]

Ethnic origin	FEMALES		MALES	
	Number persons	Average stature, in.	Number persons	Average stature, in.
British and Northwestern European Catholics	34	65.21 ± 0.42	51	70.19 ± 0.35
British Protestants	178	64.82 ± 0.17	153	69.00 ± 0.22
Eastern European Jews	188	64.00 ± 0.16	83	67.71 ± 0.30

From David C. Rife, *Heredity and Human Nature*, New York, Vantage Press, 1959, p. 144. By permission of author and publisher.

Fingerprint patterns, a multifactorial genetic character, are established in early fetal life and are probably relatively uninfluenced by common environmental factors. Although many of the Jews now living in Israel are descended from ancestral lines which have resided for many generations in other countries of Europe and the Mediterranean region, close resemblance among the Israeli Jews still remains, but the direction of differences is toward the finger pattern indices shown by the several kinds of neighbors the various migrant Jewish groups once had. A study by Sachs and Bat-Miriam showed that the migrant Jews who had returned to Israel had fingerprint pattern indices which were intermediate between those of their more recent neighbors in distant lands and those of their ancestrally even more remote Arab neighbors. In another comparison by the same authors the mean percent of fingers with whorls (having two tri-radii) was consistently lower, finger for finger, among British persons than among Arabs and Israeli Jews. The latter two populations were usually rather similar in the frequencies of whorls (Figure 27-1). Another close resemblance of Arabs and Jews and a distinctness from the British in the occurrence of loop patterns (one tri-radius) was also found. Other ethnic groups differ among themselves in respect to the mean frequencies of the whorl, loop and arch phenotypes.

When we turn from common, polymorphic characters to rarer conditions we find that the major races and even the minor-sized isolates again show both similarities and differences. A list compiled by Komai of genetic malformations occurring among the Japanese reads like a list of defects

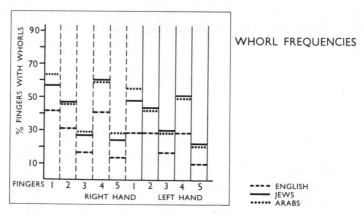

FIGURE 27-1   The mean whorl frequencies in three groups of 500 men each (Israeli Arabs, Israeli Jews, British). From L. Sachs and M. Bat-Miriam in E. Goldschmidt, ed., *The Genetics of Migrant and Isolate Populations*, New York, Association for the Aid of Crippled Children, 1963.

found also among western European peoples. Clubfoot, microcephaly and the condition we now call Trisomy 21 are found in both races and around the world. However, some sharp contrasts also exist. The recessive Tay Sachs disease is found almost exclusively among people of Jewish ancestry, but the later-acting yet similar juvenile amaurotic idiocy is not thus restricted to any race. Even among the Jewish migrants who have returned to Israel, the frequency of Tay Sach's disease is substantially greater among the Ashkenazic Jews (those from central and northern Europe) than among the non-Ashkenazic. The Ashkenazics also have Gaucher's disease more than their remote relatives from Mediterranean countries. Gaucher's disease of the reticulo-endothelial cells is found among adults of other races, and a recessive form affecting children has been described in a Negro kindred by Herndon and Bender. Mental aberrations are also distributed unevenly. Among natives in Sweden schizophrenic persons are encountered relatively much more often than are persons with manic-depressive psychosis. The reverse is true among the Hutterites residing in North America; many cases of manic-depressive psychoses are known and almost none of schizophrenia in their populations. The incidence of leukemia among various groups residing in Brooklyn, N. Y., was carefully studied by MacMahon and Koller up to 1958. No difference was found in its incidence among Negroes and whites living in Brooklyn, but the foreign-born (chiefly the Russian immigrants) had a higher incidence of leukemia than did the native born. A separate tabulation of professed Jews, Catholics and Protestants revealed that leukemia was listed as the cause of death twice as often for persons buried in Jewish cemeteries as for persons buried elsewhere.

A knowledge of population differences can be an aid in the recognition and treatment of disease and defect. The Hutterites are prepared in their way of life to allow for the swing of emotion shown time and again by manic-depressive individuals. The doctor familiar with ethnic differences may more readily diagnose a rare condition knowing that it is much less remote in one group of patients than in other kinds of patients.

INTERPRETATIONS OF DISTRIBUTIONS

The forces of selection, of migration including interbreeding, of mutation and of genetic drift may be invoked in various ways to explain one or another distribution of alleles or of phenotypes. A good explanation must naturally be based on more information than an initial discovery may provide. In the absence of information on selection, genetic drift may be blamed, or excessive mutation rate. In the absence of data on the sizes of ancient populations or of early migrations we should implicate genetic drift only after other forces have been satisfactorily evaluated.

Selective Advantage. Environments in which men live have many differences, some of them obvious and some of them subtle, and both may be selective of the kinds of persons who may survive and prosper. The selective advantage of the dark pigment in the skins of Negroes, Abyssinians, Hindus and Polynesians has been obvious for centuries. The converse advantage of a light skin to the inhabitants of cloudy northwestern Europe is not so evident until one learns about the conversion of cholesterol deep in the skin to vitamin D under the action of the ultraviolet rays in sunlight. No selective advantage was seen at first for the high frequency of the Sickle cell hemoglobin gene, Hb^S or Si, in large parts of western and equatorial Africa, the Po Valley of Italy and elsewhere, because homozygous Hb^S individuals die young of anemia from disintegration of their deformable red blood corpuscles. A gene frequency of .22 for the sickle allele was found in some African populations, a level too high to be maintained by mutation alone. It became understandable when it was noticed that the frequency of Sickle cell hemoglobin was higher in areas where there was greater exposure to mosquitoes carrying a very pathogenic malarial parasite, *Plasmodium falciparum*, and vice versa. Persons homozygous for normal hemoglobin apparently sicken and die of falciparum malaria more readily than do heterozygotes. The heterozygotes thus have the dual advantage of avoiding severe malarial infection and of avoiding the spontaneous breakdown of Sickle cell anemia; one dose of genes Hb^A and Hb^S is better in these malarial environments than are two doses of either gene. Such selective advantage of the heterozygote was not at first suspected.

Selection in some unidentified manner is doubtless acting upon the ABO blood groups because of the limited variety shown around the world in comparison with the many possible combinations. Not only are homozygous A tribes and B tribes unknown but, as Alice Brues has pointed out, a majority of representative populations have gene frequencies clustering around the values .10 to .15 i^B, .20 to .25 i^A and with the remainder being i^O alleles. Populations with frequencies of i^B above .30 are rare or unknown; frequencies of i^A above .50 are unknown except for the Blackfeet tribe of Indians. Homozygous $i^O i^O$ populations are perhaps in excess even when compared with the great number of isolates with low B, and medium low A alleles. The reasons for the observed distributions at the isoagglutinogen locus await discovery.

The gamma globulin types show inherited differences based on at least three alleles whose frequencies also show certain modes and clines. Gamma globulins may be distinguished by certain precise tests using rhesus-positive red blood cells, certain anti-Rh sera and another serum from selected patients with rheumatoid arthritis. Such tests reveal the presence of alleles at the gamma globulin locus designated as Gm^a, Gm^{ax} and Gm^b. Incidentally, these alleles seem to have the same distribution among patients with rheumatoid arthritis as among the various regional populations. The Gm(a⁺) reaction is found in nearly all persons tested among Eskimos and in equatorial regions; however, in the European peoples the range of Gm(a⁺) goes from a low of 40 percent in Italy and Greece upwards in a cline to 65 percent and higher among the Finns and the Lapps. Within these limits the subdivision according to the *a* and *ax* alleles and also the frequencies of the *b* allele show a sharp mode rather than a wide spread of the possible combinations. Selective forces as well as short distance migration are doubtless involved in the present distribution of gamma globulin types.

Color blindness may be less of a handicap now than it was among our ancestors many generations ago. The observed frequency of all kinds of color blindness in males today ranges from 1 to 10 percent with the lowest being among the Amerinds and the next lowest among African tribes (see Figure 27-2). Studies in India show a frequency of only 2.5 percent among tribal males, those residing in small villages in thatched huts and living by hunting in addition to limited agriculture; yet the Hindu, Christian and Muslim male students in a nearby government high school had 6.5 percent of color blindness, either protan, deutan or complete color blindness. In

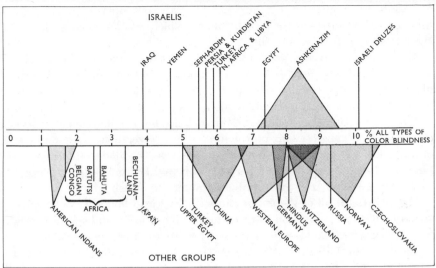

WHERE SEVERAL SAMPLES FOR A GROUP EXIST, THEIR RANGE IS INDICATED

FIGURE 27-2 Rates of color blindness among males of Israeli communities compared with other groups. Shaded guide lines show a range of sample means. The Ishihara color charts were used. From H. Kalmus and co-workers in E. Goldschmidt, ed., *The Genetics of Migrant and Isolate Populations*, New York, Association for the Aid of Crippled Children, 1963.

Australia a frequency below 2 percent was reported for the aborigines, slightly higher among the half-castes and still higher among white settlers.

Migration. The interbreeding which accompanies and follows migration helps to explain some of the gene distributions already considered above under the topic of selection. In particular the slow, steady drop in the i^B gene from its high in Mongolia westward across Siberia and into Europe has been interpreted, perhaps correctly, as evidence of the several massive invasions of eastern Tartar horsemen into the plains of Hungary and elsewhere. Some of their Maygar names and customs remain there today along with B alleles slightly in excess of those found among people living in the surrounding and protective mountains. Conversely, an absence of late migration may be the chief explanation of the absence of this same allele from the Basques in the protecting Pyrenees Mountains farther west and its absence among the American Indians and the Australians. In reality selection and migration must have been involved in various degrees.

On a smaller scale within the Nile Valley ABO gene frequencies and fingerprint indices vary systematically from Egypt upstream to the Northern Sudan and on to the Southern Sudan. (Review Table 27-2.) Rife points

out that the Arabs downstream and the Negroes upstream have intermingled for centuries in the North Sudan, which was long ago a center for
slave trading expeditions of the Arabs.

More narrowly local migrations have also left their mark within England.
The north-south gradient of A and O frequencies has already been described
above. In Wales people with Welsh surnames have a gene frequency
distribution of the ABO alleles which is significantly different from the
distribution within the group not having Welsh names. Obviously, this is a
record of one's ancestry only on the male side. Nevertheless, we may speak
of foreign names carrying foreign genes, not that the alleles are different in
kind but that the relative numbers of A, B and O from outside peoples is
not the same as the relative numbers among the Welsh.

Mutation. If all of the major races in the world had always been very
small populations, mutation alone rather than mutation and selection might
be a sufficient explanation of some of the geographical distribution maps.
On that oversimplification, the B allele might have mutated only in central
Asia and might have spread from there to other parts of the Old World.
Because genes much rarer than i^B are found in widely scattered races between which there had probably been little migration, the mutational
theory of differences is hard to apply. Perhaps an example of a unique
mutation may be the Kuru gene, which is known in New Guinea but not
elsewhere (page 239). Yet even there its presence today was doubtlessly
aided by some form of selection which scientists have not yet identified. It
should be remembered that natural selection acts on the individual and his
whole genome, not on each gene independently. Where selection is mild
enough to allow some reproduction, inheritance of linked genes in coupling
phase is more likely than crossing over between two genes linked in repulsion phase. If these adjacent genes have selective advantages one way or
another, a new mutant may prosper in its childhood generations because of
the company it keeps in the chromosome, rather than for its own intrinsic
merit, which may become evident many generations later. Selection is no
less real for favoring a new mutant and its neighbor than for favoring the
new allele itself. Thus genes which may seem to be drifting upward in frequency may actually be receiving selective help by some gene linked in the
same chromosome as well as by environmental selection acting more
directly.

Genetic Drift. Only after selection (in its many forms) and also
migration have been ruled out does a proper role for random genetic drift
begin to appear. Even so, one should have reasonable evidence that the
population was small at the time that the change in gene frequency due to
drift was alleged to have occurred. Random drift may be demonstrated

readily by using insects or other animals in population cages, and drift situations can be programmed on computers for rapid production of outcomes. Yet it is difficult to point retrospectively to specific examples of genetic drift in the distant past, although the concept of random variation is a valid one.

RACIAL MIXTURE

Interracial crosses among humans have important social and psychological implications which are not encountered in animal crossbreeding. Human experience includes many examples of unsuccessful marriages between persons of different races and even between persons from different social backgrounds within a race. Hence there must be reasons enough from the social viewpoint for a general advisory against the marriage of remotely different persons. However, there are also many other examples of couples who have made successful marriages across racial lines. The latter are more successful in some communities such as in Hawaii, in Jamaica and in parts of East Africa than in many other countries; and they are more often found in certain social climates of the larger cities of the northern United States than in rural towns and villages having customs of the "Old South." The social problem is certainly tremendous. However, the intricate racial problem will hardly be advanced toward solution if the social and the biological aspects of racial mixture are confounded. In past history this has happened. In Spain at the time of the Inquisition and in Germany during the Hitler era doctrines of religious faith or of national mission were confused with the biology of racial crossing. Allegations have been made that human racial crosses produce misfits even at the biological level.

The question of incompatible proportions of the body in hybrids from human interracial crosses has been raised many times and has had offered in support of it limited evidence from studies on animals. The animal evidence generally comes from crosses between breeds with more extreme differences than those which exist between subgroups of humans. For instance, the cross between a dachshund and any one of a number of large breeds of dogs does produce offspring with large bodies very poorly proportioned to the short legs, but it is not clear how the mating of these extremes in dogs serves as an appropriate model for the crossing of any major human races which are not that widely divergent from each other. Achondroplastic dwarf persons do exist, and pigmy tribes are found in areas of Africa; but their intermixture with Caucasians is not the social problem under discussion in South Africa nor in the United States. The desegregation problem is complicated indeed, but not in that biological sense. In Hawaii much intermixture of native Polynesian, Oriental and Caucasian stocks has taken place, and a vigorous people rather than a collection of ill-proportioned individuals seems to be the result. In a careful review of the number and kinds of birth defects recorded among some 180,000 births in Hawaii during the years 1948–1958 Morton found no elevated proportion of congenital malformations.

The chief biological consequences of intercrossing (hybrid vigor in the F_1 and more variety in later generations) have been established in dozens of species of animals and in hundreds of species of plants, and these principles presumably apply to man. When two different breeds are crossed, the recessive phenotypes formerly observed among some members of each breed may be expected to disappear in the hybrid offspring if they were not common to both stocks. Conversely, the Dominant characters will continue to appear and will contribute to hybrid vigor on one theory (or actually cause it on another). The epistatic relation of some Dominant characters over other characters cannot be predicted but has to be discovered within each species and within each of the many intervarietal crosses. Among domesticated animals the exploration of the various possible crosses, when followed by conscious selection, has produced many very desirable types of animals and birds. Hybrid corn and other currently useful plant and animal hybrids are the products of this kind of manipulation. Of course, the lack of stringent selection in man leaves many problems to be solved in the absence of established fact, but such a lack does not justify the opposite extreme position, the interdiction against all racial crossing. Such prohibitions are social, political and religious, and they should hence be discussed and settled largely in terms of those aspects of human life. The contributions of genetics to the problem of racial crossing should aid in the definition of the problems in the other realms.

Rhesus Incompatibility as a Criterion. The geneticist's answer to the question of the biological advisability of interracial crosses is neither an unqualified "yes" nor a conclusive "no." Even in narrowing the question to include only the effects from one genetic locus, Dr. Stern points out that the answer is relative. It has been known since 1940 that not all fetuses of rhesus-negative mothers are compatible with the antibodies built up in these mothers by earlier rhesus-positive pregnancies or transfusions with rhesus-positive blood (Chapter 19). Because of the danger of the infant's death by hemolytic disease among the later pregnancies, marriages of a rhesus-positive man and a rhesus-negative woman are called *rhesus incompatible marriages.* The many-fold answer to the simple question "Is racial mixture between Chinese and Americans good or bad?" in Stern's example may be pictorialized in the manner of Figure 27-3.

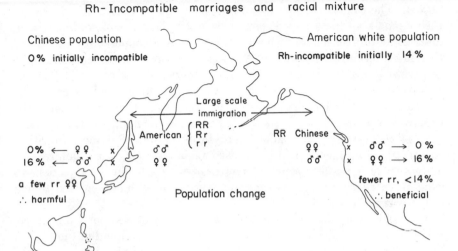

Rh-Incompatible marriages and racial mixture

FIGURE 27-3 A specific effect of migration involving an interaction phenotype, erythroblastosis fetalis. The reciprocal interracial marriages have opposite effects, regardless of the country of residence. The later population effects are intermediate between the two initial effects and are in opposite directions in the two populations. After *Principles of Human Genetics*, second edition, by Curt Stern. San Francisco: W. H. Freeman and Company, 1960.

Different answers to the broad question will be obtained (1) for the two populations concerned, (2) for the direction of the reciprocal crosses in the first generation and (3) for all later generations judged solely by the frequency of the rhesus incompatible marriages, known to predispose to hemolytic disease of the newborn. Before racial crossing began the Chinese population was all rhesus positive, and hence erythroblastosis fetalis was unknown there. Thus American men even if rhesus negative married to Chinese women would have no rhesus difficulties among their immediate offspring. However, some 16 percent of the reciprocal cross would involve rhesus-negative American women all of whom would have homozygous rhesus-positive husbands. This would be immediately disadvantageous in two ways: all marriages of these women would be of the incompatible type as contrasted with only 84 percent of the marriages which the rhesus-negative women might contract within the American population; and all fetuses by the Chinese father would be positive instead of a considerably lower proportion such as would come from a large minority of American fathers. Thus rather different answers would be given by the families involved. The Chinese women would not encounter any hemolytic disease in their infants, but the American women would run the risk of producing such diseased infants during an earlier pregnancy with a Chinese husband rather than in a later pregnancy with an American husband. These facts about the reciprocal kinds of partnerships would be revealed differently in the two countries. The immigrant American wives in China would seem to be bringing a new and dangerous disease into the native population; the Chinese husbands residing in the United States would make a slight increase, perhaps not quickly noticeable, in erythroblastotic offspring. In either country these mothers would be advised against nursing their children, an omission which psychologists say contributes to a feeling of rejection, to which an interracial hybrid in some countries might be more sensitive than a full member of one race.

Among the grandchildren and later descendants of this particular interracial cross the results would again be different in China and in the United States. The American immigrants of both sexes would be introducing rh^- genes into the Chinese population not only via the rhesus-negative women those children had revealed trouble but also via the few male homozygotes and the heterozygotes of both sexes. These alleles would in later generations segregate to produce a few rhesus-negative women, previously absent or very rare among the typical Chinese. Such instances might be pointed out as a harmful result of Chinese-American crossing. In the United States by contrast the introduction of more rhesus positive alleles would dilute the rh^- gene pool via the Chinese immigrants of both sexes, and so the results in later generations would be called beneficial, in spite of the first generation risks which were increased for those American women marrying Chinese men. If the question "Is Chinese–American intermarriage good or bad?" has such diverse answers in regard to a specified interaction between maternal phenotype and child's phenotype merely in respect to one locus, rh, broader conclusions about more loci and other phenotypes may involve similar complexities and might require much longer study.

SUMMARY

The polytypic human species has been described as if subdivided into six major races and many more minor races which in turn are composed of several or many Mendelizing populations. Each such descriptive subdivision is typified by a certain combination of gene frequencies at 15 or more loci for which man is polymorphic and by the possession of certain phenotypic characters at various frequencies. Occasionally, a genetic type may be rare or practically absent from one or more other races. The gene frequencies often show geographical gradients or clines suggestive of past migrations, past selective forces or even mutational history. Because of the clines it is difficult to draw boundary lines between races, and intermixture in boundary zones is very often encountered. The present picture of distributions of genes and genetic phenotypes is the net product of migration, selective advantage of certain genotypes in certain environments, mutation and random drift in small isolates interacting in unrecorded sequences and strengths.

SUGGESTED READING

Boyd, W. C., *Genetics and the Races of Mankind*, Boston, Little, Brown, 1950, 453 pp. A readable popular book written by a well-known hematologist.

Dronamraju, K. R., and P. M. Khan, Frequency of colour blindness among the tribal and nontribal peoples of Andhra Pradesh. Ann. Hum. Genet. **27**: 17–21 (1963). A recent study with references to research on other continents.

Garn, S. M., *Human Races*, Springfield, Ill., Thomas, 1961, 137 pp. A very concise, authoritative and objective account.

George, W. C., *The Biology of the Race Problem*, 1962, 87 pp., available from National Putnam Letters Comm., Box 3518, Grand Central Sta., New York, N.Y. 10017. This article contrasts sharply with the other suggested readings.

Howells, W. W., The distribution of man. Sci. Amer. **203**(3): 112–129 (and reprint series, Sept. 1960) San Francisco, Freeman, 1960. Changes with time and place discussed from the biological point of view.

MacMahon, B., and E. K. Koller, Ethnic differences in the incidence of leukemia. Blood **12**: 1–10 (1957). A recent, large study in New York.

Morton, N. E., Genetics of interracial crosses in Hawaii. Eugen. Quart. **9**(1): 23–24 (1962). A careful review of births in a large crossbred population.

Steinberg, A. G., and H. Matsumoto, Studies on the Gm, Inv, Hp and Tf serum factors in Japanese populations and families. Hum. Biol. **36**: 77–85 (1964). The analysis of new genetic differences by established methods.

PROBLEMS

27–1 Give an example of a human race which is
    (a) High in allele i^B
    (b) High in allele i^O
    (c) Low in rhesus negative
    (d) High in sickling hemoglobin

27–2 What frequencies of color-blind women would you expect in three different populations chosen from Figure 27-2?

27–3 (a) If blood group AB persons have more than half of their offspring also of group AB, as Matsunaga has pointed out, would you expect to find populations of any size homozygous for i^A (or for i^B)?
    (b) Explain your answer.

chapter 28

Genetic Changes in Virulence and in Resistance

The knowledge of those organisms which threaten and parasitize man is often as important, and knowledge of their genetics is as important, as the knowledge of human genes. We are known and tried by the company we keep, and we cannot escape some of the infective diseases of childhood nor some of the viruses associated with congested urban life. We may therefore consider some of the ecological aspects of genetics, first in regard to chemicals and then in respect to neighboring organisms of different species, some of them always parasitic and others of them capable of becoming parasitic.

RESPONSES OF ORGANISMS TO NEW CHEMICALS

Pharmaceuticals which are administered to humans are not uniformly helpful to all persons receiving them; some persons may be harmed by a reasonably well-chosen drug. Suxamethonium is one such drug which is of considerable help during surgical operations because it slows the breathing of most patients. Some few persons have a very delayed recovery from this relaxant; and all such persons have a lowered level of plasma pseudocholinesterase, an enzyme which is stable enough to be demonstrated in old blood spots and therefore is of occasional use in criminal investigations. The *suxamethonium-sensitive* individuals are homozygous recessive at a single locus, and their parents and offspring are usually recognizable as heterozygotes. The heterozygotes may be phenotypically distinguished from the two kinds of homozygotes with little or no overlapping by what is called a dibucaine test. By another test of the pseudocholinesterase level the abnormals overlap a little with the heterozygotes, and the heterozygotes overlap considerably with the homozygous normals.

Primaquine sensitivity is shown by some persons ill with malaria and treated with this drug, which is effective against more strains of malaria than are certain other drugs. These same persons have a low level of g-6-P-d activity of their red blood cells, and hence *primaquine sensitivity* may be considered as one of the pleiotropic effects of the sex-linked partially Dominant gene causing either normal or deficient levels of production of the enzyme glucose-6-phosphate dehydrogenase. Males show only two phenotypic levels for this enzyme, and they are easily segregated into two contrasting classes. Heterozygous females, however, overlap both normal and g-6-P-d deficient persons of either sex in the activity of this enzyme.

Other instances of variable response of humans to medicines are well known and comprise the basis for the prescription of drugs by the family doctor specifically for individual patients. Likewise an anesthesiologist needs to be a competent and well-trained person both in respect to the use of agents and in regard to human responses due to genetic and constitutional variability.

Chemicals chosen to eliminate a parasite or a pest are also not effective against all individuals in a species. Many species of Trypanosomes parasitize the blood stream of humans, and one of the drugs used to combat them is Antricide. This had only weak effects against several of the species but was for a time rather effective against *Trypanosoma congolense;* however, the parasite is now represented by strains resistant to Antricide. Some other drugs used to combat other Trypanosomes have diminished usefulness because of the presence now of strains resistant to one or another of those drugs. It appears that the killing of susceptible strains had left opportunity for one or another rare resistant strain to fill the void by the usual rapid reproduction of successful parasites and to take over the ecological niche left vacant after the first use of a devastating drug.

The appearance of DDT resistance and its inheritance has now been studied in many insects which once were expected to be exterminated by the use of this new and powerful insecticide. In 1948 the common housefly was scheduled for extinction, and most of the sprayed individuals doubtless died. However, today's descendants of those who withstood the extermination attempts are now highly resistant to this chemical. Similarly, among fleas five species are now immune to DDT. As an outgrowth of this disappointing development studies of resistance to chemicals have been made on laboratory populations of insects, and careful analyses of DDT resistance have been made in crosses between unselected normal and DDT-resistant strains of *Drosophila*. Here it was found that each of the six large chromosomes of the female flies of a resistant strain contributed something to the survival of its possessor under uniform tests with DDT. The three pairs of chromosomes could be assorted in 16 different combinations starting with all being from the resistant stock and going through substitutions of one or another chromosome, or several chromosomes from the susceptible strain to the other extreme of all being from the unselected, susceptible strain. Many different degrees of survival were found among these genotypic classes, according to the expectations of multifactorial inheritance (Chapter 14). Resistance to a chemical may follow any one of several modes of inheritance depending on the organism and on the chemical.

VARIABILITY IN PARASITES AND HOSTS

Organisms react variously to their biological surroundings as well as to known chemicals and perhaps by reason of the chemicals the neighbor releases. Resistance or susceptibility may characterize a given host; and weak or strong virulence may be an attribute of a certain parasite. These may be described first as fixed attributes, but their origin by mutational change has been demonstrated in several microorganisms.

People differ in their resistance to infection not only from season to season but more fundamentally for genetic reasons. Most children contract measles from infection by and multiplication of a virus, but among close relatives some suffer severely from the disease and some escape it. In a comparison of monozygotic twins and fraternal twins at least one of whom has measles the concordance for the MZ twins is significantly higher than the concordance among DZ twins, 95 against 87 percent, respectively. If exposure is assumed to be similar for twins regardless of their origin, this difference indicates genetic variability. Poliomyelitis is also due to a virus which perhaps invades most children but does visible damage to only a few. Herndon and Jennings studied paralytic cases of polio among twins and found a distinct difference between the two types; 5/14 of monozygotic twins were concordant while only 2/33 of dizygotic twins both had paralytic poliomyelitis. Bacterial infection resulting in tuberculosis in some members of a family may miss most other members unless they be monozygous twins (Table 20-4).

Epidemiological studies and laboratory investigations show that the invading organisms likewise are not genetically uniform. Variation in Asian influenza viruses from year to year have been experienced. Different strains of Pneumococci ranging from mild to severe in their pathogenic effects are known. Even better understood, however, are the numerous mutations measured and studied among the viruses. As a prelude to a brief account of microbial genetics, we may gain some ecological perspective by reviewing Burkholder's summary of all possible ways in which two different species of organisms may interact.

Burkholder's arrangement of the nine possible kinds of coaction of associated or symbiotic species was designed particularly in respect to cooperation and conflict among microorganisms, but it has wide application to higher forms including man (Table 28-1). For example, the smaller species of the table would be a virus and the larger organism a bacterium; at a higher level the bacterium might be living in or on a larger organism, man. We note that two familiar relationships, parasitism and predation, are at opposite corners of the table and that neutrality and commensalism are intermediate in position. A range of shades of adaptation has been suggested by a three-point scale of +, 0 and — to designate species (or individuals) of greater, average or subnormal effectiveness, respectively, in the business of living. An association of + — or of — + means that one species lives at the expense of the other, while 0 means that one organism,

TABLE 28-1 Forms of coaction between larger and smaller symbionts[a]

Adaptation of the smaller (species) is	of the larger (species) is relatively		
	lagging —	average 0	advanced +
+ favorable	+ — parasitism	+ 0 commensalism	+ + mutualism
0 average	0 — allolimy	0 0 neutrality	0 + allotrophy
— deficient	— — synnecrosis	— 0 amensalism	— + predation

[a]Modified after P. R. Burkholder, Amer. Sci., **40**: 605 (1952).

the larger or the smaller, is not demonstrably affected by the other organism. Since there are degrees of parasitism, it should be no surprise that there are borderline examples belonging somewhere between parasitism and commensalism. More important than the average relation of species pairs is the observation of mutations in the individuals (in a larger neighbor-host or in a smaller neighbor-parasite) such that the relationship between their descendants may shift from commensalism to parasitism or to neutrality — back and forth in a rather rapid kind of evolution.

INTERACTIONS OF BACTERIA AND PHAGE

The bacteria which inhabit the human intestine as does *Escherischia coli* may often have their own inhabitants called *bacteriophages*, or simply *phages*. These phages can exist for periods of time outside living cells, but they multiply only inside one or another strain of bacterium. The shapes of phage particles in their completed stage can be studied by means of the electron microscope. Their chemical content can be deduced in general terms by growing them in bacteria which have been supplied with a radio-isotope-labeled category of foodstuffs such as nucleic acid precursors or alternatively with sulfur-containing amino acids destined to become parts of the protein molecules. It has been found that the T4 phage consists of densely packed nucleic acid surrounded by a protein coat which also forms a tail-like structure able to attach to the surface of the *E. coli* bacterial cell wall. When infection occurs, the DNA of phage T4 (or the RNA of many other types of viruses) is injected into the host cell, but the protein coat remains outside and is lost.

In the life cycle of a phage the injected nucleic acid multiplies sooner or later in typical infections, new protein coats are made, the completed phage particles escape and may cause new infections elsewhere. The injected phage DNA is hard to demonstrate at first during a latent period, which may be short or long. When multiplication begins, a few phage particles, or many dozens, may be formed within the cell and soon acquire new protein coats thus becoming ready for release when the host cell disintegrates. An experiment with a known strain of phage mixed with a known susceptible bacterial suspension for the length of time required for infection and multiplication to be completed once is called a single-burst experiment. Further cycles of infection and rupture of neighboring bacterial cells on an agar plate produce a larger and larger clear area, a *plaque*, on a uniformly grown spread of bacterial cells called a lawn.

Unlike the simple viruses the bacteria have most of the principal structures and properties of typical cells. The bacterium has a cell membrane through which some substances pass and others do not. Its nucleus is either indistinct or diffuse. The nucleus contains genes in linear segments of DNA (as shown by transfer experiments), but surprisingly these linear arrangements are closed as a circle most of the time. Breaks may occur, but they open preferably at one place on the loop. Some DNA material exists separately from the chromosomal DNA as an *episome*, or else attached to the chromosome in a temporary or relatively permanent manner. The bacterial genes mutate. Under certain conditions genes from different sources recombine after a process of sexual fusion described by J. Lederberg. Because of the rapid growth of bacterial cells and their short generation time, it is possible to get millions and even billions of bacterial cells, among which rare processes of mutation and recombination may be studied, and in which the new genetic phenomena of DNA transformation and viral transduction have been discovered.

Some ecological relationships of bacteriophages and of their host cells can also be studied advantageously because of the short generation times of the two organisms. Rates of attack and of destruction can be measured in mixtures of temperate phage or of virulent phage with either susceptible or resistant host strains. A *temperate phage* will multiply slowly without killing the host cell. A strain of phage which is virulent to a certain strain of bacterium will quickly *lyse* (cytolyse) cells of that strain. From each such lysed bacterial cell many dozens of new phage particles will be released into the medium and will attack and lyse a large number of neighboring cells. In a few cycles of multiplication and infection the whole bacterial population may be wiped out; if not, the resistant bacterium may often be shown to be a mutant form. Bacteria can have mutations altering their cell wall in such a way that certain kinds of phage can no longer attach to the wall as a preliminary to injecting their DNA. Conversely, phages can occasionally mutate to wider "host range" phenotypes; they now have the ability to attack and lyse a strain previously unharmed by the ancestral viral strain.

In contrast to the lysing action of the virulent phages described above, the temperate phages reveal a very special kind of relationship between invader and host. The DNA of the temperate phage resides in the host cell for long periods as *prophage*, which multiplies slowly and in step with bacterial multiplication. Such a temperate phage is said to *lysogenize* a host cell and its descendants, although ultimately some small fraction of the clone of lysogenized cells will be lysed under special or transient environmental conditions, such as ultraviolet irradiation. Thus the temperate phage occasionally becomes virulent and vice versa.

The synchrony of reproduction of prophage and of the bacterial cell seems to be achieved by the attachment of the prophage to a particular place on the bacterial chromosome. Different phages map at different locations on the bacterial chromosomes. However, it is doubtful that the phage material is inserted into the linear sequence of the host chromosome. According to Jacob and Wollman it is a variety of episome, DNA material attached laterally as a hook or cleat on the bacterial chromosome. Thus it can be released on occasion, and when released the viral DNA is free to multiply rapidly and in a short time to lyse the cell which for many bacterial generations had been merely lysogenized. In this way many replicates of the lysing virus become available for experimental analysis.

THE ENTRANCE OF NEW DNA INTO CELLS

Sometimes the viral material from a burst bacterium is variant from the DNA originally entering a bacterium. The released virus may possess one or more marker genes from the bacterial chromosome, as may be demonstrated when subsequent infections are studied. A virus can thus *transduce* genetic material belonging to one bacterial variety into a strain with different genetic markers in which the transduced genes may be detected through a phenotypic change. Because several closely linked markers from the bacterial chromosome of one lysed strain can be expressed at the same time in a newly infected strain, an explanation via gene mutation is ruled out by the high improbability of simultaneous mutation of two or three adjacent gene loci. Because of the transduction of material by viruses between bacteria, it is difficult to say from a long range view what DNA is viral and what DNA is bacterial in the systems currently being studied so intensively. From generation to generation, however, stability of each genome is probably the rule.

A second method of transferring genetic material from one bacterial cell to another occurs when rarely two bacteria *conjugate*. When this happens one cell seems to push its "chromosome," always with the same end first, into the recipient cell. The bacterial DNA is usually circular but breaks at a specifiable point during early conjugation. By shaking apart bacterial pairs at various times after conjugation has begun, the sequence of genetic loci in the incoming material can be demonstrated.

A third method of genetically changing several closely linked loci in bacteria is historically the first way, as demonstrated in 1944 by Avery, MacLeod and McCarty. It had been known that heat-killed cells of one strain placed in the medium where another and different strain was growing could *transform* the growing strain into possessing some of the genetic characteristics of the killed strain. Avery, MacLeod and McCarty tested the transforming ability of various components of the cellular debris from encapsulated bacteria and found that the DNA fraction had the greatest ability to produce capsules as new cells of the nonencapsulated strain were growing. With this discovery investigation of the nature of the genetic material turned increasingly from proteins to the nucleic acids.

The methods and concepts of bacterial genetics are now finding increasing application to studies in mammalian cell cultures. Hamster tissue and mouse tissue cells, among others, have been found to change their form, their rate of multiplication and their antibody responses to superinfection after a first infection with animal viruses. Many cells are attacked and lysed by a heavy viral intermixture, but a small percentage of survivors seem to be resistant to further viral infection and are said to be transformed by the animal virus. Present usage does not restrict the meaning of the term transformation as narrowly as in the definition above. Because some of the viruses cause sarcomas, the details of their survival and multiplication should prove to be most interesting. Whether irradiation of a tumor in a person produces changes more effectively in the viral DNA, in the tumor chromosomes or in the healthy cells of the host may be found by present and future research to depend on the tumor, the virus, the time of treatment and the manner of treatment. Past experience shows that genetic actions are that specific.

SUMMARY

Much of man's environment is biological — his plant and animal foods, his enemies among the bacteria and viruses. These are not static. These other biological species also undergo mutation, and they in turn are selected by their environment. Human disease can occur because the person is less resistant or because the virus is more virulent or for some combination of time and circumstance. The microorganisms go in and out of variable environments more often than does the human species, and their generation time is very short. Therefore a mutation rate per generation of bacteria may be a tremendous quantitative threat to man, whereas mutation in humans might be of only remote help or hindrance. Because of mutations ecological classifications can change. Once a parasite is not always a parasite, and once a commensal or neutral does not always mean the continuation of that steady state. Not only do the distinctions between strains, races and species wash out from time to time, but the activities of the bacteriophages not only raise the question "The DNA is where?" but also "The DNA is whose?"

SUGGESTED READING

Brit. Med. Bull. **20:** 87–164 (1964). Mechanisms of carcinogenesis: chemical, physical and viral.

Jacob, F., and E. L. Wollman, *Viruses and Genes* (Sci. Amer. reprint series 89, June, 1961), San Francisco, Freeman, 1961, 16 pp.

Stent, Gunther S., *Molecular Biology of Bacterial Viruses*, San Francisco, Freeman, 1963, 474 pp. A fascinating account written with an historical perspective.

Zinder, Norton D., *"Transduction" in bacteria* (Sci. Amer. reprint series 106, Nov. 1958), San Francisco, Freeman, 1958, 8 pp.

PROBLEMS

28–1 What kind of mutation in what organism would change a relationship
  (a) Of parasitism to commensalism?
  (b) Of neutrality to commensalism?
  (c) Of allotrophy to predation?

28–2 Why does it seem that microorganisms mutate and evolve more rapidly than do mammals?

28–3 What are some differences in the shape and the location of DNA in mammals, bacteria and viruses?

28–4 Briefly define

temperate phage
episome
bacterial conjugation
bacterial transformation
transduction
lysis
lysogeny